Mineral-Filled Polymer Composites

Mineral-Filled Polymer Composites

Perspectives, Properties, and New Materials

Edited by

Hanafi Ismail, S.M. Sapuan, and R.A. Ilyas

CRC Press is an imprint of the
Taylor & Francis Group, an **informa** business

First edition published 2022
by CRC Press
6000 Broken Sound Parkway NW, Suite 300, Boca Raton, FL 33487-2742

and by CRC Press
2 Park Square, Milton Park, Abingdon, Oxon, OX14 4RN

© 2022 Taylor & Francis Group, LLC

CRC Press is an imprint of Taylor & Francis Group, LLC

Reasonable efforts have been made to publish reliable data and information, but the author and publisher cannot assume responsibility for the validity of all materials or the consequences of their use. The authors and publishers have attempted to trace the copyright holders of all material reproduced in this publication and apologize to copyright holders if permission to publish in this form has not been obtained. If any copyright material has not been acknowledged please write and let us know so we may rectify in any future reprint.

Except as permitted under U.S. Copyright Law, no part of this book may be reprinted, reproduced, transmitted, or utilized in any form by any electronic, mechanical, or other means, now known or hereafter invented, including photocopying, microfilming, and recording, or in any information storage or retrieval system, without written permission from the publishers.

For permission to photocopy or use material electronically from this work, access www.copyright.com or contact the Copyright Clearance Center, Inc. (CCC), 222 Rosewood Drive, Danvers, MA 01923, 978-750-8400. For works that are not available on CCC please contact mpkbookspermissions@tandf.co.uk

Trademark notice: Product or corporate names may be trademarks or registered trademarks and are used only for identification and explanation without intent to infringe.

ISBN: 978-1-032-11656-3 (hbk)
ISBN: 978-1-032-11659-4 (pbk)
ISBN: 978-1-003-22094-7 (ebk)

DOI: 10.1201/9781003220947

Typeset in Times
by KnowledgeWorks Global Ltd.

Contents

Preface vii
Authors Biography ix
Contributors xiii

Chapter 1   Bio Mineral Fillers Reinforced Polymer Composites 1

*Yamuna Munusamy, Sumathi Sethupathi, Hanafi Ismail,
and Zunaida Zakaria*

Chapter 2   Mechanical Properties of Geopolymer Filler in Polymer
Composites 15

*Yusrina Mat Daud, Mohammad Firdaus Abu Hashim,
and Rozyanty Rahman*

Chapter 3   Basalt Fiber-Reinforced Polymer Composites: A Review 31

*R.A. Ilyas, T.M.N. Afiq, R.M. Affiq, T.H. Tahrim, S.M. Sapuan,
M.S.N. Atikah, A. Atiqah, and Hanafi Ismail*

Chapter 4   Properties Enhancement of Poly(Lactic Acid) Using
Functionalized Mineral Fillers 71

Keemi Lim and Wen Shyang Chow

Chapter 5   Ageing of Mineral-Reinforced Polymer Composites 85

Emel Kuram

Chapter 6   Halloysite Nanotubes-Filled Natural Rubber Composite:
Mechanical and Other Related Properties 111

Nabil Hayeemasae and Hanafi Ismail

Chapter 7   Halloysite Nanotubes-Filled Natural Rubber Composite:
Morphology and Crystallization of the Composites 135

Nabil Hayeemasae and Hanafi Ismail

Chapter 8 Alumina Filled Rubber Composites: Application, Mechanical
Properties, Morphological Characteristics and Processability 159

Noraiham Mohamad, Jeefferie Abd Razak,
Hairul Effendy Ab Maulod, Andanastuti Muchtar,
Mariyam Jameelah Ghazali, Dahlan Hj. Mohd,
and Che Husna Azhari

Chapter 9 Magnetite Filler Reinforcement for Magnetorheological
Elastomer Damping Performance 195

Raa Khimi

Chapter 10 Characterization and Properties of Montmorillonite-Reinforced
Thermoplastic Composites 211

Sung Ting Sam, Pei Gie Gan, Sin Yee Lew,
Nik Noriman Zulkepli, and Hanafi Ismail

Chapter 11 Mineral-Filled Polymer Composites: Reliability, Challenges,
Opportunities and Future Perspectives 235

R.A. Ilyas, M. Izzat, S.M. Qusyairi, S.M. Sapuan,
M.S.N. Atikah, H.A. Aisyah, and Hanafi Ismail

Index 263

Preface

Mineral Filled Polymer Composites: Perspective, Properties, and New Materials provides an exhaustive overview of the latest research and future directions of advanced mineral fiber-reinforced polymer composites. Mineral-filled polymers are widely used in industries across the globe and the applications are continuously increasing. These materials are desirable because they have comparable strength and toughness ratios to those used in metal alloys while being lightweight and more economical. A wide variety of these composite applications were found in the shipping, manufacturing and renewable energy sectors. In the mineral-filled polymer composite, the key factor for good incorporation between filler and the polymer is the filler volume, particularly when processing highly viscous material. Thus, this book features chapters looking at the properties of specific mineral-filled polymer composite materials such as organic, inorganic, basalt, calcium carbonate, nanotube, clay, feldspar, zinc oxide, silica, zeolite, sepiolite, alumina, magnetite, montmorillonite, rubber, dolomite, halloysite and biomineral fiber-reinforced polymer composites. Moreover, this book highlights the resources for bio-based mineral production and presents the comparison between bio-based minerals with commercial mineral fillers. This book reviews the various properties of macro-sized up to nano-sized mineral-reinforced polymer composites. Covering novel methods for the synthesis of mineral-filled polymer composites, the book starts by reviewing the properties of new biomineral fillers such as silica and $CaCO_3$. Effects of aging on the properties of mineral-reinforced polymer composites were also discussed. This book also shares the potential of using mineral fillers to enhance the properties of biopolymer and synthetic polymers. The use of halloysite and montmorillonite in the thermoplastic matrix to improve the overall properties of the composites was also highlighted. This book is aimed at researchers, advanced students and industry professionals working in materials science and engineering. It covers fundamentals, recent progress and new materials involved in mineral filler polymers and also includes a wide-ranging list of comprehensive chapters authored by an international team of experts.

Authors Biography

Hanafi Ismail is currently the Director of Innovation Centre and Consultation, Universiti Sains Malaysia, Fellow Academy of Science Malaysia (FASc) and ex-Dean School of Materials and Mineral Resources Engineering. Professor Hanafi has won many awards including Khwarizmi International Award 2000; APCTT (Asia Pacific) 2000 International Award; ISESCO Prize in Science & Technology 2001 and the silver medal at the International Exhibition of Invention in 2002, 2004 and 2009. In 2005, he won the gold medal at the International Trade Fair IENA, and in 2007 he won the gold medal with special mention by jury at the 56th World Exhibition of Innovation, Research and New Technologies. He also won the gold medal at the International Invention, Innovation, Industrial Design and Technology Exhibition (I-TEX 2003, 2004, 2007, 2008 and 2010) and silver medal at the Science & Technology Expo 2003, 2006 and 2010. In 2010 Professor Ismail won the gold medal, double gold and the Special Award from Russia at the British Invention Show (BIS 2010) and the gold medal at the Seoul International Invention Fair. In 2011, he won the gold medal and Best Invention Award at the 22th International Invention, Innovation, Industrial Design and Technology Exhibition (I-TEX 2011) and the gold medal and Grand Eco Award Prize at the International Trade Fair, Ideas, Inventions and New Products. In 2012, Professor Hanafi won the KIWIE Prize and Thailand Special Award at the Korea International Women's Invention Exposition (KIWIE 2012). In 2013, he won the gold medal at the 24th International Invention, Innovation & Technology Exhibition (ITEX 2013) and the gold medal at the 6th International Invention Fair in the Middle East (IIFME). In 2014, Professor Hanafi won the gold medal and Special Award from Asia Invention Association (AIA) at the 25th International Invention, Innovation & Technology Exhibition (ITEX 2014). In 2016, he won the gold medal and three Special Awards from Highly Innovative Unique Foundation Saudi Arabia and Universitatea Technics Din Cluj-Napoca Romania at the 8th European Exhibition of Creativity and Innovation (EUROINVENT 2016). At the International Conference on Innovation in Polymer Science and Technology (IPST2019) in 2019, Professor Hanafi was awarded the Innovation in Polymer Science & Technology Award by the Indonesian Polymer Association. He also was awarded the Excellent Research Award for his outstanding international scholastic achievement in polymer science and technology by the Croatian Inventors Network. He has published more than 722 research papers in various polymer International Scientific Indexing (ISI) international journals and is currently on the Editorial Board for *Polymer Plastic Technology & Engineering* (ISI, Marcel Dekker), *Research Journal of Environmental and Earth Sciences* (Maxwell Science), *ASEAN Engineering Journal, Iranica Journal of Energy and Environment, Iranian Polymer Journal* (ISI, Springer), *Central European Journal of Engineering* (Springer), *Journal of Composites and Biodegradable Polymers* (Savy Publishers) and *Journal of Vinyl and Additive Technology* (ISI, Wiley). He is also on the Editorial Board for *Polymer Testing* (ISI, Elsevier) and *Journal of*

Rubber Research (ISI, Springer) and is the Chief Editor for *Progress in Rubber Plastic and Recycling Technology* (SAGE). At the national level, he is also on the Editorial Board for *Journal of Physical Science* (Scopus), *International Journal of Automotive and Mechanical Engineering* (Scopus) and *Journal of Electron Microscopy Malaysia*. Professor Hanafi is a Fellow at the Science Academy of Malaysia and was the Top Malaysian Scientist 2012 and 2014.

S.M. Sapuan is a Professor of composite materials at Universiti Putra Malaysia. He earned his B. Eng. degree in mechanical engineering from the University of Newcastle, Australia, in 1990; MSc from Loughborough University, UK, in 1994 and Ph.D. from De Montfort University, UK, in 1998. His research interests include natural fiber composites, materials selection and concurrent engineering. To date, he has authored or co-authored more than 1521 publications (730 papers published/accepted in national and international journals, 16 authored books, 25 edited books, 153 chapters in books and 597 conference proceedings/seminar papers/ presentation (26 of which are plenary and keynote lectures and 66 of which are invited lectures). S.M. Sapuan was the recipient of the Rotary Research Gold Medal Award 2012; The Alumni Medal for Professional Excellence Finalist, 2012 Alumni Awards, University of Newcastle, NSW, Australia and Khwarizmi International Award (KIA). In 2013, he was awarded the 5 Star Role Model Supervisor award by Universiti Putra Malaysia (UPM). He has been awarded Outstanding Reviewer by Elsevier for his contribution to reviewing journal papers. He received the Best Technical Paper Award in UNIMAS STEM International Engineering Conference in Kuching, Sarawak, Malaysia. S.M. Sapuan was recognized as the first Malaysian to be conferred Fellowship by the U.S.-based Society of Automotive Engineers International (FSAE) in 2015. He was the 2015/2016 recipient of SEARCA Regional Professorial Chair. In the 2016 ranking of UPM researchers based on the number of citations and h-index by SCOPUS, he is ranked 6th of 100 researchers. In 2017, he was awarded the IOP Outstanding Reviewer Award by the Institute of Physics, UK; National Book Award; The Best Journal Paper Award, UPM; Outstanding Technical Paper Award, Society of Automotive Engineers International, Malaysia and Outstanding Researcher Award, UPM. He also received the 2017 Citation of Excellence Award from Emerald, UK, SAE Malaysia; the Best Journal Paper Award; IEEE/TMU Endeavour Research Promotion Award; Best Paper Award by Chinese Defence Ordnance and Malaysia's Research Star Award (MRSA) from Elsevier. In 2019, he was awarded Top Research Scientist Malaysia (TRSM 2019) and Professor of Eminence Award from AMU, India.

R.A. Ilyas is an Assistant Professor in the School of Chemical and Energy Engineering, Faculty of Engineering, Universiti Teknologi Malaysia, Malaysia. He received his Diploma in Forestry at Universiti Putra Malaysia, Bintulu Campus (UPMKB), Sarawak, Malaysia in 2012. In 2012, he was awarded the Public Service Department (JPA) scholarship to pursue his BSc in Chemical Engineering at Universiti Putra Malaysia (UPM). Upon completion of his BSc in 2016, he was again awarded the Graduate Research Fellowship (GRF) by UPM to undertake a PhD degree in the field of Biocomposite Technology & Design at the Institute of Tropical Forestry and Forest

Products (INTROP) UPM. He was the recipient of the MVP Doctor of Philosophy Gold Medal Award UPM 2019 for Best Ph.D. Thesis and Top Student Award, INTROP, UPM. In 2018, he was named Outstanding Reviewer by *Carbohydrate Polymers*, Elsevier, UK; Best Paper Award (11th AUN/SEED-Net Regional Conference on Energy Engineering); Best Paper Award (Seminar Enau Kebangsaan 2019, Persatuan Pembangunan dan Industri Enau Malaysia) and National Book Award 2018. R.A. Ilyas also was listed among the World's Top 2% Scientist (Subject-Wise) Citation Impact during the Single Calendar Year 2019. His main research interests are polymer engineering (biodegradable polymers, biopolymers, polymer composites and polymer-gels) and material engineering (natural fiber-reinforced polymer composites, biocomposites, cellulose materials and nanocomposites). To date he has authored or co-authored more than 221 publications (68 papers published/accepted/submitted in national and international journals, 1 authored book, 10 edited books, 68 chapters in books, 2 research bulletins, 5 Journal Special Issues as Guest Editor and 6 editor/co-editor for conference/seminar proceedings and 61 conference proceedings/seminar papers/presentations.

Contributors

T.M.N. Afiq
Department of Mechanical and
  Manufacturing Engineering
Universiti Putra Malaysia
Serdang, Malaysia

R.M. Affiq
Department of Mechanical and
  Manufacturing Engineering
Universiti Putra Malaysia
Serdang, Malaysia

H.A. Aisyah
Institute of Tropical Forestry and Forest
  Products (INTROP)
Universiti Putra Malaysia
Serdang, Malaysia

M.S.N. Atikah
Department of Chemical and
  Environmental Engineering
Universiti Putra Malaysia
Serdang, Malaysia

A. Atiqah
Institute of Microengineering and
  Nanoelectronics
Universiti Kebangsaan Malaysia
Bangi, Malaysia

Che Husna Azhari
Entruss Ventures Sdn Bhd
Bangi, Malaysia

Wen Shyang Chow
School of Materials and Mineral
  Resources Engineering
Universiti Sains Malaysia
Gelugor, Malaysia

Yusrina Mat Daud
Center of Excellence Geopolymer and
  Green Technology (CEGeoGTech)
Universiti Malaysia Perlis
Aaru, Malaysia

Pei Gie Gan
Center of Excellence Geopolymer and
  Green Technology (CEGeoGTech)
Universiti Malaysia Perlis
Aaru, Malaysia

Mariyam Jameelah Ghazali
Faculty of Engineering
Universiti Kebangsaan Malaysia
Bangi, Malaysia

Mohammad Firdaus Abu Hashim
Center of Excellence Geopolymer and
  Green Technology (CEGeoGTech)
Universiti Malaysia Perlis
Aaru, Malaysia

Nabil Hayeemasae
Department of Rubber Technology and
  Polymer Science
Prince of Songkla University
Hat Yai, Thailand

R.A. Ilyas
School of Chemical and Energy
Centre for Advanced Composite
  Materials (CACM)
Universiti Teknologi Malaysia
Johor Bahru, Malaysia

Hanafi Ismail
Polymer Engineering Department
Universiti Sains Malaysia Engineering
  Campus
Nibong Tebal, Malaysia

M. Izzat
Advanced Engineering Materials and
  Composites (AEMC)
Universiti Putra Malaysia
Serdang, Malaysia

Raa Khimi
School of Materials and Mineral
  Resources Engineering
Universiti Sains Malaysia
Nibong Tebal, Malaysia

Emel Kuram
Department of Mechanical
  Engineering
Gebze Technical University
Gebze, Turkey

Sin Yee Lew
Center of Excellence Geopolymer and
  Green Technology (CEGeoGTech)
Universiti Malaysia Perlis
Arau, Malaysia

Keemi Lim
School of Materials and Mineral
  Resources Engineering
Universiti Sains Malaysia
Gelugor, Malaysia

Hairul Effendy Ab Maulod
Fakulti Teknologi Kejuruteraan
  Mekanikal and Pembuatan
Universiti Teknikal Malaysia Melaka
Melaka, Malaysia

Noraiham Mohamad
Fakulti Kejuruteraan Pembuatan
Universiti Teknikal Malaysia Melaka
Melaka, Malaysia

Dahlan Hj. Mohd
Malaysian Nuclear Agency
Selangor, Malaysia

Andanastuti Muchtar
Faculty of Engineering
Universiti Kebangsaan Malaysia
Bangi, Malaysia

Yamuna Munusamy
Faculty of Engineering and Green
  Technology
Universiti Tunku Abdul Rahman, Jalan
  Universiti
Kampar, Malaysia

S.M. Qusyairi
Advanced Engineering Materials and
  Composites (AEMC)
Universiti Putra Malaysia
Serdang, Malaysia

Rozyanty Rahman
Center of Excellence Geopolymer and
  Green Technology (CEGeoGTech)
Universiti Malaysia Perlis
Aaru, Malaysia

Jeefferie Abd Razak
Fakulti Kejuruteraan Pembuatan
Universiti Teknikal Malaysia Melaka
Melaka, Malaysia

Sung Ting Sam
Center of Excellence Geopolymer and
  Green Technology (CEGeoGTech)
Universiti Malaysia Perlis
Aaru, Malaysia

S.M. Sapuan
Advanced Engineering Materials and
  Composites (AEMC)
Laboratory of Biocomposite
  Technology
Institute of Tropical Forestry and Forest
  Products (INTROP)
Universiti Putra Malaysia
Serdang, Malaysia

Contributors

Sumathi Sethupathi
Faculty of Engineering and Green
 Technology
Universiti Tunku Abdul Rahman, Jalan
 Universiti
Kampar, Malaysia

T.H. Tahrim
Advanced Engineering Materials and
 Composites (AEMC)
Universiti Putra Malaysia
Serdang, Malaysia

Zunaida Zakaria
School of Materials Engineering
Universiti Malaysia Perlis
Aaru, Malaysia

Nik Noriman Zulkepli
Faculty of Chemical Engineering
 Technology
Universiti Malaysia Perlis
Aaru, Malaysia

1 Bio Mineral Fillers Reinforced Polymer Composites

Yamuna Munusamy, Sumathi Sethupathi
Universiti Tunku Abdul Rahman, Jalan Universiti
Kampar, Malaysia

Hanafi Ismail
Universiti Sains Malaysia Engineering Campus
Nibong Tebal, Malaysia

Zunaida Zakaria
Universiti Malaysia Perlis
Aaru, Malaysia

CONTENTS

1.1 Introduction to Bio Mineral Fillers 1
1.2 Production of Bio Mineral Fillers 3
1.3 Modification of Bio Mineral Fillers 5
1.4 Production of Bio Mineral-Filled Hybrid Composites 10
1.5 Gaps and Future Challenges in Bio-Based Mineral Application
    in Polymer Composites 10
1.6 Conclusions 10
References 12

1.1 INTRODUCTION TO BIO MINERAL FILLERS

Polymeric materials are heavily loaded with mineral fillers such as talc, calcium carbonate ($CaCO_3$) and silica from non-renewable resources such as limestone, sand, metamorphic rocks and rock deposits. These mineral fillers are found to increase the mechanical properties, thermal stability, process ability and fire retardancy of polymer composites. However, mining of these fillers can cause adverse effects on the environment such as depletion of natural flora and fauna, erosion of soil, instability of soil and rock masses and changes in the environmental landscape.

DOI: 10.1201/9781003220947-1

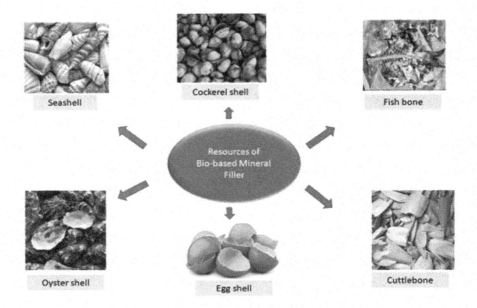

FIGURE 1.1 Resources of bio-based mineral fillers.

Thus, attempts had been made to substitute the usage of mineral-based fillers from non-renewable resources with bio-based mineral fillers. Bio-based mineral fillers can be defined as mineral fillers derived from renewable biomaterials from animal or plant resources. The resources for bio-based mineral fillers from animals and plants are illustrated in Figures 1.1 and 1.2, respectively.

FIGURE 1.2 Plant resources of bio-based mineral fillers.

1.2 PRODUCTION OF BIO MINERAL FILLERS

Bio mineral fillers, such as silica and $CaCO_3$, from renewable resources could be obtained through various processes such as grinding, chemical extraction or treatment and burning in controlled conditions. Examples of few processes used to obtain bio-fillers are presented in Figure 1.3. Properties of bio mineral fillers compared with commercial $CaCO_3$ and commercial silica are shown in Tables 1.1 and 1.2, respectively.

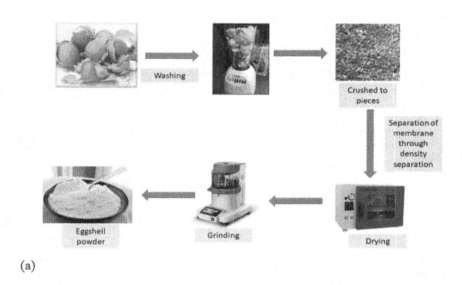

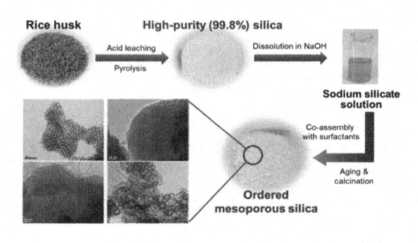

FIGURE 1.3 Preparation of bio mineral fillers: (a) preparation of calcium carbonate from eggshell and (b) preparation of mesoporous silica from rice husk.

TABLE 1.1
Comparison of Calcium Carbonate Bio Mineral Fillers with Commercial Grounded Calcium Carbonate

Properties	Grounded Commercial Calcium Carbonate (GCC)	Chicken Eggshell Bio-Filler	Cockerel Shell Bio-Filler
CaO content	~99%	~95%	~98%
	Contains very small amount of Mg and SiO_2	Contains ~4% carbon and very small amount of Fe_2O_3 and SrO	Contains small amount of carbon and Fe_2O_3
Crystal structure	Calcite	Calcite	Calcite and aragonite
Morphology			
Surface area BET ($m^2 \times g^{-1}$)	10.0140	14.0140	12.0220

TABLE 1.2
Comparison of Silica Bio Minerals with Commercial Silica

Properties	Commercial-Grade Fused Silica	Silica from Rice Husk	Cockerel Shell Bio-Filler
SiO_2	~98	~97%	~55%
			Contains large amount of K_2O (10.67%), CaO (10.13%), Fe_2O_3 (5.69%), SO_3 (4.92%), P_2O_5 (4.17%), Al_2O_3 (3.31%) and MgO (3.49%).
Crystal structure	Amorphous	Amorphous	Crystalline cristobalite
Morphology			
Surface area BET ($m^2 \times g^{-1}$)	2.73	11.35	4.5337

Source: Fernandas et al. (2018) and Rizal et al. (2020).

1.3 MODIFICATION OF BIO MINERAL FILLERS

A great deal of work has been done to modify the bio mineral fillers to be more compatible with the polymer matrix. These modifications involve changes in surface morphology and functional groups of the fillers. Changes in surface morphology create higher surface area for interfacial interaction between polymer chains and fillers and cause physical entrapment of polymer chains on the surface of the fillers. Meanwhile, introduction of functional groups on the surface of bio mineral fillers act as a bridge between polymer chains and the fillers.

In research conducted by Murugan et al. (2018), eggshell powder was grafted with a silane coupling agent to improve compatibility between the filler and high-density polyethylene (HDPE). The tensile strength, tensile modulus and thermal decomposition stability were found to be higher for composites with silane-grafted eggshell powder compared with composites with pure eggshell powder. In another review by Pahlevani and Sahajwalla (2019), seashell powder was treated with an amino silane coupling agent. The reaction between amino silane and the seashell powder happens in four steps: hydrolysis, condensation, hydrogen bonding and bond formation (Figure 1.4). Hydrolysis occurs when the amino silane is mixed with water (Reaction 1). The hydrolyzed mixture is then mixed with seashell powder filler to promote condensation (Reaction 2). During the mixing process, the active groups in the amino silane with a hydrolytically sensitive center will bind with the surface of the seashell powder to form hydrogen bonds (Reaction 3). Finally, formation of covalent bonds occurs on heating the mixture at 120°C for 90 minutes with removal of water (Reaction 4). The organic end of the treated powder acts as a bridge, which interacts with the polymeric matrix. The formation of this interaction causes improvement in mechanical properties of the composite.

Amino silane treatment was also carried out on bio silica from rice husk to produce high-performance coating material using an epoxy composite. Composite with 4 vol% treated bio silica showed a highest value of storage modulus of 7.2 GPa, glass transition temperature of 91°C and improvement in thermal conductivity by 67% compared with non-treated bio silica. These bio silica-filled composites could be used as coating materials for aircraft passenger air ducts (Karthigairajan et al., 2020).

Shah et al. (2018) treated oyster shells with polyvinyl alcohol (PVA) using dry ball milling. The treated oyster shell powder was blended into a polypropylene (PP) matrix. PVA treatment on the oyster shell powder improved the filler distribution and increased interfacial bonding between filler and polymer matrix, which lead to the improvement of mechanical and thermal properties of the composites. PVA treatment also improved the flame-retardant property of the composites by increasing the burning time up to 29% in horizontal burning test. Demobilization of PP chains on the surface of PVA-treated oyster shell powder increased the stiffness of the composite system and reduced internal flaws and bubbles, which makes the composites more uniform, thus prolonging their burning time.

Modification on the bio mineral fillers could also be done by modifying or controlling the production process. Normally modification on the production process will change the morphology of the bio mineral fillers and thus influence the surface area and porosity of the fillers. Examples of bio mineral morphological changes due

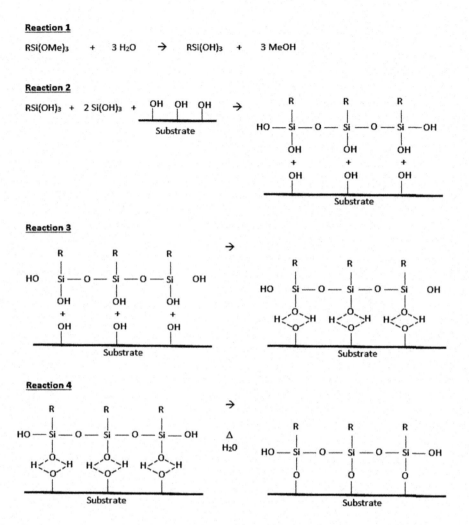

FIGURE 1.4 Modification of seashell powder with amino silane coupling agent. (Adapted from Farshid Pahlevani and Veena Sahajwalla, 2019).

to implementation of control in processing conditions and its effect on the interaction with polymer macromolecules are shown in Figure 1.5. Figure 1.5(a) shows amorphous bio silica produced from rice husk, whereas in Figure 1.5(b) porous silica structure is formed when the process condition is controlled with the formation of carbon in its structure. Porous silica provides larger surface area for interaction with polymer chains and the chains can penetrate through the pores in the fillers and form hydrogen bonds with the silanol group of silica. A study by Hsieh et al. (2017) proved that the carbon/silica produced from rice husk has surface area and equal pore volume of 305 m^{2}g^{-1} and 0.2 cm^{3}g^{-1}, respectively, compared with that of petroleum-based carbon/silica, which is around 35 m^{2}g^{-1} and 0.03 cm^{3}g^{-1}. Thus, the rice husk

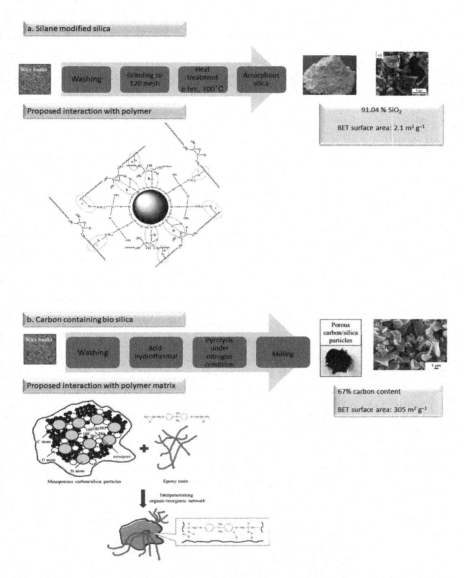

FIGURE 1.5 Modification of bio based mineral fillers. (Adapted from Hsieh et al., 2017; Pongdong et al., 2018.)

carbon/silica is categorized as a high-porosity filler, whereas the petroleum-based carbon/silica is categorized as a low-porosity filler.

The main purpose of introducing carbon into the bio silica is to improve the thermal conductivity of the bio-filler as shown in Figure 1.6. Thermal conductivity (K) of 29 wt% rice husk carbon/silica-filled epoxy increases by 57.7% from 0.186 W/mK for neat epoxy. This increment is attributed by the carbon content in the bio silica

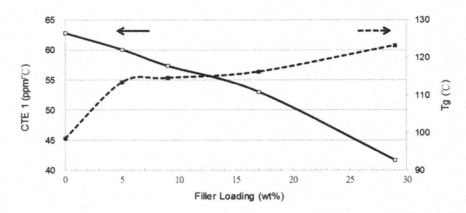

FIGURE 1.6 Effect of rice husk carbon/silica filler loading on thermal conductivity of epoxy composite. (Adapted from Hsieh et al., 2017.)

filler, which serves as a thermal transport medium. The scanning electron microscope image in Figure 1.7 shows good distribution of filler. Formation of composite without any air void between the filler and matrix can reduce thermal boundary resistance and thus increase thermal conductivity of the composite system.

Calcination is another common method to modify the surface morphology of bio mineral fillers. In bio mineral fillers that contain $CaCO_3$, calcination process oxidizes $CaCO_3$ to calcium oxide (CaO) with the release of carbon dioxide gas. In fact, the main purpose of calcination process is to increase CaO content in the filler. Many researchers have focused their attention on determining the right calcination temperature and time to optimize the phase change from $CaCO_3$ to CaO. Figure 1.8 shows the calcination route for eggshell powder and the resulting properties of the filler after calcination.

Calcined chicken eggshell powder exhibits larger surface area compared with pure chicken eggshell powder due to the elimination of impurities and release of carbon dioxide, which produces a rougher or uneven surface of the filler. Fourier transform

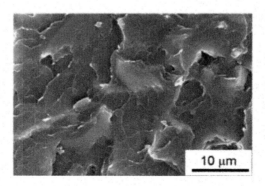

FIGURE 1.7 Epoxy composite filled with 29 weight% rice husk carbon/silica filler (Adapted from Hsieh et al., 2017.)

Bio Mineral Fillers Reinforced Polymer Composites

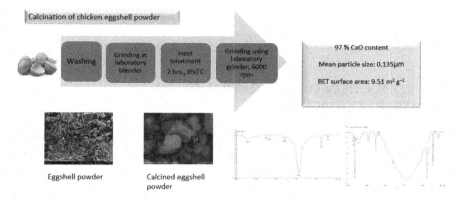

FIGURE 1.8 Calcination of chicken eggshell powder.

infrared spectroscopy (FTIR) analysis is often used to confirm the conversion of $CaCO_3$ to CaO by referring to the presence of a new sharp and strong transmission peak at the wavelength of 572 cm^{-1} and a strong and broad band at the wavelength of 3643 cm^{-1}, which corresponds to Ca–O and calcium hydroxide ($Ca(OH)_2$) bonds, respectively. In findings by Chai et al. (2016), calcined eggshell-filled composites were found to exhibit better tensile strength, tensile modulus and thermal decomposition stability compared with pure eggshell-powder-filled composites. These improvements are caused by larger surface area of the calcined chicken eggshell powder that promotes better interfacial bonding between the filler and polymer matrix.

Preparation of calcined waste white scallop powder (WWSP) in a study conducted by Wu et al. (2019) is shown in Figure 1.9. At 1000°C, $CaCO_3$ inside WWSP

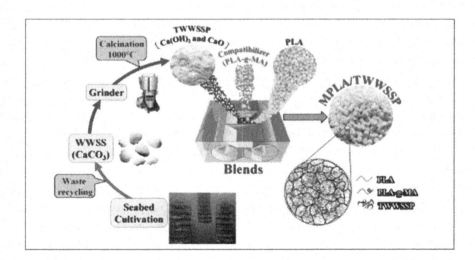

FIGURE 1.9 Preparation of PLA composites with calcined WWSP (Adapted from Wu et al., 2019.)

was transformed completely to CaO and $Ca(OH)_2$, and the calcined WWSP exhibited better interaction with polylactic acid (PLA) matrix, which resulted in greater tensile strength, thermal stability and antimicrobial properties.

1.4 PRODUCTION OF BIO MINERAL-FILLED HYBRID COMPOSITES

Recently attention has also been paid to the production of a hybrid composite with a bio mineral component. The addition of bio mineral fillers into these composite systems was found to impart certain properties required by the final product such as thermal conductivity, antimicrobial properties, mechanical properties and thermal stability. The improvements imparted by the bio mineral fillers on hybrid composites are listed in Table 1.3.

1.5 GAPS AND FUTURE CHALLENGES IN BIO-BASED MINERAL APPLICATION IN POLYMER COMPOSITES

The first challenge in the production of bio-based minerals is mainstreaming and collecting the waste resources to fulfill the demand of fillers in the polymer industry. Even though tons of waste materials containing minerals are generated annually, a system needs to be set up to collect this waste. Moreover, most of the waste collections such as eggshell collections are from the food industry, but a large fraction of waste is also generated by household consumers. Up till now, there has been no system set up to collect waste with a high mineral content from households.

Second, the origin of resources for bio-based minerals will influence the mineral content and impurities in the produced minerals. For example, the rice husk from Malaysia might contain different levels of silica compared with rice husk from India. Non-uniformity of the mineral content in bio-based minerals will cause variation in the quality of the final product.

Grinding methods are largely applied to convert shells and other hard substances into smaller particles of bio-based minerals. This process can be energy intensive, cause noise pollution, and cause wear and tear to machinery. Moreover, some surface modification methods of bio-based minerals, such as calcination, require a high-temperature environment in which the process becomes energy intensive. Precise control is also required in both methods to ensure that the particle size distribution of the bio-based minerals is narrow.

1.6 CONCLUSIONS

Bio-based mineral fillers have great potential to substitute commercial mineral fillers from non-renewable resources. The bio-based mineral fillers have similar physical and chemical properties as commercial mineral fillers such as $CaCO_3$, silica and talc. Previous studies proved that the bio-based mineral fillers could be prepared at desired particle size, shape and surface chemistry by using chemical modifications and controlling the preparation parameters. Some of the bio-based fillers could

TABLE 1.3
Properties of Bio Mineral Filler Hybrid Composites

Composite System	Findings	Reference
Epoxy LY556 resin was mixed with reinforcements of seashell and e-glass fiber	Addition of more seashell components reduced the hardness of the composite. Addition of 35 and 45 wt% of seashells into the composites improved the tensile strength of the system	Krishna et al. (2021)
Epoxy resin composite prepared with e-glass fiber (primary reinforcement) and crab shell powder (secondary reinforcement) with various weight fractions (0%, 3%, 5% and 7%) using the wet hand layup method	The density of the composites increases when the crab shell powder loading increases, because the density of the crab shell powder is 1.3 g/cc Scanning electron microscopy micrographs showed that in the composite with only e-glass fiber, large pores are observed. Whereas, when secondary reinforcement in the form of crab shell powder is added, the amount of pores drop significantly, especially at 5 wt% crab shell powder loading All the composites reinforced with crab shell powder showed better hardness and ultimate tensile strength compared with composites without crab shell powder The crab shell powder is found to fill in the pores and voids between the fiber and the epoxy matrix, thus increasing the mechanical properties	Prasad et al. (2021)
Unsaturated polyester reinforced with jute fiber/ carbon fiber and fishbone powder nanofillers The fishbone is made up of calcium and phosphate in the form of hydroxyapatite $Ca_{10}(Po_4)_6(OH)_2$	The addition of fishbone powder increases the tensile strength of the composites, with the highest value of improvement achieved at 5 wt% fishbone powder Improvement of tensile strength is caused by improvement in adhesive strength with the addition of fishbone powder, which enhances the stress transfer between the polymer matrix and fibers	Singh et al. (2020)
Epoxy reinforced with (5–20 wt%) individual or combination of eggshell and snail shell powder	Both contain ~99 wt% $CaCO_3$. The density of eggshell powder (2.66 g/m^3) is higher compared with the density of snail shell powder (1.4 g/m^3). The particle shape of both are different, whereby the shape of eggshell powder particles is in uniform sphere, whereas the snail shell powder exhibits an irregular particle shape. Both are prepared at particle sizes less than 50 nm Elemental analysis revealed that snail shell contains 22.25% carbon compared with eggshell which contains 14.93% carbon The higher elemental carbon content in snail shell was found to contribute to the increment in tensile strength in the composites due to better interaction between the snail shell powder and the polymer matrix To be precise, the addition of 5 wt% of eggshell improves epoxy composite strength by 4.83%, whereas the addition of 5 w% snail shell increases strength by 27.8% and hybrid reinforcement increases the tensile strength by 35.01%	Gbadeyan et al. (2020)

impart additional properties to the composites, such as thermal conductivity and anti-microbial properties, compared with their commercial counterparts, because they contain elements such as carbon in their structure. This advantage led to the production of many hybrid bio-based mineral-filled composites. However, to move forward in the application of bio-based mineral fillers in polymer composites, streamlining the resources for production of bio-based minerals is important. A robust waste collection and management system needs to be implemented to ensure a continuous supply of bio-based minerals to the polymer composite industry. Shortage of supply will interrupt the production chain and force the industry to go back to mineral fillers from non-renewable resources.

REFERENCES

Chai, Chun Leong. "Development polypropylene (PP)-modified chicken eggshell composites." PhD dissertation, UTAR, 2016.

Fernandes, Iara Janaína, Ramon Vieira Santos, Emanuele Caroline Araujo dos Santos, Tatiana Louise Avila Campos Rocha, Nei Sebastião Domingues Junior, and Carlos Alberto Mendes Moraes. "Replacement of commercial silica by rice husk ash in epoxy composites: a comparative analysis." *Materials Research* 21, no. 3 (2018). https://doi.org/10.1590/1980-5373-MR-2016-0562

Gbadeyan, Oluwatoyin Joseph, Sarp Adali, G. Bright, Bruce Sithole, and Awogbemi Awogbemi. "Studies on the mechanical and absorption properties of achatina fulica snail and eggshells reinforced composite materials." *Composite Structures* 239 (2020): 112043.

Hsieh, Ya-Yu, Tsung-Yi Chen, Wei-Chiao Kuo, Yi-Shao Lai, Ping-Feng Yang, and Hong-Ping Lin. "Rice husk-derived porous carbon/silica particles as green filler for electronic package application." *Journal of Applied Polymer Science* 134, no. 15 (2017).

Karthigairajan, M., P. K. Nagarajan, R. Raviraja Malarvannan, BR Ramesh Bapu, D. Jayabalakrishnan, T. Maridurai, and V. K. Shanmuganathan. "Effect of silane-treated rice husk derived biosilica on visco-elastic, thermal conductivity and hydrophobicity behavior of epoxy biocomposite coating for air-duct application." *Silicon* (2020): 1–10. https://doi.org/10.1007/s12633-020-00772-z

Krishna, U.B. Gopal, C. S. Srinivasa, N. S. Amara, and Sanganabasu Gudoor. "Processing, characterization and property evaluation of seashell and glass fibre added epoxy based polymer matrix composite." *Materials Today: Proceedings* 35, no. 3 (2021): 417–422.

Murugan, Sharmeeni, Yamuna Munusamy, Mathialagan Muniandy, and Hanafi Ismail. "Development of HDPE-modified eggshell composite." *Polymer Composites* 39, no. 5 (2018): 1630–1637.

Pahlevani, Farshid, and Veena Sahajwalla. "Effect of different waste filler and silane coupling agent on the mechanical properties of powder-resin composite." *Journal of Cleaner Production* 224 (2019): 940–956.

Pongdong, Wiphawadee, Claudia Kummerlöwe, Norbert Vennemann, Anoma Thitithammawong, and Charoen Nakason. "A comparative study of rice husk ash and siliceous earth as reinforcing fillers in epoxidized natural rubber composites." *Polymer Composites* 39, no. 2 (2018): 414–426.

Prasad, G. Vara, S. Nagappa, Y. Ravi Kanth, I. Gopi Lakshmi, and J. Babu Rao. "Effect of brachyura shell particles on glass fibre reinforced epoxy polymer composite." *Materials Today: Proceedings* 42 (2021): 555–562.

Rizal, Samsul, H. M. Fizree, Md Sohrab Hossain, Deepu A. Gopakumar, Eunice Chong Wan Ni, and HPS Abdul Khalil. "The role of silica-containing agro-industrial waste as reinforcement on physicochemical and thermal properties of polymer composites." *Heliyon* 6, no. 3 (2020): e03550.

Shah, Atta Ur Rehman, M. N. Prabhakar, Huifeng Wang, and Jung-Il Song. "The influence of particle size and surface treatment of filler on the properties of oyster shell powder filled polypropylene composites." *Polymer Composites* 39, no. 7 (2018): 2420–2430.

Singh, Harsimran, N. K. Batra, and Iti Dikshit. "Development of new hybrid jute/carbon/fishbone reinforced polymer composite." *Materials Today: Proceedings* 38, no. 1 (2020): 29–33.

Wu, Chin-San, Dung-Yi Wu, and Shan-Shue Wang. "Antibacterial properties of biobased polyester composites achieved through modification with a thermally treated waste scallop shell." *ACS Applied Bio Materials* 2, no. 5 (2019): 2262–2270.

2 Mechanical Properties of Geopolymer Filler in Polymer Composites

Yusrina Mat Daud, Mohammad Firdaus Abu Hashim, and Rozyanty Rahman
Universiti Malaysia Perlis
Aaru, Malaysia

CONTENTS

2.1 Introduction 15
2.2 Geopolymer Filler in Polymeric Materials 18
2.3 Geopolymer Filler in Epoxy Hybrid Composite 20
    2.3.1 Effect of Fly Ash-Based Geopolymer Filler Loading on
        Compressive Strength 21
2.4 Geopolymer Filler in Epoxy Glass Fiber Composites 22
    2.4.1 Effect of Fly Ash-Based Geopolymer Filler Loading on
        Compressive Strength in Glass-Reinforced Epoxy Pipe 22
    2.4.2 Effect of Fly Ash-Based Geopolymer Filler on Hydrostatic
        Pressure Strength in Glass-Reinforced Epoxy Pipe 25
2.5 Conclusion 26
References 27

2.1 INTRODUCTION

To meet technical, technological and economic requirements imposed by the oil industry to increase new technologies and materials for manufacturing numerous productions, the need for current composite materials becomes increasingly evident.

The remaining and unique properties of polymeric composite materials include advanced mechanical, counting stiffness and specific strength properties; anti-corrosive properties; light weight; extended lifetime against fatigue phenomenon and higher natural frequencies. These properties have made these materials a modest contender for a wide range of engineering applications (Hollaway, 2010). At the present time, numerous modern industrial technologies and applications require resources with properties such as great fatigue strength, higher specific stiffness, greater specific strength and good impact characteristics, which cannot be provided by conservative monolithic materials like alloys materials, polymers and ceramics (Karpuz, 2005).

DOI: 10.1201/9781003220947-2

Fiber-reinforced plastic (FRP) pipe has many advantages because of its polymeric nature and glass fibers (Martins *et al.*, 2014). Excellent corrosion resistance, light weight and inner wall smoothness create a product with great hydraulic performance due to its low friction coefficient. The key feature of glass fiber-reinforced plastic (GFRP) pipes makes them a primary competitor of traditional steel, concrete pipe and asbestos, which are damaged by chemical corrosion. GFRP pipes are produced because they have characteristically high corrosion resistance (Rafiee, 2013). This tendency provides a smooth internal surface over a long period of operation time and lower head loss (Kozyra, 2005). GFRP pipes are comprised of high specific strength and comparatively low elastic modulus and are lightweight. Although GFRP pipes are more durable, the steel pipes and concrete pipes are more resistant against vibrations and internal shocks (Anderson, 2000).

Fiber-reinforced composites are increasingly used as alternatives for conventional materials primarily because of their high specific strength, specific stiffness and adaptability. In addition, the viscoelastic character of composites renders them suitable for high-performance structural applications in the aerospace, marine and automobile industries (Fabian *et al.*, 2002; Mangalgiri, 1999; Wróbel *et al.*, 2004). The unique properties of polymeric composite materials make them appropriate for a wide range of engineering projects. As the most important composite category, polymeric composites are active in high-tech industrial applications like military sectors and aerospace, and in low-tech industries like sanitary wares (Rafiee, 2016). Table 2.1 presents a consolidated view of the fiber-reinforced/mineral-filled epoxy composite parameters used by different researchers.

Pipes made of composite glass fiber polyester resin are used in the chemical industry. Under the influence of static and dynamic loads, pipes made for this purpose are being abused. Considering the conditions of future use in the chemical industry, the topic of this analysis was the estimation of the useful life of glass fiber-reinforced epoxy (GRE) composite pipes (Stamenović *et al.*, 2011). The application of composite materials in the oil industry contributes significant savings because of their beneficial material properties of excellent strength and stiffness to weight ratio and corrosion resistance (Mallick, 2007). Engineers have focused on the challenge of designing structures that will be fit over their lifetimes, typically lasting 20–30 years (Frost & Cervenka, 1994).

The idea of filament winding development was presented in the 1940s and recorded as a method that created high strength and lightweight products that contain fundamentally two elements: tape type reinforcement or filament and a matrix or resin (Abdalla *et al.*, 2007). It is often used in wide areas such as aerospace, industrial, sports and recreational and commercial areas. Tubes, pressure containers, reservoirs, pipes, drive shafts and many other structures are formed using this method. Filament winding development utilizes numerous dissimilar fibers and resins to achieve preferred features and appearance for the end constituent (Soutis, 2005).

Islam *et al.* (2013) and Abu Hashim *et al.* (2016) researched geopolymer materials as a matrix resin for filament winding applications, but they studied mostly silica-based geopolymer matrix resin without an epoxy system. Mat Daud *et al.* (2015a,b,c) used epoxies/thermosetting polymers as a matrix and added geopolymer filler without using any fiber reinforcement.

TABLE 2.1

Studies on Fiber-Reinforced/Mineral-Filled Epoxy Composites on Mechanical and Physical Properties

Composite Component	Descriptions	Result	Reference
SiO_2/epoxy nanocomposite	Studied the crack propagation path and fractured surface behavior using field emission SEM and SEM, respectively, to analyze the distribution of SiO_2 particles	SiO_2 particles were uniformly distributed. They were also found in the formation of the cup and cone fracture on the tested specimens	Yao *et al.* (2008)
Fiberglass/ epoxy	Similar analysis on explosion-produced underwater severe shock loads was done for epoxy composite filled with different weight fractions of glass fibers and fly ash	Composites filled with glass fiber and fly ash showed less impact on explosion	Singlal & Chawla (2010)
Fiberglass/SiO_2/ epoxy	Polymer composites were fabricated using glass fiber with the addition of 10 wt% of silica nanoparticles Fatigue life of the composite was studied	Addition of silica particles has increased the fatigue life threefold There is suppressed cracking in the matrix, which in turn reduced the crack propagation rate in the nanoparticle-modified composite system	Manjunatha *et al.* (2010)
Bamboo fiber/ epoxy	Epoxy composites were reinforced with bamboo fiber, Al_2O_3, SiC and industrial wastes, such as copper slag and red mud fillers. Synergistic effects were studied	Tensile strength of epoxy composites reinforced with bamboo fiber were mostly decreased because the composite system contains voids. Minimum void fraction was found in red mud-filled composites compared with SiC	Biswas *et al.* (2010)
Slag/epoxy	Epoxy matrix composites filled with different weight fractions of slag particulate by hand layup method were fabricated	Flexural and tensile properties enhanced by 20% while the impact properties were reduced. Addition of slag and cement has improved the mechanical properties	Ramesh *et al.* (2012)
Fiberglass/ epoxy	Studied the mechanical properties of glass epoxy composite materials filled with Al_2O_3, $CaCo_3$, SiO_2 and PbO	Mechanical properties were improved. Addition of PbO filler has improved the tensile strength. Addition of SiO_2 created better torsional and hardness properties compared with other fillers	Akram *et al.* (2013)

(Continued)

TABLE 2.1 (*Continued*)

Studies on Fiber-Reinforced/Mineral-Filled Epoxy Composites on Mechanical and Physical Properties

Composite Component	Descriptions	Result	Reference
Glass/carbon fiber/epoxy	The glass/carbon fiber/epoxy hybrid composites were developed by varying the reinforcements in terms of weight percentage of 15%, 30%, 45% and 60% of glass fiber and carbon fiber in 40% of epoxy matrix	The inclusion of carbon fiber materials in glass/epoxy composite significantly enhanced the ultimate tensile strength, yield strength and peak load of the composite. The ductility of carbon fiber-reinforced composite is higher than the other composites	Jagannatha & Harish (2015)
Fly ash/epoxy	Fly ash-filled epoxy polymer composites are produced with different fly ash particles by weight. Mechanical properties were investigated in this study	The toughness and hardness maximum for 40% fly ash contained composites that are 2 J and Rf106.50, respectively, but tensile strength is better for 30% of fly ash-based composites	Patra *et al.* (2018)

Abbreviations: SEM, scanning electron microscopy.

Geopolymer functionalities with polymeric materials have been reported in some organic polymers such as polypropylene (PP) (Liu and Liang, 2011). The PP fiber was added to reinforce the geopolymer, resulting in improved tensile failure, shrinkage and high brittleness. There have been other studies using polyvinyl alcohol (PVA) short fibers to improve the ductility of hardened geopolymeric cement (Yunsheng *et al.*, 2008). The addition of PVA fiber changed the impact failure mode of the geopolymer from brittle to ductile, resulting in great impact toughness; whereas Du *et al.* (2016) reported the use of epoxy resin in geopolymers to study the thickening properties of epoxy resin. The addition of epoxy enhanced the compressive strength of hardened geopolymer paste. The studies also reveal the potential of epoxy resin as a compatibilizer when diluted and dispersed in geopolymer suspension.

2.2 GEOPOLYMER FILLER IN POLYMERIC MATERIALS

Hussain *et al.* (2005) combined geopolymer and epoxy matrices for automobile and marine applications. The geopolymer in viscous paste was added into a mixture of epoxy resin and curing agent and then allowed to cure. This combination helped improve thermal stability and fire resistance of the epoxy. However, there was no mechanical testing data reported to discuss the effect of geopolymer filler on the mechanical properties of epoxy composite.

Fiber-reinforced composites based on the geopolymer matrix have been well known for more than 20 years, since the first patent was filed by Davidovits *et al.* (2002). These materials can be manufactured and cured at room temperature or thermoset in a simple autoclave. After a few hours of curing, these new materials exhibit excellent features, such as light weight and high strength, and with an ideal fire resistance that can maintain temperatures up to 1200°C with long-term exposure, nontoxic fumes and smokes and resisting all organic solvent that can only be affected by highly strong hydrochloric acid (Davidovits, 2020). These superior properties help to use geopolymer matrix composites more competently in high-tech technologies such as aerospace, ground transportation or automotive industries and naval architecture, particularly for applications that involve high temperature resistance (Davidovits, 2020). Furthermore, geopolymeric matrices are regulated or controlled easily and do not need to be heated at high temperatures because they are made up at room temperature or thermoset in a simple autoclave (basically below 150°C) for several hours. Furthermore, most categories of fibers can be used with geopolymer matrices and singular ones can protect carbon from oxidation (Abu Hashim *et al.*, 2016; Tran *et al.*, 2011; Lyon *et al.*, 1997).

Mat Daud *et al.* (2015a) investigated the effect of fly ash-based geopolymers in epoxy-layered silicate nanocomposites through flexural properties and morphological characterization. A series of nanocomposites with fly ash-based geopolymers containing 1–7 wt% were prepared. The addition of 1–2% of fly ash showed a lower flexural strength of 6.09 MPa compared with the flexural strength of nanocomposites without fly ash (9.19 MPa). However, at 3 wt% of fly ash geopolymer material, flexural strength unexpectedly increased (14.98 MPa) compared with the original. The study was prepared using epoxy forms of bisphenol A diglycidyl ether (DGEBA) as a polymer matrix and montmorillonite surface modified as a nanofiller with 35–45 wt% dimethyl dialkyl amine (C14–C18). The fly ash raw materials with particle sizes ranging from 50 to 100 μm were sourced from Saudi Arabia.

Mat Daud *et al.* (2015b) studied the effect of a fly ash-based geopolymer in epoxy-layered silicate nanocomposites using a compressive test. A series of nanocomposites were prepared with fly ash-based geopolymer content of 1–7 per hundred resin (phr). Qualitative assessment of the three-dimensional shape of a geopolymer surface centered on fly ash and the origin was defined by scanning electron microscopy (SEM). The addition of 1–2% of fly ash shows lower compressive strength (12.69 MPa) than nanocomposites without fly ash (24.26 MPa). However, compressive strength (31.06 MPa) suddenly increased at 3 phr of fly ash geopolymer content compared with nanocomposites without fly ash.

Mat Daud *et al.* (2015c) used a compression test to study the effects of kaolin-based geopolymers on epoxy-layered silicate nanocomposites. A series of kaolin-based geopolymer nanocomposites containing a content of 1–7 phr was prepared. This research led to the discovery that the addition of kaolin-based geopolymer lead to a compressive strength lower than nanocomposites without kaolin-based geopolymer, which is a phr material. Nevertheless, the compressive properties unexpectedly increased compared with nanocomposites without 3 phr of kaolin.

Tran *et al.* (2009) explored the curing temperature at which adhesion between silica-based geopolymer matrix and carbon fiber could be accomplished. The continuous fibers were saturated with the geopolymer resin using a homemade impregnation machine. This machinery was intended to stimulate the real pultrusion or filament winding technique. The speed of the fiber during the impregnation process was selected based on the best penetration of geopolymer resin into the fiber; this value was around 34 m/h. Composite samples were manually produced in silicon molds and cured at various temperatures under hot vacuum bagging techniques. Flexural strength properties were conducted using the three-point bending mode. The comparatively broad curing temperature range from 70°C to 100°C achieved high flexural properties, maximum flexural strength values of 570 MPa, and flexural module 65 GPa; relative composite deformation was 0.98% percent when the composite was cured and dried at 75°C. The adhesion of the geopolymer matrix to carbon fiber was very good and the variances within the range of optimum curing temperature were barely defined by SEM observation.

Tran *et al.* (2010) studied mechanical properties of silica-based geopolymer composite cured at ambient conditions in accordance with the size-independent method. Silica-based geopolymer matrix composites containing generally 35 wt%, 50 wt% or 55 wt% of carbon; advance basalt or electrical grade glass (which is fiber glass type E) or roving fibers, respectively, were synthesized and fabricated at ambient temperature. The flexural property of the resulting composites, which is high toughness compared with other ceramic matrix composites, was determined on a universal testing machine under three-point bending mode; whereas the adhesion between the fibers and geopolymer matrix was analyzed under SEM. This showed the adhesion between geopolymer matrix and fibers is very good, and microcracks on both cross-sectional and surface geocomposites are determined as inborn defects of inorganic matrix composites.

Another investigation of developing nanocomposites via geopolymer and thermoplastic mixing was performed by Yuana *et al.* (2004) using low-density polyethylene (LDPE) for glass ceramic application. The LDPE powder was added to a viscous paste of metakaolin-based geopolymer and mixed in the mechanical processor. To improve the adhesion between inorganic powders and polymeric matrix, a coupling agent was used along with preheating in the oven. The preliminary results obtained from the study showed the potential of the geopolymer to enhance the mechanical properties of LDPE. However, this research only involved the application of geopolymer filler produced from one source of geopolymer material (metakaolin), thereby limiting the information on geopolymer composition and subsequent effects on polymer composite properties.

These studies suggest there is very little research about combining a geopolymer and polymer, especially when using the geopolymer as filler material in the polymer matrix. Moreover, the published works only reported the application of geopolymer filler in viscous paste form rather than dry powder form.

2.3 GEOPOLYMER FILLER IN EPOXY HYBRID COMPOSITE

Geopolymers and polymers have good prospective when combined together, which opens a new dimension for plastics and composites leading to the new development of hybrid composites with geopolymer filler. Geopolymer sources using fly ash

Mechanical Properties of Geopolymer Filler in Polymer Composites

have been successful in the last decade, emerging as a new cement alternative in the field of building and construction (Mat Daud et al., 2015b). Fly ash is a silica-rich material made from products discovered from coal-fired electricity generation. It can be used as a source material to react with a liquid alkaline activator within sodium silicate solution (Na_2SiO_3) and sodium hydroxide (NaOH) mixture (Mat Daud et al., 2015b). Current research reviews the potential of fly ash-based geopolymer in an epoxy-layered silicate hybrid composite system and epoxy glass fiber composites and subsequent mechanical properties of the composites from past studies.

2.3.1 Effect of Fly Ash-Based Geopolymer Filler Loading on Compressive Strength

The effect of fly ash-based geopolymer filler loading (0–7 phr) on compressive strength has been studied in epoxy-layered silicate composites by Daud et al. (2014). Based on Figure 2.1, adding fly ash with 3-phr geopolymer content enhanced the compressive strength to 31.06 MPa and modulus to 4727 MPa of the nanocomposite system compared with nanocomposite without geopolymer filler (24.26 MPa and modulus 4259 MPa). Daud et al. (2014) reports a strong interaction between geopolymer filler and polymer chains; however, addition of geopolymer filler loading at 5% and 7% decreased the compressive strength. This may due to an increase of viscosity when added with a higher content of geopolymer filler, which effects the filler distribution in the epoxy matrix. Poor distribution of filler in the polymer matrix will affect the load transfer and reduce the compressive strength.

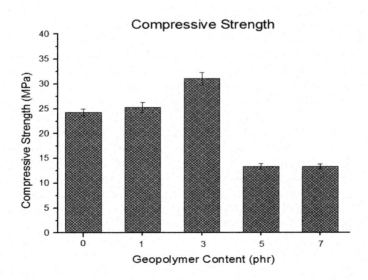

FIGURE 2.1 Compressive strength for nanocomposite filled with fly ash geopolymer of 0–7 phr.

2.4 GEOPOLYMER FILLER IN EPOXY GLASS FIBER COMPOSITES

For several years, non-metallic pipe systems such as GFRP pipes and non-metallic material-lined steel pipes have been widely used in the oil and gas industry because of high corrosion resistance, light weight, low cycle time and short installation time (Qi *et al.*, 2010). GRE pipes are normally designed to withstand high pressure. Their lightweight, relatively thin-walled structure makes them easy to handle and transport, resulting in reduced installation costs. These advantages also make GRE pipes commonly preferred in the fields of aviation and structural engineering (Hahn, 1982). The high usage of these non-metallic pipe systems demands reliable testing methods to ensure they are safe to use and to predict their long-term performance. Nevertheless, previous research reported that GRE pipes also have the following disadvantages: less strength compared with the metallic pipe; cannot stand at high temperature due to epoxy properties and low corrosion resistance, causing strain corrosion in acidic environments (Knox *et al.*, 2000; Salibi, 2001). The aim of this study is to overcome all of these disadvantages and to use GRE pipes in the offshore oil and gas industry, in particular composite pipelines for aqueous liquids, and to produce higher GRE pipe strength. Geopolymer filler such as fly ash is used in this research to solve these problems. Fly ash contains finely divided ash produced by pulverized coal in power stations. The spherical shape of the fly ash improves the consolidation of the pipe and reduces its permeability (Pacheco-Torgal *et al.*, 2008). Therefore materials, such as fly ash, kaolin and white clay, have great potential to be used as a source material to react with liquid alkaline activator within sodium silicate solution (Na_2SiO_3) and sodium hydroxide (NaOH) mixture (Temuujin *et al.*, 2010).

2.4.1 EFFECT OF FLY ASH-BASED GEOPOLYMER FILLER LOADING ON COMPRESSIVE STRENGTH IN GLASS-REINFORCED EPOXY PIPE

Effect of fly ash-based geopolymer filler loading (0–40 wt%) on compressive strength has been studied on glass-reinforced epoxy pipe. Figure 2.2 (a) and (b) shows the schematic diagram of pipe samples being tested in vertical and horizontal positions. Figures 2.3 and 2.4 clearly show great differences in compressive strength in both vertical and horizontal positions, because in a vertical position, when loads were applied to the top of the samples, the entire areas of the samples hold the strength of the pipe (Figure 2.5). When loads were applied on the surface in a horizontal position, only two points held that area to support the whole sample (see Figure 2.3). In this situation, resin plays an important role in creating high compressive strength on pipe samples in vertical position tests compared with samples tested in the horizontal position. In the vertical position, the tendency for glass fiber to slip is very high compared with samples tested in the horizontal position because the glass fiber stacked up when load was applied to the pipe samples in the vertical position, thus creating a big difference in compressive strength.

Figure 2.3 shows the compressive strength of GRE filled with fly ash-based geopolymer samples with 0–40 wt% of filler loading in the vertical position. GRE filled with 30 wt% of fly ash-based geopolymer filler shows the highest result of 94.64 MPa

Mechanical Properties of Geopolymer Filler in Polymer Composites

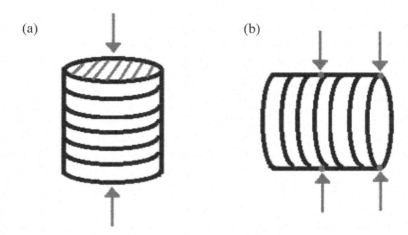

FIGURE 2.2 Schematic diagram of testing pipe sample in (a) vertical and (b) horizontal positions.

for samples with 12M NaOH concentration compared with other pipe samples. Compressive strength of GRE filled with fly ash-based geopolymer pipe increased from 0 to 30 wt% of filler loading. From 0 to 30 wt% of filler loading, 30 wt% of filler loading recorded the highest strength in the range of 75.49–94.64 MPa, whereas GRE pipe without any geopolymer filler recorded the lowest strength of 53.36 MPa.

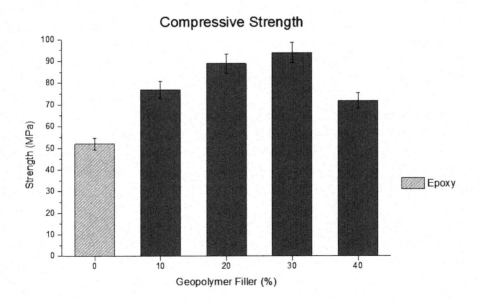

FIGURE 2.3 Compressive strength of GRE-filled fly ash-based geopolymer pipe in the vertical position.

The compressive strength increased with the increasing weight percentage of filler loading until the optimum results were achieved.

At 40 wt% of filler loading, the resin was unable to be mixed due to higher viscosity and lower workability then the strength was able to acquire. This situation showed that the percentage of filler loading was correlated to the viscosity and workability and thus to the compressive strength of the samples. This reduction is recognized as the incapability of the filler to sustain tensions relocated from the polymer matrix, and poor interfacial connection produces incomplete spaces among filler and matrix materials, which produces a weak arrangement (Sudheer *et al.*, 2014). This finding was supported by Shakuntala *et al.* (2014) who reported that higher filler loading reduces the interaction between the matrix and filler, thus producing poor compressive strength.

Figure 2.4 shows the compressive strength development of GRE filled with fly ash-based geopolymer pipe samples with various filler loadings (0 wt% to 40 wt%) being tested on horizontal positions. The results show that the sample with 30 wt% of filler loading and 12M NaOH concentration for fly ash-based geopolymer filler have the highest compressive strength (6.73 MPa).

Figure 2.4 also shows reduction in compressive strength from 6.73 to 6.24 MPa for epoxy filled with fly ash-based geopolymer of 12M NaOH concentration pipe samples after 30 wt% of filler loading. This is due to higher viscosity and lower workability of the resin, which decreases the compressive strength.

The compressive strength of samples that have higher filler loading and higher NaOH concentration is low due to the excessive concentration of NaOH in a mixture. A high concentration of NaOH and filler loading complicates the mixing process

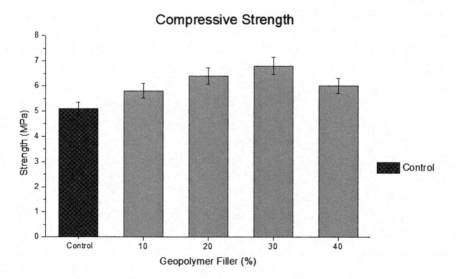

FIGURE 2.4 Compressive strength of GRE-filled fly ash-based geopolymer pipe on the horizontal position.

Mechanical Properties of Geopolymer Filler in Polymer Composites

more evenly and cause improper geopolymerization, thus affecting the compressive strength of the sample. Also, higher concentrations of NaOH will increase the sodium content and decrease OH⁻, enabling the production of sodium carbonate via carbonation atmosphere. This condition interferes with the geopolymerization and it coincides with the findings by Barbosa *et al.* (2000).

2.4.2 EFFECT OF FLY ASH-BASED GEOPOLYMER FILLER ON HYDROSTATIC PRESSURE STRENGTH IN GLASS-REINFORCED EPOXY PIPE

Short-time hydrostatic failure pressure strength tests were conducted to determine the static hydraulic pressure, which causes failure of the pipes. The hydrostatic pressure tests were performed with the same pressurizing system employed in previous work done by Martins *et al.* (2012), where the closed-end condition was under biaxial pressure loading. Hydrostatic pressure leak tests were carried out using a hydrostatic-pressure machine capable of applying pressure at a uniform rate until the failure of the test specimen. The two ends of the samples were sealed using endcaps with rubber rings to prevent any longitudinal load from being transmitted to the pipe. A special device was developed and built to measure the circumferential length, as the pressure was increased. Figure 2.5 shows the apparatus for hydrostatic pressure test.

The hydrostatic pressure or burst test results of control samples (GRE pipe without geopolymer filler) compared with the best compressive strength for both GRE filled with fly ash-based geopolymer pipe samples (12M NaOH concentration and 30 wt% of filler loading) are shown in Figure 2.6. The samples for each pipe (GRE without any geopolymer filler and GRE-filled fly ash-based geopolymer filler pipe) were produced with two patterns of filament winding types with a hoop pattern (90° angle) and helical pattern (55° angle). Figure 2.6 shows that the samples with a hoop

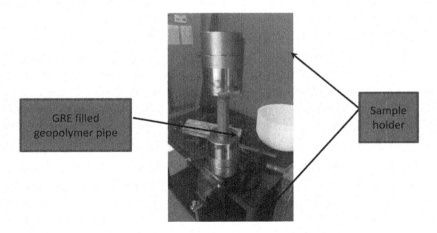

FIGURE 2.5 Hydrostatic pressure leak testing apparatus.

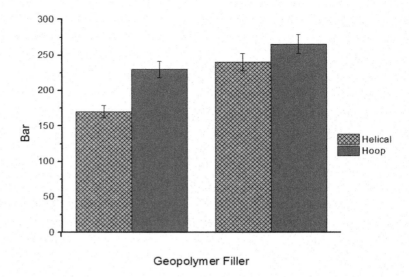

FIGURE 2.6 Burst test of the control sample and GRE filled with fly ash-based geopolymer pipe.

pattern produce higher pressure strength (225 and 261 bar) compared with the helical pattern (181 and 233 bar) for each control sample and GRE filled with fly ash-based geopolymer pipe, respectively. The test results proved that the geopolymer filler does significantly affect he pressure resistance of the GRE pipes because energy is absorbed in the development of plastic deformation of matrix material and debonding occurs at the matrix/reinforcement interface and in the fracture of reinforcing material. Thus, the geopolymer filler is applicable and suitable to use in matrix resin with fiberglass pressure pipes, according to the hydrostatic pressure leak tests results.

2.5 CONCLUSION

This study concludes that fly ash geopolymer filler enhances the compressive strength of epoxy composite filled with geopolymer and GRE pipe filled with fly ash-based geopolymer. Based on the results obtained from the compressive test for nanocomposite filled with fly ash geopolymer, the compressive test (horizontal and vertical) for GRE-filled fly ash-based geopolymer pipe and the burst test of the control GRE filled with fly ash-based geopolymer pipe, the following conclusions can be drawn:

1. Compressive strength of nanocomposite filled with fly ash geopolymer increases with the increase of geopolymer filler loading due to good interaction between geopolymer filler and epoxy matrix.
2. Compressive strength for both horizontal and vertical position testing for GRE-filled fly ash-based geopolymer pipe shows an incremental trend with the addition of geopolymer filler. Addition of 30% geopolymer filler contributed the highest compressive strength for both testing positions.

Mechanical Properties of Geopolymer Filler in Polymer Composites

3. GRE-filled fly ash-based geopolymer pipe shows significant effect on the pressure resistance compared with the control sample. Geopolymer filler enables the absorption of energy in the development of plastic deformation, debonding matrix to reinforcement interface and overall composite failure.

REFERENCES

Abdalla, F., Mutasher, S., Khalid, Y., Sapuan, S., Hamouda, A., Sahari, B. & Hamdan, M. 2007. "Design and fabrication of low cost filament winding machine." *Materials & Design*, 28, 234–239. https://doi.org/10.1016/j.matdes.2005.06.015

Abu Hashim, M., Abdullah, M. M. A., Ruzaidi, C., Kamarudin, H. & Binhussain, M. 2016. "Effect of geopolymer filler in glass reinforced epoxy (GRE) pipe for piping application: mechanical properties." *IOP Conference Series: Materials Science and Engineering.* https://doi.org/10.1088/1757-899X/133/1/012044

Akram, W., Chaturvedi, S. K. & Syed Mazhar, A. 2013. "Comparative study of mechanical properties of e-glass/epoxy composite materials with Al_2O_3, $CaCo_3$, SiO_2 and PBO fillers." *International Journal of Engineering Research & Technology*, 2, 1029–1034.

Anderson, L. R. 2000. Preliminary ring design. In *Structural Mechanics of Buried Pipes*. Edited by R. K. Watkins. Boca Raton: CRC Press LLC, 12.

Barbosa, V. F., Mackenzie, K. J. & Thaumaturgo, C. 2000. "Synthesis and characterisation of materials based on inorganic polymers of alumina and silica: sodium polysialate polymers." *International Journal of Inorganic Materials*, 2, 309–317. https://doi.org/10.1016/S1466-6049(00)00041-6

Biswas, S., Satapathy, A. & Patnaik, A. 2010. "Effect of ceramic fillers on mechanical properties of bamboo fiber reinforced epoxy composites: a comparative study." *Advanced Materials Research*, 123–125, 1031–1034. https://doi.org/10.4028/www.scientific.net/AMR.123-125.1031

Daud, Y. M., Kamarudin, H., Ruzaidi, C. M., Osman, A. F. & Al-Bakri, M. 2014. "Epoxy layered-silicates filled with fly ash based geopolymer: compressive properties." *Materials Science Forum*, 803, 58–62. https://doi.org/10.4028/www.scientific.net/MSF.803.58

Davidovits, J. 2002. "30 years of successes and failures in geopolymer applications. Market trends and potential breakthroughs." *Keynote Conference on Geopolymer Conference.* https://www.geopolymer.org/category/library/technical-papers/

Davidovits, J. 2020. *Geopolymer Chemistry and Applications.* 5th Ed. Saint-Quentin, France: Geopolymer Institute, 67.

Du, J., Bu, Y., Shen, Z., Hou, X. & Huang, C. 2016. "Effects of epoxy resin on the mechanical performance and thickening properties of geopolymer cured at low temperature." *Materials & Design*, 109, 133–145. https://doi.org/10.1016/j.matdes.2016.07.003

Fabian, P., Rice, J., Munshi, N., Humer, K. & Weber, H. W. 2002. "Novel radiation-resistant insulation systems for fusion magnets." *Fusion Engineering and Design*, 61, 795–799. https://doi.org/10.1016/S0920-3796(02)00205-3

Frost, S. & Cervenka, A. 1994. "Glass fibre-reinforced epoxy matrix filament-wound pipes for use in the oil industry." *Composites Manufacturing*, 5, 73–81. https://doi.org/10.1016/0956-7143(94)90058-2

Gibson, A. 1989. "Composite materials in the offshore industry." *Metals and Materials (Institute of Metals)*, 5, 590–594.

Hahn, H. 1982. "Fatigue of composites – environmental effects." *Fatigue and Creep of Composite Materials*, 19–35.

Hussain, M., Varely, R., Cheng, Y. B., Mathys, Z., & Simon, G. P. (2005). Synthesis and thermal behavior of inorganic-organic hybrid geopolymer composites. *Journal of Applied Polymer Science*, 96(1), 112–121.

Hollaway, L. 2010. A review of the present and future utilization of FRP composites in the civil infrastructure with reference to their important in-service properties. In *Construction and Building Materials*. Edited by M. C. Forde. Amsterdam: Elsevier Ltd., 24, 2419–2445. https://doi.org/10.1016/j.conbuildmat.2010.04.062

Islam, M. S., Masoodi, R. & Rostami, H. 2013. "The effect of nanoparticles percentage on mechanical behavior of silica-epoxy nanocomposites." *Journal of Nanoscience*, 2, 1–10. https://doi.org/10.1155/2013/275037

Jagannatha, T. D. & Harish, G. 2015. "Mechanical properties of carbon/glass fiber reinforced epoxy hybrid polymer composites." *International Journal of Mechanical Engineering and Robotics Research*, 4, 131–137.

Karpuz, P. 2005. "Mechanical characterization of filament wound composite tubes by internal pressure testing." MSc. Dissertation, Middle East Technical University, Ankara Turkey. http://etd.lib.metu.edu.tr/upload/12606128/index.pdf

Knox, E., Cowling, M. & Hashim, S. 2000 "Fatigue performance of adhesively bonded connections in GRE pipes." *International Journal of Fatigue*, 22, 513–519. https://doi.org/10.1016/S0142-1123(00)00015-3

Kozyra, M. K. 2005. *Fiberglass Pipe Design: AWWA Manual of Practice*. Second Ed. Denver: American Water Works Association.

Liu, S. P. & Liang, C. W. 2011. "Preparation and mechanical properties of polypropylene/montmorillonite nanocomposites – after grafted with hard/soft grafting agent." *International Communications in Heat and Mass Transfer*, 38, 434–441. https://doi.org/10.1016/j.icheatmasstransfer.2010.12.030

Lyon, R. E., Balaguru, P., Foden, A., Sorathia, U., Davidovits, J. & Davidovics, M. 1997. "Fire-resistant aluminosilicate composites." *Fire and Materials*, 21, 67–73. https://doi.org/10.1002/(SICI)1099-1018(199703)21:2≤67::AID-FAM596≥3.0.CO;2-N

Mallick, P. K. 2007. *Fiber-Reinforced Composites: Materials, Manufacturing, and Design*. Third Ed. Boca Raton: CRC Press, 57.

Mangalgiri, P. 1999. "Composite materials for aerospace applications." *Bulletin of Materials Science*, 22, 657–664. https://doi.org/10.1007/BF02749982

Manjunatha, C. M., Taylor, A. C., Kinloch, A. J. & Sprenger, S. 2010. "The tensile fatigue behaviour of a silica nanoparticle-modified glass fibre reinforced epoxy composite." *Composites Science and Technology*, 70, 193–199. https://doi.org/10.1016/j.compscitech.2009.10.012

Martins, L., Bastian, F. & Netto, T. 2014. Reviewing some design issues for filament wound composite tubes. In *Materials & Design*. Edited by K. L. Edwards. Amsterdam: Elsevier Ltd., 55, 242–249. https://doi.org/10.1016/j.matdes.2013.09.059

Martins, L. A., Bastian, F. L. & Netto, T. A. 2012. "Structural and functional failure pressure of filament wound composite tubes." *Materials & Design*, 36, 779–787. https://doi.org/10.1016/j.matdes.20123.11.029

Mat Daud, Y., Hussin, K., Ruzaidi, C. M., Osman, A. F., Al-Bakri, M. & Binhussain, M. 2015a. "Epoxy layered silicates with fly ash-based geopolymer: flexural properties." *Materials Science Forum*, 819, 290–294.

Mat Daud, Y., Hussin, K., Ruzaidi, C. M., Osman, A. F., Al Bakri Abdullah, M. M. 2015b. "Epoxy layered-silicates filled with fly ash based geopolymer: compressive properties." *Materials Science Forum*, 803, 58–62. https://doi.org/10.4028/www.scientific.net/MSF.803.58

Mat Daud, Y., Hussin, K., Ruzaidi, C. M., Osman, A. F., Al Bakri Abdullah, M. M. & Binhussain, M. 2015c. "Kaolin-based geopolymer filled epoxy-layered silicates: compressive properties." *Applied Mechanics and Materials*, 754–755, 220–224.

Pacheco-Torgal, F., Castro-Gomes, J. & Jalali, S. 2008 "Alkali-activated binders: a review: Part 1. Historical background, terminology, reaction mechanisms and hydration products." *Construction and Building Materials*, 22, 1305–1314. https://doi.org/10.1016/j.conbuildmat.2007.10.015

Patra, A., Das, M., Anwar, K., Khan, B., Kamran, K. & Dipak Ranjan, J. 2018. "Investigation on mechanical and physical properties of fly ash reinforced epoxy resin composite." *IOSR Journal of Mechanical and Civil Engineering (IOSR-JMCE)*, 15, 64–68. doi: 10.9790/1684-1501046468

Qi D, Yan M, Ding N, Cai X, Li H & Zhang S 2010 "Application of polymer composite pipes in oilfield in china," *The 7th International MERL Oilfield Engineering with Polymers Conference*. London, UK.

Rafiee, R. 2013. Experimental and theoretical investigations on the failure of filament wound GRP pipes. In *Composites Part B: Engineering*. Edited by D. Hui and L. Feo. Amsterdam: Elsevier Ltd., 45, 257–267. doi.org/10.1016/j.compositesb.2012.04.009

Rafiee, R. 2016. "On the mechanical performance of glass-fibre-reinforced thermosetting-resin pipes: a review." *Composite Structures*, 143, 151–164. https://doi.org/10.1016/J.COMPSTRUCT.2016.02.037

Ramesh C. H., Jeevan Kumar N. & Kumar, M. A. 2012. "Fabrication and mechanical properties of iron slag matrix composite materials." *International Journal of Engineering Research and Development*, 5, 34–46. http://dx.doi.org/10.17577/IJERTV9IS070480

Salibi, Z. 2001. "Performance of reinforced thermosetting resin pipe systems in desalination applications: A long-term solution to corrosion—the Arabian Gulf example." *Desalination*, 138, 379–384. https://doi.org/10.1016/S0011-9164(01)00287-9

Shakuntala, O., Raghavendra, G. & Samir Kumar, A. 2014. "Effect of filler loading on mechanical and tribological properties of wood apple shell reinforced epoxy composite." *Advances in Materials Science and Engineering*, 38651, 9. https://doi.org/10.1155/2014/538651

Singlal, M. & Chawla, V. 2010. "Mechanical properties of epoxy resin – fly ash composite." *Journal of Minerals & Materials Characterization & Engineering*, 9, 199–210. https://doi.org/10.4236/jmmce.2010.93017

Soutis, C. 2005. "Carbon fiber reinforced plastics in aircraft construction." *Materials Science and Engineering: A*, 412, 171–176. https://doi.org/10.1016/j.msea.2005.08.064

Stamenović, M., Putić, S., Rakin, M., Medjo, B. & Čikara, D. 2011. "Effect of alkaline and acidic solutions on the tensile properties of glass–polyester pipes." *Materials & Design*, 32, 2456–2461. https://doi.org/10.1016/j.matdes.2010.11.023

Sudheer, M., Prabhu, R., Raju, K. & Bhat, T. 2014. "Effect of filler content on the performance of epoxy/PTW composites." *Advances in Materials Science and Engineering*, 970468, 11. https://doi.org/10.1155/2014/970468

Temuujin, J., van Riessen, A. & MacKenzie, K. 2010 "Preparation and characterisation of fly ash based geopolymer mortars." *Construction and Building Materials*, 24, 1906–1910. https://doi.org/10.1016/j.conbuildmat.2010.04.012

Tran, D., Kroisová, D., Louda, P., Bortnovsky, O. & Bezucha, P. 2009. Effect of curing temperature on flexural properties of silica-based geopolymer-carbon reinforced composite. *Manufacturing Engineering*, 37, 492–497.

Tran, D. H. P. L., Kroisiva, D. & Bortnovsky, O. 2010. "Thermal mechanical behavior of silica-based geopolymer-carbon composite." Paper presented at the 7th International Conference, TEXSCI.

Tran, H., Louda, P., Kroisová, D., Bortnovsky, O. & Xiem, N. T. 2011. New generation of geopolymer composite for fire-resistance. In *Advances in Composite Materials - Analysis of Natural and Man-Made Materials*. Edited by P. Tesinova. London: IntechOpen Limited. https://doi.org/10.5772/17933

Wróbel, G., Szymiczek, M. & Wierzbicki, Ł. 2004. "Swagelining as a method of pipelines rehabilitation." *Journal of Materials Processing Technology*, 157–158, 637–642. https://doi.org/10.1016/j.jmatprotec.2004.07.150

Yao X. F., Zhou D. & Yehb, H. Y. 2008 "Macro/microscopic fracture characterizations of SiO2/epoxy Nano composites." *Aerospace Science and Technology*, 12, 223–230. https://doi.org/10.1016/j.ast.2007.03.005

Yuana, X. W., Easteal, A. J. & Bhattacharyyaa, D. 2004. "Geopolymer reinforced polyethylene nanocomposites." In *Composite Technologies for 2020*. Edited by L. Ye, Y.-W. Mai and Z. Su. Cambridge, UK: Woodhead Publishing Limited, 796–802. https://doi.org/10.1016/B978-1-85573-831-7.50135-8

Yunsheng, Z., Wei, S., Zongjin, L., Xiangming, Z., Eddie & Chungkong, C. 2008. "Impact properties of geopolymer based extrudates incorporated with fly ash and PVA short fiber." *Construction and Building Materials*, 22, 370–383. https://doi.org/10.1016/j.conbuildmat.2006.08.006

3 Basalt Fiber-Reinforced Polymer Composites
A Review

R.A. Ilyas
Universiti Teknologi Malaysia
Johor Bahru, Malaysia

T.M.N. Afiq, R.M. Affiq, T.H. Tahrim, S.M. Sapuan, and M.S.N. Atikah
Universiti Putra Malaysia
Serdang, Malaysia

A. Atiqah
Universiti Kebangsaan Malaysia
Bangi, Malaysia

Hanafi Ismail
Universiti Sains Malaysia
Nibong Tebal, Malaysia

CONTENTS

3.1 Introduction 32
    3.1.1 Basalt Fiber 32
    3.1.2 Polymer Composites 35
3.2 Basalt Fiber-Reinforced Polymer Composites 36
3.3 Mechanical and Thermal Properties of Basalt Fiber Reinforcement 49
    3.3.1 Mechanical Properties 49
    3.3.2 Thermal Properties 57
3.4 Applications 59
    3.4.1 Laminates and Pre-Pregs 59
    3.4.2 Transportation 59
3.5 Conclusions 60
References 61

DOI: 10.1201/9781003220947-3

3.1 INTRODUCTION

A composite material is a non-uniform solid produced by combining two or more materials that are mechanically bonded together. Each material in the composite retains its properties and when combined, the individual properties are improved (Ilyas and Sapuan 2020a,b; Alsubari et al. 2021; Omran et al. 2021). In general, composites are composed of two phases, matrix and reinforcement (Abral et al. 2019; Aisyah et al. 2019). The matrix has the responsibility of bonding the reinforcements and the reinforcements are responsible for attaining the composite's strength. Today, fiber and polymer is the most popular type of composite material and it is widely applied in various types of industries. It also has the potential to substitute conventional metal in structural applications like in the aerospace, automobile and wind turbine blade manufacturing industries. The most well-known composites are fiber-reinforced polyester composites. They contain fiber material embedded in a polyester matrix and include natural fiber-reinforced polyester (NFRP), glass-fiber reinforced polyester (GFRP), and carbon fiber-reinforced polymer (CFRP) (Meenakshi and Krishnamoorthy 2018). The viscoelasticity of composites make them suitable for high-performance structural applications like in the aerospace, marine and automobile industries; satellites; sporting goods; robots; thermal insulation structures like cryostats for low-temperature technology; hydrogen technology tanks; superconductivity and in biomedicine for body-compatible implants.

Berozashvili (2001) stated that basalt fiber (BF) is a novel fiber that appeared in recent years. It offers high strength, excellent fiber or resin adhesion, and can be easily processed using conventional means and equipment. Furthermore, BFs do not contain any other additives when used in a single producing process, which is an advantage in production cost compared with glass fiber. Compared with E-glass fiber, BFs have higher tensile strength, and compared with carbon fibers, the strain to failure of BF is larger. Also, basalt fibers have high chemical stability, outstanding mechanical properties, noise-dampening properties, perfect thermal resistance (superior to glass fibers), are chemical resistant and are low water-logging materials. On the top of that, basalt fibers are non-toxic, non-combustible, bioinert and harmless. According to Wei et al. (2010), the basalt fibers are suitable for various applications, such as corrosion-resistant material in the chemical industry, wear and friction material in the automobile industry, the target area of anti-low-velocity impact, construction reinforcement material, and high-temperature insulation of automobile catalysts. This chapter will review the current research on basalt fiber-reinforced polymer (BFRP) composites.

3.1.1 BASALT FIBER

In the last few decades, strong demand for basalt fiber caused the polymer industry to grow rapidly. Figure 3.1 shows widely used BF and carbon-woven fabrics. These fibers are currently used to produce lightweight, strong hybrid composite materials for the construction of infrastructure and civilian use (Tehrani Dehkordi et al. 2013). BF is currently the preferred material. It is also an inorganic fiber with an excellent high modulus, outstanding durability, enhanced failure strain, low toxicity

Basalt Fiber-Reinforced Polymer Composites

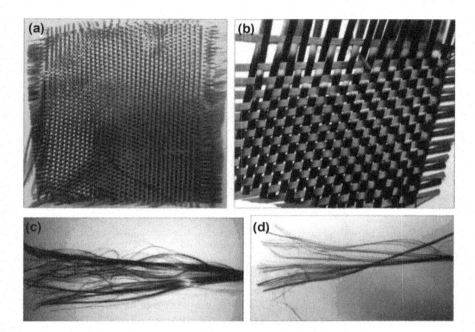

FIGURE 3.1 Woven fabrics: (a) Basalt fiber fabric; (b) carbon fiber fabric; (c) carbon fiber strands; (d) basalt fiber strands. (Adapted with copyright permission from Dhand et al. 2015.)

and is natural, eco-friendly and affordable to process (Dhand et al. 2015). BF's positive characteristics include acoustic insulation features, higher heat tolerance, good chemical attack tolerance, and minimal permeability of water (Sim, Park and Moon 2005).

BFs are made from the extrusion of melted granitic rock formations contained in the basalt-centered volcano eruption (Banibayat and Patnaik 2014). After solidification, basalt rocks are developed from molten lava, known as volcanic rock, and are dark or gray in appearance (Sapuan et al. 2020). Extruding BF is simpler and therefore more energy efficient than other existent fibers (Fiore, Di Bella and Valenza 2011). For the composite applications required, continuous BF is cut in diameters of 10–20 μm and lengths between 3 and 130 mm (Khandelwal and Rhee 2020). Basalt fiber is strong and compatible with various polymer matrices compared with conventional fibers like glass fiber and asbestos fiber. It is used to reinforce thermoset polymers such as epoxy, polyester, and vinyl ester (Khandelwal and Rhee 2020). Table 3.1 lists the mechanical characteristics of BFs and other fibers are evaluated.

Dhand et al. (2015) mentioned that "basalt is chemically high of oxide of magnesium, calcium, sodium, potassium, silicon and iron, and traces of alumina". Figure 3.2 presents the overall percentage distribution of the chemical constituents in basalt.

Basalt's main components are the metal oxides SiO_2, Al_2O_3, Fe_2O_3, CaO, MgO and FeO. Some additional components include K_2O, Na_2O and TiO_2 The chemical

TABLE 3.1
Comparison of Mechanical Properties of Basalt Fiber and Other Fibers

Fiber	Density (gm/cm³)	Tensile Strength (GPa)	Elastic Modulus (GPa)	Elongation at Break (%)
E-glass	2.56	1.4–2.5	76	1.8–3.2
Carbon	1.4	4.0	230–240	1.4–1.8
Basalt	2.8	2.8	89	3.15
Jute	1.3	0.3–0.7	26.5	1.5–1.8
Flax	1.5	0.5–1.5	27.6	2.7–3.2

Source: From Afroz, Patnaikuni and Venkatesan (2017).

structure of basalt fiber is close to glass fiber and both fibers have comparable strength and properties.

The classification of basalts rocks is based on the SiO_2 content as acidic basalts (over 46% SiO_2), mildly acidic basalts (43 to 46% SiO_2) and alkaline basalts (up to 42% SiO_2) (Deák and Czigány, 2009). The most suitable basalt rocks for basalt fiber production are basalt rocks containing 46% SiO_2 (acid basalt). The extrusion process manufactures basalt fibers to form thin threads. Finely powdered basalt is melted around 1500°C–1700°C, and then yields a glassy molten liquid to be extruded (Dhand et al. 2015).

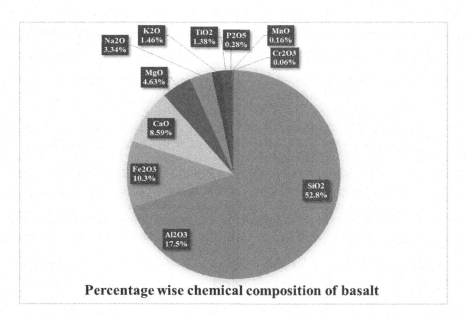

FIGURE 3.2 Percentage distribution of chemical constituents in basalt. (Adapted with copyright permission from Dhand et al. 2015.)

Basalt Fiber-Reinforced Polymer Composites

3.1.2 POLYMER COMPOSITES

Sawyer (2003) reported that in the polymetric matrix there are thermoplastic resins (polypropylene, polyphenylene sulfone, polyamide, polyetheretherketone, etc.) and thermoset resins (polyesters, phenolics, melamines, silicones, polyurethanes and epoxies). There are four polyester resin types: unsaturated polyester resin, saturated polyester resin, alkyd resin and vinyl ester resin.

Composites are composed of two or more different phases, and although they are a single substance, the components remain recognizable and separable (Ilyas et al. 2018a, 2019a, 2020a,b; Syafri et al. 2019; Asrofi et al. 2020). By integrating two or more components, the resulting composite benefits from the properties of various materials of the two constituent stages, which have properties that cannot be achieved by a single constituent (Middleton 2016; Azammi et al. 2019; Ayu et al. 2020; Nazrin et al. 2020; Nurazzi et al. 2020; Sabaruddin et al. 2020; Syafiq et al. 2020). A composite material consisting of a fiber-reinforced polymer (FRP) is a polymer matrix embedded with high-intensity fibers, for example, glass, aramid and carbon (Atiqah et al. 2019).

The primary function of the matrix phase in a composite is to bend the fibers together and roll the medium, which disturbs the externally applied stress to the fibers so only a small portion will get through to the matrix phase (Asyraf et al. 2020a,b,c). Furthermore, the matrix phase acts to maintain the shape of a component and transfers the applied load to the reinforced fibers, protects the reinforced fibers from degradation due to abrasion or environmental attack, and protects the reinforced fibers against chemical attack and mechanical damage (Callister and Rethwisch 2003; Aisyah et al. 2019).

Generally, polymers can be categorized as thermoplastics and thermosets. As matrices for bio-fibers, thermoplastic materials presently dominate; starch, polyethylene, polypropylene (PP), and polyvinyl chloride (PVC) are the most widely used thermoplastics for this purpose (Ku et al. 2011; Jumaidin et al. 2019a,b). Meanwhile, the most frequently used thermosetting matrices are phenol, epoxy, and polyester resins (Norizan et al. 2020; Nurazzi et al. 2019, 2020; Baihaqi et al. 2021). As lightweight metal alternatives, polymer matrix composites are often used and benefit from being lightweight, stiff and rigid, and generally have lower production costs than metals. The range of polymer matrix composites is wide with a vast range of possible polymer matrix materials combined with several different reinforcement forms that can be arranged in different architecture (Middleton 2016; Jumaidin et al. 2020; Kumar et al. 2020;). Polymers have replaced many of the existing materials in various applications over the last couple of decades. This is possible due to the massive benefits polymers offer over conventional materials. Recently, natural fibers have drawn the interest of scientists and technologists (Ilyas et al. 2017, 2019a,b,c,d, 2021; Ilyas, Sapuan, and Ishak 2018; Abral et al. 2020). Fibers with low-density and high basic properties are low-cost fibers. These are, unlike other reinforcing fibers, biodegradable and nonabrasive (Rozilah et al. 2020; Abral et al. 2021). Furthermore, they are also easily accessible and their particular properties are equivalent to those of other reinforcement fibers (Saheb and Jog 1999).

3.2 BASALT FIBER-REINFORCED POLYMER COMPOSITES

Composite material is a combination of dissimilar materials that are mixed and forma a bond on a microscopic level. For instance, cement, rocks, sand and water form the basis of concrete (Nagavally 2017). The first composite bow was invented by the Mongols in 1200 AD using a mixture of "animal glue," wood and bone. They pressed the bows and covered them with birch bark. The bows were strong and precise (Ngo 2018). Lopresto et al. (2011) studied the mechanical characterization of basalt fiber-reinforced polymer. Basalt and glass fiber-reinforced plastic laminates with 300 × 300 mm in plane dimensions compared with glass and BFRP composite's mechanical characteristics. The tensile strength and flexural strength created followed ASTM D3039 and ASTM D790 standards, respectively. Figure 3.3 shows the results of Young's modulus from tensile, flexural and compression tests. The best results obtained with the basalt composite showed 35%–42% higher values than the tested glass composite. Figure 3.4 illustrates the ultimate strength results of Young's modulus from tensile, flexural and compression tests. The glass composite performed better in the tensile case, which is higher than the basalt composite. Lopresto et al. (2011) concluded that "basalt composite showed a 35%–42% higher Young's modulus as well as a better compressive strength and flexural behavior, whereas a higher tensile strength was found for glass material."

Essentially, a composite material is composed of reinforcement (fibers, particles, flakes and/or fillers) embedded in a matrix (polymers, metals or ceramics). The matrix preserves the reinforcement to form the desired shape, whereas the reinforcement enhances the matrix's overall mechanical properties. When appropriately designed, the new combined material possesses better strength than each actual material (Nagavally 2017). Currently, the composite industry continues to develop, with some development based on renewable energy. In particular, the wind turbine

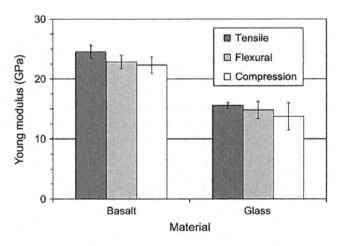

FIGURE 3.3 Young's modulus of tensile, flexural and compressive comparison between basalt and E-glass fiber composites. (Adapted from Lopresto, Leone and De Iorio 2011.)

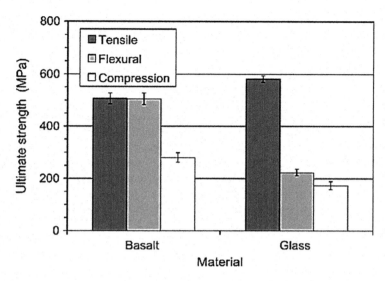

FIGURE 3.4 Ultimate strength of tensile, flexural and compressive comparison between basalt and E-glass fiber composites. (Adapted from Lopresto, Leone and De Iorio 2011.)

blade industry requires enhanced composite materials that engineers can modify based on performance needs. This will create a very sturdy composite layer by positioning the fibers in one direction, making the other direction, where toughness is unnecessary, weaker (Ngo 2018).

In a comprehensive study of chemical sustainability and performance of altered basalt fiber in concrete medium, Afroz, Patnaikuni, and Venkatesan (2017) found that the chemical composition of basalt fiber is almost identical to glass. Strong base 1 M NaOH and 1 M $Ca(OH)_2$ solutions were used for alkaline ion contamination. The effect of chloride and sulfate ions has been determined by 3% NaCl and $CaCl_2$ and by 10% Na_2SO_4 and $CaSO_4$ solutions. The result showed that the enhanced fiber has outstanding characteristics compared with the unmodified fibers based on morphological and chemical analysis. This study showed that silane-modified basalt fibers have sufficient long-term capabilities that are often used in concrete as a fiber reinforcement in extreme environments.

A recent study by Sapuan et al. (2020) on the mechanical characteristics of longitudinal basalt reinforced unsaturated polyester-resin hybrid composites examined the fusion of glass fibers with other types of fiber, which provides both high strength and is more environmentally sustainable. As a sandwich-structured composite by hand layup method in a steel mold, the fibers and the unsaturated polyester resin were combined into the composites and then compressed using compression molding. The glass fiber in a glass-basalt reinforced hybrid composite with a fiber percentage proportion of 25% glass fiber and 75% basalt fiber enhanced its total density, flexure and tensile capabilities. These studies concluded that a significantly higher density of 1.8% compared with B22.5/G7.5 hybrid composites was introduced by roving basalt fiber (BF) composites with basalt fiber. For the proportion of basalt fibers, the tensile and flexural properties improved; the tensile strength for BF composites increased by 69% in relation to G composites, then subsequently rose by 26% in relation to B22.5/G7.5 hybrid composites.

More recent attention has been dedicated to investigating analytical evaluation of the impact of resin matrix in BFRP composites under static and fatigue loading, Zhao et al. (2020) found BFRPs have higher creep and fatigue properties than glass fiber-reinforced polymer composites. Four different forms of BFRP composite resin-based composites were described using refined fatigue test equipment combined with an in situ scanning electron microscope (SEM) for strength, fatigue and microdamage mechanisms. More ductile BFRP matrices such as toughened vinyl ester and epoxy systems curing at ambient temperature have less damage to crack than typical vinyl ester and epoxy systems curing at an elevated temperature. This smaller amount of fatigue damage will minimize both fatigue life and initial stiffness. Overall, this study strengthens the idea that a clear resin effect for BFRP's long-term fatigue life is due to an insufficient set of data. Further testing will help to measure these effects and provide further guidance for enhancing the fatigue life of BFRP products.

In the study conducted by Shishevan et al. (2017) on how weak velocity affects the behavior of BFRP composites, it was shown that the demand of basalt fibers has grown as a completely new, environmentally friendly reinforcing material because of their high mechanical characteristics and good thermal properties. Two homogenous BFRP and CFRP composites reinforced with epoxy matrix composites with carbon and basalt fibers were fabricated by vacuum-assisted resin transfer molding (VARTM) method. As a result, the impact performance of BFRPs was higher than that of CFRPs. Moreover, penetration in BFRPs had a higher energy than in CFRPs. The high toughness and good impact performance of basalt fibers are the main reasons for BFRPs' good impact performance. This study has shown that the fabrication process and the curing process of BFRP composites have been modified by the VARTM method and the curing temperature and pressure increased to 100°C and 1.2 atm to determine the effect of the manufacturing process on the low velocity effects of these composites. The change in fabrication process led to the improvement of the impact behavior of BFRPs. In previous studies to evaluate strain and damage of self-sensing BFRP laminates manufactured with carbon nanofiber (CNF)/epoxy composites under stress, Wang et al. (2018) found that different contents of CNFs were dispersed into a basalt fiber fabric and infused into a conductive network for straining and damage self-sensing BFRP laminates. Prepared CNF/epoxy suspensions were created using a wet layup approach and spread across four layers of unidirectional basalt fiber fabrics. BFRP laminates containing 1.0 wt% and 1.5 wt% of CNF can monitor the evolution of damage in monotonic tensile loads until failure. Their electrical resistance response may have divided into three phases, which correspond to various damage modes. The investigation results show that an analysis of the electrical resilience strain responses during cyclical tensile loading in the elastic region verified stable and repeatable CNF/BFRP laminate strain self-sensing capabilities. However, the effect of tunneling conduction on a small deformation of CNF/BFRP laminates is the nonlinear variation of the electrical resistance at the start and end of each cycle.

In a study investigating experimental investigation of BFRP bar-reinforced concrete slabs (BRCSs) under contact explosions, Yu et al. (2020) reported that in extreme service environments, BFRP bars are often used as an option for ordinary steel bars. Eight slabs were tested, four of which were normal reinforced concrete slab (NRCS) and four of which were BFRP BRCSs. Explosions from cylindrical explosives of 0.8, 1.0, 1.6 and 1.9 kg were subjected to slabs to gain various damage levels. The BRCS anti-blasting capability is superior to NRCS. BRCS demonstrated greater blast resistance compared with the NRCS based on smaller crater and spall sizes, lack of a cross-shaped crack and fewer cracks. These experiments confirmed that established formulas for predicting damage to concrete in the close-in explosion, in particular for a thick reinforced concrete (RC) slab, are not correct for contact explosion. An incorrect formula can result in a hazardous calculation that predicts the defection of the concrete slab inaccurately. Recently, a study by Chen et al. (2017) involved quasi-static and dynamic tensile properties of BFRP, and basalt fiber was shown to be an environmentally friendly material with exceptional characteristics, including a high weight resistance, acoustic ductility and resilience, greater heat tolerance and excellent corrosion tolerance, in addition, it is affordable. The Shimadzu test system has been used to perform many quasi-static and dynamic tensile tests for BFRP material characteristics and strain rate-dependent characteristics. The BFRP has been known to be responsive to the strain rate. BFRP dynamic toughness is almost twice its quasi-static strength. These findings suggest that empirical formulas were derived for the tensile material characteristics of BFRPs in relation to the strain rate from test data that could be used to model the dynamic loading BFRP material characteristics in numerical simulations.

A study by Alaimo et al. (2016) on the durability of BFRP panels for cladding examined BFRP laminates used in the manufacture of exterior building panel coverings. The study consisted of testing performance aspects of mechanical and physical or chemical parameters of two basalt composite panels formed from a distinct sequence of basalt fiber layers. The hybrid laminate composites exhibited better performances in durability, even though their initial mechanical properties are lower than unidirectional laminate composites and these properties remain relatively unchanged. This study confirmed that the unidirectional laminate composites should be more acceptable for applications in which greater mechanical toughness than durability is required, whereas the hybrids are better suited in the long-term application of technical elements. Also, various studies have explored the effect of thermal stimulation on the tensile failure of basalt fiber. Militký et al. (2002) found that basalt is indeed still primarily used in molded goods such as flagstones and pipes with improved abrasion, chemical and temperature resistance. The ultimate tensile mechanical properties were examined after tempering to 50, 100, 200, 300, 400, and 500°C at room temperature and the three Weibull form model parameters of the fibers were used to define the strength distribution of basalt filaments. These results assumed that fractures occur because of non-homogeneities in fiber volume (possibly close the small mineral crystallites). These experiments confirmed that during basalt fabric abrasion, an evaluation of the fibrous fragment is possible, although quite long, thin basalt fragments can be harmful when inhaled. Ramraji et al. (2019) investigated numerous crucial research studies trying to explain the cutting dimensionality by abrasive water jet machine tools on basalt fiber/fly ash-reinforced polymer composite. It was reported that this machine tool is the leading technology in non-traditional machining for processing advanced and complicated-to-cut materials with favorable cutting methods, disposal of coatings, surface treatment and machining. Composites were prepared with different fly ash loading (5–20 wt%) by a compression molding technique. The high quality of the surface and the minimum of fiber delamination and fiber pullouts were seen in hybrid composite-reinforced fly ash. This concludes that the fly ash particle-reinforced fiber composite is an acceptable material to machine tool any engineering product.

Recently, there was a study conducted by Santosh et al. (2020) on experimenting and recognizing basalt and jute fiber reinforced in polymer matrix hybrid composites. It was shown that composites in a polymer matrix usually have strong characteristics such as advanced rigidity, low weight and high strength. Polymer hybrid composites were made using the hand layup technique and the compression molding method was used with basalt and jute as reinforcement and polyester as a matrix. This was done by preserving the thickness of the laminate and maintaining an acceptable temperature of 80°C while the laminate was being prepared and cured. There was an improvement in the tensile strength of 4B4J2 tensile modulus relative to the 4B4J3 composites, whereas the compression strength of 4B4J2 was reduced compared with 4B4J3. In conclusion, the 4B4J2 damping ratio is 5.78% higher than the 4B4J3 damping ratio, where the difference in laminate stiffness and differences in thickness and volume fraction may be attributed to the different composite behavior. Moreover, there has been a great deal of previous study investigating the versatile quality of basalt fiber laminates at ambient and cooler temperatures. Papa et al. (2019) reported that many marine and aerospace systems are mechanically shocked at low temperatures and the toughness of the material shifts is also compatible with normal conditions, creating different damage mechanisms. Laminates made of basalt fibers in a matrix of vinyl ester resin developed by overlapping plain woven fabrics with a resin infusion technique impacted ambient temperature and –50°C at a velocity of about 4 m/s with an increased amount of energy before penetration. This is contrary to what is often found in the literature where less energy is used on delaminates by using thinner laminates, because much of the energy consumed is used to bend the laminate. The findings obtained at low temperatures confirmed those of carbon fiber laminates, with greater areas of damage linked to lower absorbed energies. This demonstrates the function of the temperature as the thickness rises. A number of studies have begun to examine fatigue deterioration and life estimation of BFRP composites after saltwater oxidation. A study conducted by Wang et al. (2019) showed durability without loading BFRP in marine environments and that BFRP composites are resilient to salt oxidation. BFRP composites contained saltwater corrosion damage effects with a fatigue life and microdamage mechanism explained by a progressive fatigue test apparatus and in situ SEM. The specimens' fatigue life is significantly impacted by corrosion of the saltwater. The fatigue life declines with an aging period below a stress ratio of 0.8. With a low fatigue life stress proportion of 0.1, fatigue life can recover with a quick corrosion duration and decline after a long period of saltwater corrosion. The research also showed that fatigue life forecast for the worst scenario in the studies, and fatigue toughness decreases for 10^7 cycles at approximately 11%, with 0.1 and 0.8 stress ratios. When using BFRP in cables, the fatigue strength is reasonable.

A comprehensive study of acoustic emission (AE) analyzed the effect of temperature and hybridization on drop weight influence, and post-impact residual strength of hemp and BFRP composite laminates. Suresh Kumar et al. (2019) found that hybridization of various fibers is one of the effective ways to improve resistance to impact damage by composite materials. A drop-weight performance impact tower machine impacted the specimen at temperatures of 30°C and 65°C and was subsequently submitted to a three-point bending test for residual strength evaluation, while online AE signals during the test were registered. Hybrid laminates demonstrated greater impact tolerance at high temperatures than non-hybridized laminates. Furthermore, the AE-based methods, the sentry feature and the cumulative rise angle (RA) value were capable of detecting the hybridized laminates' gradual failure and damage-tolerant nature. This study concluded that AE was susceptible to the effects of temperature and hybridization of natural FRP composite laminates on impact resistance. The study on bond integrity of aramid, basalt and carbon FRP bonded wood composites at elevated temperature by Zhou et al. (2020) established that the FRP wood composite has attracted researchers' interest in its feasibility, mechanical performance, economic viability, durability etc. The experiment proposed in this work involves the tensile tests to assess the mechanical features of the bonded wood specimens aramid fiber-reinforced polymer (AFRP), BFRP and CFRP, and single shear tests to prove bond integrity at elevated temperatures for AFRP, BFRP and CFRP. The deterioration of the BFRP and CFRP bonded wood is due to the degradation of epoxy and wood substrates with a rise in the exposure temperature to 210°C. This finding may enhance understanding of the actions of fire in FRP and wood and provide essential insights for developing adhesives or wood-coating materials with better fire resistance fibers.

A current study by Dhand et al. (2015) contained a short review on BFRP composites and how basalt fibers can be used as a reinforcement material for composites and as a choice of fiber for glass. Essentially no materials, such as glass fiber, are added during its production. Basalt is literally washed and then melted, turning into glass fibers. The outcomes revealed that the composite characteristics (stiffness and modulus) were 45% and 18% greater than the unregulated ones, respectively. Also, they displayed a major increase in fiber wettability and development of fiber surface functionalization by physical etching. It was inferred from the analysis that the basalt was discovered to create better characteristics than the combined traditional characteristics of asbestos and glass fibers. Basalt fibers are as beneficial as carbon fibers and are eco-friendly, non-toxic and renewable. There have been a number of studies on BFRP composites.

A previous study by Branston et al. (2016) involved the mechanical behavior of basalt fiber RC. They evaluated the relative merit of two types of BFs shaped like a bundle of dispersion fibers and minibars (MBs) in boosting the mechanical behavior of concrete and compared the pre-cracking and post-cracking mechanical behavior of concrete reinforced with plain chopped BFs, basalt MBs and commonly used hooked-end steel fibers (SFs). Mix designation indicates chopped basalt bundle dispersion fibers 36 mm long were used at 8 kg/1 m^3 of plain concrete (8 kg/m^3). The percentage of blows from a 4.54-kg of compaction hammer with a 457-mm fall was necessary to cause noticeable surface failure, and eventual failure was reported for each specimen. The addition of BF improved the first-crack strength of concrete subjected to flexural loading, but it was not massively effective when exposed to impact loading. In MB specimens, the ductile post-cracking behavior was indeed the reason for failure by incremental pullout. In the end, it can be reported that after 9 months, physical changes to the BF surface were found and were assumed to be reflective of mechanical property deterioration. Therefore, because of higher fiber-matrix bond strength and poor fiber tensile strength, BF composites' brittle behavior can be due to fiber rupture.

Researches done by Colombo et al. (2012) on static and fatigue characterization of new basalt fiber-reinforced composites showed a contrast was made between composites with such fibers and other reinforcement fibers in terms of mechanical properties. To determine their effect on the assessed parameters, two matrices, vinyl ester and epoxy, were considered. Various mechanical tests were designed and carried out including static tests of tensile and compression, static tests of delamination and classical and stepwise tests of fatigue. On the other hand, in the classical fatigue tests, a stepwise test was also carried out on an uncycled sample. Stepwise testing takes the form of fatigue testing at variable stress amplitudes, at 20 Hz, with different cycle blocks. With respect to basalt fiber reinforced composite with vinylester matrix (BV) composites, basalt fiber reinforced composites with epoxy matrix (BE) specimens' ultimate tensile strength showed a rise of 29%, particularly in compression behavior, where this rise is more obvious at about 85%. It is clearly apparent that in the linear region, the BV and BE specimens show a similar slope, while the applied load increases, curves diverge and different trends are evident. In conclusion, basalt-reinforced epoxy composites showed higher mechanical properties with respect to vinyl ester. Thermally regulated checks were also described, both static and stepwise for the basalt-epoxy composite, and both in the tensile and compressive behavior and together with mechanical results.

Bhat et al. (2015) focused on the fire structural resistance of basalt fiber composites. In their studies woven basalt fiber composite's fire resilience properties were experimentally evaluated using fire structural tests involving combined tensile loading and one-sided unstable-state heating indicative of potential fire. Basalt fabric was arranged so that the warp tows were aligned to produce a fiber pattern of cross-ply. Using the vacuum bag resin infusion process, vinyl ester resin was combined into the fabric at ambient temperature. The vinyl ester matrix was meshed and slightly cured under ambient conditions following infusion of 23°C, 50% R_H and then post-cured for 2 hours at 80°C. The BF composite's heated surface temperature increased due to front-face ignition at around 675°C at a greater heat flux of 50 kW/m². However, the glass fiber laminate did not ignite with the same heat flux, even after long-term heat exposure. Since its emissivity (e ~0.92 at 20°C) is higher than the glass fiber composite (e ~0.65 at 20°C), the basalt fiber composite has become hotter. From the result, it can be inferred that when subjected to the same heat flux, a basalt fiber composite has poorer tensile fire resistance than an identical glass fiber laminate, reflecting a potential fire situation. This enabled the basalt composite to endure softening and decomposition of the polymer matrix and rapid weakening of the fibers, leading to a lower fire resistance under combined tensile loading and one-sided radiant heating compared with the glass fiber composite.

In a recent study by Esnaola et al. (2015) on quasi-static and tensile properties of BFRP, a number of dynamic tensile and quasi-static tests were performed to determine properties of the BFRP material and strain rate-dependent features using the Shimadzu test method and the Instron® VHS 160/100-20. Tests were used to obtain the mechanical qualities of BFRP at various strain evaluations. The Shimadzu AGS-X 300 kN series universal testing machine was used to conduct a quasi-static test. The maximum load of the machine is 300 kN and the speed variation of the test is 0.001e1000 mm/min. The Instron VHS 160-20 high-speed servo hydraulic testing system (Instron VHS 160-20 testing machine) was used to perform the dynamic tensile test. With the strain rate, the composite strength's tensile strength increases, particularly the composite strength rises exponentially when the strain rates were higher than 120 s^{-1}. The complex research strain rate in this analysis was up to 259 s^{-1}. The BFRP was discovered to be responsive to the strain rate. After the strain rate exceeded 120 s^{-1}, the BFRP mechanical qualities and tensile strength, failure strain and elastic modulus rose significantly through the strain rate. Its quasi-static power was almost doubled by the dynamic strength of BFRP. During the dynamic testing, diagonal defects were identified and the samples were delaminated. The experimental formulas for BFRP's mechanical properties with regard to the strain rate were drawn from test data that could be run in numerical simulations to prototype the properties under dynamic loading of BFRP materials.

Current studies on natural FRP composites by Yuan et al. (2019) reported consequences of cumulative size on bond behavior between BFRP sheets and concrete. The single-lap shear testing procedure and its impact on the coarse cumulative size of the bond properties between FRP and concrete was researched. In experiments, concrete prisms with a substrate of 350 (L) × 150 (H) × 150 (W) mm were removed 24 hours after casting and then treated for 28 days at room temperature in water tanks. The mechanical properties of concrete, including compressive durability and splitting tensile durability, were calculated with specific coarse aggregate sizes. As the coarse aggregate size increased, the debonding loads reduced. A decrease of 6.55% and 10.04% can be observed for the specimens with the cumulative size of 10–15 mm and 15–20 mm, respectively, relative to the specimens with the aggregate size of 5–10 mm. By considering the interfacial fracture energy and depending on the maximum aggregate size, debonding loads could be expected. The testing research revealed that with the aggregate size, the effective bond length improved. A growth of 21.62% and 45.95% for samples 10–15 mm and 15–20 mm was verified, respectively, relative to samples with the cumulative size of 5–10 mm. For specimens with cumulative sizes of 10–15 mm and 15–20 mm, an improvement of 11.61% and 21.43% was evaluated compared with specimens with cumulative sizes of 5–10 mm. In summary, it should be noted that with the increasing cumulative scale, the comparative slip between BFRP and concrete at the highest point bond stress also rose due to the weakened concrete tensile capacity. Current bonded stiffness and interfacial bond-slip models are implemented and readjusted against all the experimental outcomes in which all the cumulative size effect is included.

In a study by Inman et al. (2017) on the mechanical and environmental evaluation and contrast of rebars and steel rebars of BFRP in concrete beams, the comparison of both of these features in a systematic method, the technique for mechanical test and evaluation and the strength and reliability outcomes from mechanical testing are explained. The BFRP beams were pre-stressed and had a diameter of 2×10 mm. As suggested by the American Concrete Institute (ACI) recommendations for FRP, separate tendons were pre-stressed to about 50% from their ultimate strength. In contrast, up to 85% of their yield power is usually strained by steel wires. The calculated steel reinforcement was intense heat rolled B500 NC. The concrete strength was calculated 28 days after casting as the mean strength of concrete of three tests conducted on concrete rod. The regular temperature in the laboratory was 20°C, and during the healing of the concrete the relative humidity was 30%. The BFRP RC 1200-mm-long beam shows better performance in all 18 environmental metrics, in contrast to the steel RC beam that was 1250 mm long. The BFRP experiences 14.7 $kgCO_2Eq/FU$ of pollution from climate change, while the steel RC beam experiences nearly twice the quantity of contained releases at 23.7 $kgCO_2eq/FU$. The mechanical test results suggest that BFRP rebar has double the steel rebar toughness, which is not influenced. In conclusion, the BFRP is a valuable building material and, more precisely, favorable as a concrete beam reinforcement material. The research examines that in further construction uses, like prefabricated sandwich panels that need thin concrete facades and thin constructional foundations, BFRP may also be acceptable. Compared with traditional RC components, BFRP in thinner concrete parts is expected to have similar low environmental emissions.

Research by Fernando et al. (2016) on BFRP-enhanced timber laminates under tensile mounting showed that the behavior of BFRP-strengthened timber sections and evaluation and theoretical study into the behavior of lumber stick panels under tensile loading improved with BFRP. Series I attempted to research the impact of BFRP reinforcement of control lumber samples. At a steady displacement rate between 0.01 and 0.02 mm/s, the load was exerted. During the test using the mounted strain gauges, strain at various spots of the sample was evaluated. The applied load and total displacement were obtained from the system analysis on each 0.5-s cycle. Research studies have shown that BFRP under tensile loading can significantly promote both the axial stiffness and lumber samples' strength. Twenty-six percent was the highest rise in axial stiffness, whereas 65% was the maximum increase in strength achieved. BFRP had a serious influence on the samples' post-ultimate load responses, mainly when damaged lumber was used. The rise in the 95th percentile output of the elastic module was 12.5% from a study focused on lumber parts without any flaws and a BFRP-to-lumber axial stiffness proportion of 0.1, whereas that of strength was 13%. In conclusion, BFRP reinforcement is an effective strategy to improve the strength and rigidity of lumber under tensile loading.

In recent research on flexural enhancement of unreinforced masonry (URM) out-of-plane wallets using BFRP composite, Padalu et al. (2019) further explained the influence of various parameters, for example, the reinforcement ratio of BFRP. In other words, they explained the loading path parallel bending tension to bed-joints portraying horizontally spanning walls and perpendicular bending tension to bed-joints portraying vertically spanning walls and BFRP specification. Along with their constituent components, 8 URM and 28 reinforced wallets were checked in two orthogonal directions. The masonry wallets are mounted horizontally and examined under two-point (line) out-of-plane loading in a single-way bending situation. The toughening approach's effectiveness was verified by analyzing failure modes, endurance, toughness, energy absorption capability and hardness. The strengthened wallets' flexural strength improved up to 2.9 and 6.4 times compared with URM wallets when bending stress parallel and perpendicular to the bed-joints. The total midspan displacement of strengthened wallets was up to 6.7 and 30 times much better parallel and perpendicular to the bed-joints under bending stress than correlating URM wallets. The BFRP wallets indicated a total ductility of up to 6.0 and 6.8 for bending tension parallel and perpendicular to the bed-joints. In conclusion, the use of mechanical connectors in avoiding debonding error may also be examined. The efficacy of this reinforcing method for seismic loading can be further evaluated by extending the study to full workout specimens with usual pre-compression caused by gravitation, due to two-way bend under cyclic loading.

A recent study was done by Li et al. (2017a) on the influence of extreme temperature on the connection performance between BFRP bars and concrete. The study proved that the bond properties between BFRP bars and concrete were applied in extreme temperatures via a direct specimen complete withdrawal test. Variables include temperature, embedding length, diameter and size of FRP bars, concrete durability thickness of the concrete cover and fireproof material availability. The diameters of the BFRP bars were 6, 8 and 10 mm, respectively, and the polymer matrix of the BFRP and GFRP bars was epoxy resin. The temperature of the tests included ambient temperature, which is 20, 70, 120, 170, 220, 270 and 350°C. The specimens were demolded after being cured for 48 hours, transferred to the laboratory setting for curing for 28 days and then put in an extreme temperature heat treatment furnace. The heating rate was 5°C/min. The connection resilience of the BFRP bar samples weakened by 2.45%–7.11% compared with the connection resilience at ambient temperature 70°C–220°C, and the connection resilience of the GFRP bar samples plummeted by 6.99% till reaching 14.24%. At 270°C, the connection resilience of the BFRP and GFRP bar samples falls by almost 32%. The bonding hardness of the BFRP and GFRP bar specimens plummeted significantly at 350°C, and the remaining bonding forces were, respectively, 12.20% and 23.14% of their actual numbers. The bonding resilience of the bars and concrete of the BFRP was considerably higher than those of the bars and concrete of the GFRP and the rate of change ranged from 42.4% till 57.3%. In summary, it should be acknowledged that the mechanical and physical properties between the BFRP bar and concrete significantly reduced with the rise of the bonding size and BFRP bar diameter with the growth of the bonding size and BFRP bar diameter; the bonding resilience between the BFRP bar and concrete improved with the addition of the concrete intensity and the thickness of the concrete cover. Extra information is necessary to assess the influence of the fireproof insulation material on the concrete surface.

Several studies have begun to compare which fiber suits the production of concrete the most. In a study, mechanical and environmental examination and comparative analysis of the rebar and steel bar of BFRP in concrete beams was conducted by Inman et al. (2017). It is claimed that basalt fiber has attracted attention in the last two decades due to its low cost, significant environmental compatibility and functional properties during the manufacturing process. These mechanical properties are expected to affect the environmental quality of BFRP as a construction material. The mechanical test and life cycle assessment (LCA) approach was conducted in the study. Then, after the LCA findings, the strength and reliability outcomes from mechanical testing were demonstrated. In terms of reliability and strength, nine BFRP and three steel-reinforced beams were tested. BFRP beams were pre-stressed and used tendons of 2×10 mm in diameter. To promote concrete bonding, the BF tendons were fastened with epoxy resin and had a coarse finish. With end anchors, the pre-stressed BFRP beams were fixed and glued with threaded M24 bolts with steel plates at the ends of the beams. As suggested by the ACI guidelines for FRP, every other tendon was pre-stressed to about 50% of its optimal potential. The mechanical results indicated that the rebar strength of BFRP is strong, with a tension strength of about double the tension strength of steel reinforcement for the identical cross-sectional area. Overall, this shows that BFRP rebar is a sturdier and lighter option to reinforcing concrete beam steel; therefore it is a very good potential building material for the long term.

Recent developments in the study of experimental testing of BFRP bars in concrete beams were research by Elgabbas et al. (2016). In the study, the new FRP composite materials designed to improve the protection and durability of structural structures were BFRP bars. Because of their cost-effectiveness, high-temperature resistance, freeze-thaw performance and ease of manufacture, BFRP bars have attracted attention. In addition, for very low temperatures between $-200°C$ and comparative high temperatures, basalt fibers can be used around $600°C -800°C$ and have better fatigue performance. Six concrete beams reinforced with BFRP bars were designed and examined for failure. The test beams were, respectively, 200 mm wide, 300 mm high and 3100 mm long. BFRP bars sized 10, 12 and 16 mm were used with sand-coated surfaces over a helical covering. The beam specimens were constructed and tested under four-point bending over a clear period of 2700 mm before failure. Overall, the experimental result indicated that the BFRP composite beams showed strong increases in strains and deflection at cracking with low reinforcement ratios. The sudden increase in strain led to wider and deeper cracks, representing the cracked section's neutral axis stiffness and position.

A study was begun to examine the influence of basalt fiber hybridization when exposed to high velocity effects on carbon/epoxy laminates. A study by Tirillò et al. (2017) was conducted on the influence of larger velocity on the behavior of hybrid basalt-carbon/epoxy composites. For the purpose of experimental analysis, hybrid interply specimens were tested with four distinct stacking orders (sandwich-like and laminated model) and contrasted with non-hybrid laminates made of either carbon or basalt layers only. By measuring the impact and residual velocities of the projectile and the ballistic limit, measured using investigational data, the response to high velocity impact tests was evaluated by comparing the outcomes obtained by an analytical model, showing good promise. Destructive (optical microscopy) and non-destructive (ultrasonic phased array) methods were used to investigate damage to the composite laminates. One interesting finding was that basalt composites indicated a damage pattern mainly characterized by debonding, whereas the fracture was brittle in the case of carbon structure, with visible signs of fracturing. Therefore, the observed decrease in the static mechanical properties of hybrid composites is mostly offset by enhanced impact responses.

Research on the dynamic efficiency of basalt fiber laminates at ambient and decreased temperatures conducted by Papa et al. (2019) stated that the mechanical properties of natural fibers such as sisal, kenaf, coconut, flax and banana are reduced and are very susceptible to thermal and hygroscopic loads. The alternative may be basalt fiber laminates, balancing the environmental and mechanical issues. To begin with, basalt fiber-reinforced plastic laminates in vinyl ester resin were acquired through overlapping plain woven fabrics through the resin infusion technique. From the main panels, rectangular samples of 100–150 mm were sliced and affected at two different room temperatures and –50°C at penetration and rising energy values. In fact, the result was compared with carbon fiber laminates; the lesser absorbed energy associated with the reduction extension of delamination does not contribute to major load decreases, which means that they do not affect the material stiffness and potentially the residual strength. Hence, it can be concluded that the findings gained at low temperatures verified what had already been observed on laminates of carbon fiber: there were greater areas of damage associated with lower energy absorption.

Extensive research on quasi-static crush energy absorption capability of E-glass/polyester and hybrid E-glass-basalt/polyester composite structures was conducted by Esnaola et al. (2015). The research showed that in various stacking series, unidirectional and bidirectional E-glass fibers were used to decide which is the most efficient arrangement in terms of precise energy absorption. In addition, bidirectional basalt laminates are measured to enhance the ability of composite structures to absorb energy. For the purpose of analysis, semi-hexagonal composite structures with piling orders of E-glass and basalt fibers were tested at a compression speed of 10 mm/min during a collapse distance of 50 mm under quasi-static crush circumstances and specific energy absorption (SEA) capacity. From the analysis, samples of unidirectional and bidirectional E-glass fibers display the highest SEA values (~30 kJ/kg). Basalt/polyester samples showed unstable collapse during the crushing process due to buckling effect. The crush behavior of the latest basalt/polyester arrangement is therefore not appropriate for automotive crash applications.

A study on extended BF-reinforced epoxy matrix composite incorporating erbium oxide on radiation shielding properties was conducted by Li et al. (2017). In advanced materials with strong shielding ability, low density and great mechanical toughness and modulus are greatly desired to protect the human body and apparatus from radiation in the nuclear power field, for radiation remedy and for use in the aerospace field. To begin, the pre-preg-autoclave procedure was used to make composites reinforced with BF using the hot-melting method. The autoclave was heated at 2°C/min from ambient temperature to 130°C, maintained for 1 hour at 130°C and then raised to 180°C and maintained for 3 hours at 180°C. During the curing process, 0.1 MPa vacuum pressure was used. When temperatures increased to 130°C, 0.1 MPa external pressure was used, and 0.6 MPa was used after temperatures were sustained for an hour at 130°C. The composite laminates were post-cured in the oven at 200°C for 2 hours following the autoclave process. Further statistical tests revealed that there is a maximum deviation between experimental and theoretical findings of 10.3%. Thus, the approach is assumed to be ideal for guessing the protecting efficiency of extended composite materials reinforced with fiber.

Previous research on the effect of exposure heat on the behavior of composites of slightly pyrolyzed hybrid BFs conducted by Chlup et al. (2018a) established that from the point of observation of the strengthening effects, composites using long fibers as reinforcement are the most successful. A brittle matrix enhanced by brittle fibers was examined. In the studied composite, polysiloxane resin was applied as the matrix precursor, while extended BFs acted as reinforcement. In the first step in this process, the polymeric precursor was converted into a so-called hybrid matrix containing nano-domains of pyrolytic SiOC glass and untransformed polysiloxane polymer by an optimized pyrolysis process carried out at 650°C under nitrogen atmosphere. It was found that the pyrolysis temperature of 650°C was optimum. Interestingly, when introduced to 300°C/1000 h for about 41.7 days and a maximum of 60 MPa pressure, the flexural intensity decreased to 50% of the initial value. The decline in strength of the fracture and flexural strength could be due to the weakening of the matrix after shrinking.

A study on sticky and hybrid-bonded binding of composites based on basalt and carbon fiber-reinforced polybenzoxazine was executed by Wolter et al. (2019). In the study it was established that because of their exceptional qualities in terms of chemical tolerance, inherent flame retardancy and mechanical quality, polybenzoxazine-based composites were an exceptional option for durable structures. To begin, the vacuum infusion technique accompanied by convection oven curing was used to produce BFRP and CFRP. Using a wet abrasive cutoff system, the BFRP and CFRP plates were cut following the fiber path. Rivet insertion into cured joints bonded with a structural adhesive has created hybrid joints. As a result of the analysis, adhesive bonding has been shown to be an effective joining technique that has strong substratum adhesion and sufficient cohesive strength. Prior to failure, hybrid-bonded joints had a fail-safe rupture and better energy absorption than their counterparts that were sticky bonded. Thus, CFRP joints demonstrated higher lap-shear strength than their BFRP counterparts with respect to the form of fiber reinforcement, which was consistent with interlaminar shear strength (ILSS) performance.

Composite materials are widely used because they have high mechanical properties. A research study on the impact of thermal cycling on mechanical and thermal qualities of basalt fiber-reinforced epoxy composites by Azimpour-shishevan and Akbulut (2020) claimed that the demand for BFRP composites has increased in industries where high thermal resistance is important. The first step in the study was to analyze the influence of thermal fatigue on mechanical and thermal characteristics, for 20, 40, 60, 80 and 120 cycles. Thermal cycling experiments were carried out between −40°C and +120°C. In addition, to determine the influence of thermal cycling on the thermal characteristics of BFRPs, a dynamic mechanical analyzer (DMA) was used. The hydrophobicity test investigated the effect of thermal cycling on the water absorption properties of BFRP composites. The research revealed that tensile force, flexural modulus and ILSS values increased with a rise in the quantity of cycles to 80 cycles. In other words, a rise in the quantity of cycles enhanced the hydrophobicity of BFRP composites by decreasing the contact angles.

Several studies have investigated BFs because of their high intensity, and they have gained considerable attention in both academia and industry. A recent research improvement of BF performance with polymer-based nanocomposite dimensioning by Miao et al. (2020) claimed that during the manufacture of BF, sizing was a key component to mitigate the damage to the fiber during processing and transport, and to strengthen the interactions between the fiber and the matrix, such as metal, polymer or ceramics. To begin, under mechanical stirring, epoxy was pre-emulsified. Water was added into the mixture dropwise and stirred for another 2 hours at 55° C at the same level, creating an emulsion of epoxy in water. To achieve the optimal formulation of sizing, a full-scale experiment with quantitative research on liquid stability, wettability, conductivity and morphology was applied. The results showed that during the fiber-spinning process, nanocomposite sizing was deposited on the fiber surface. The sizing increased the BF's electrical and tensile toughness significantly, revealing the efficacy of nanocomposites as a multifunctional material.. Thus, the hybrid laminate composites showed higher efficiency in terms of durability (Table 3.2).

3.3 MECHANICAL AND THERMAL PROPERTIES OF BASALT FIBER REINFORCEMENT

BFRP composites enhance the physical properties of composites. This section addresses the mechanical and thermal qualities of the enhanced composites of BFRP as shown in the review journals.

3.3.1 MECHANICAL PROPERTIES

BFs as a fiber reinforcement source have attracted much interest because they have better mechanical properties than any other conventional fillers (Lopresto, Leone and De Iorio 2011; Dhand et al. 2015; Li et al. 2017b; Sapuan et al. 2020). It was confirmed that the elastic modulus of the BF-reinforced composite depends heavily on the chemical affinity and composition of the particular BF (Dhand et al. 2015). Basalt is popular for its greater tensile resilience and elongation at break, and due to these enhanced criteria (Khandelwal and Rhee 2020), the impact strength and sustainability of the materials within the composite can also be improved (Tirillò et al. 2017). A recent study by Banibayat and Patnaik (2014) involved the variability of mechanical properties of BFRP bars manufactured by the wet-layup approach. The research showed that the new type of bars known as BFRP bars were manufactured using BF in the civil engineering sector specifically for buildings and bridges. Three bar sizes with nominal diameters of 4.3, 7.1 and 9.8 mm (0.17, 0.28 and 0.39 in.) were used in these studies and identified as R4, R7 and R10. The corresponding net fiber diameters were 3, 5 and 7 mm (0.12, 0.2 and 0.28 in.) in all three bars' measurements. The minimum test number of 99.875% confidence level as advised by ACI was shown by combining data sets for the three different bar diameters tested in this study due to normal distribution of test data. This study identified the results of the three data sets of 10–14 specimens of BFRP bars produced using an automated wet layup method. They were found to be normally distributed according to statistical K-S tests. In an

50

Mineral-Filled Polymer Composites

TABLE 3.2
Reported Work on Basalt Fiber-Reinforced Polymer Composites

Polymer	Characteristics	Effect of Reinforcement	References
Epoxy	Long-term creep behavior	• The mechanical properties of composite increased	Sokairge et al. (2020)
Vinyl ester	Mechanical characteristics	• Thermal properties of composites increased • The mechanical characteristics of composite increased	Banibayat and Patnaik (2014)
Epoxy	Tensile mechanical properties	• The tensile strength of composite increased	Xu et al. (2019)
Epoxy	Low velocity impact behavior	• The impact behavior of composite improved	Shishevan et al. (2017)
Unsaturated polyester	Mechanical properties	• The physical properties of composite increased • The mechanical properties of composite increased	Sapuan et al. (2020)
Epoxy	Static and fatigue behavior	• The static strength and fatigue life of BFRTP composite was similar to BFRP at high-stress levels	Wang et al. (2020)
Epoxy	Strain and damage self-sensing	• The composite had stable and repeatable strain self-sensing capacity	Wang et al. (2018)
Vinyl ester and epoxy	Static and fatigue loading	• The long-term fatigue strength level of composite increased • The static toughness of the composite was minimal	Zhao et al. (2020)
Polyester	Tensile characteristics, compressive properties, and dynamic behavior	• The tensile properties of composite increased • The compressive properties of composite increased • The damping ratio obtained for 4B4J2 hybrid composite was higher than for 4B4J3	Santosh Gangappa and Sripad Kulkarni (2020)
Epoxy	Fatigue degradation and life prediction	• The estimation of fatigue life demonstrated that fatigue strength of BFRP disrupts to an appropriate level	Wang et al. (2019)
Vinyl ester	Cutting dimensionality by coarse water jet machining	• Good surface quality with minimal fiber delamination • Fiber pullouts were exhibited in composite	Ramraji et al. (2019)
Epoxy	Mechanical properties, interfacial fracture energy and effective bond length	• The mechanical properties of composite reduced • The interfacial rupture energy decreased with increasing exposure temperature • Effective bond length of composite bonded wood increased with rising exposure temperature	Zhou et al. (2020)

Polydimethylsiloxane and epoxy	Fracture resistance	• In-plane fracture characteristics of the composite were considerably lower	Chlup et al. (2020)
Epoxy	Peak limit interfacial shear stress, and bond-slip relationship	• Debonding loads decreased • Effective bond length increased • Shear stress experienced significant increase	Yuan et al. (2019)
Epoxy	Drop weight impact and post-impact residual strength	• Hybrid improved the resistance to impact and caused a gradual damage evolution	Suresh Kumar et al. (2019)
Epoxy	Quasi-static and dynamic tensile properties	• Tensile toughness, elastic modulus and failure strain increase rapidly • The dynamic strength of composites almost doubled their quasi-static toughness	Chen et al. (2017)
Epoxy	Fatigue behavior	• The fatigue strength of composite tendons degraded under a marine environment	Shi et al. (2017)
Hybrid phenolic	Hot wear properties	• Flexural toughness and shear toughness surged up to 30 vol% total fiber quantity • Compression strength increased with increasing fiber content • Coefficient of friction rose with surged BF quantity in hybrid composites	Öztürk et al. (2007)
Nonpolymeric	Thermal treatment on tensile failure	• Strength and dynamic acoustical modulus dropped significantly at 300°C • Long, thin fragments may be dangerous when inhaled	Militký et al. (2002)
Polypropylene and Polyamide	Mechanical properties reinforced hybrid composites.	• Lead to significant increase in the bending strength in all composites • Qualities of the composites were doubled by treating the BF in hybrid matrix	Czigány (2005)
Polyester resin	Mechanical properties affected by basalt fiber length and its content	• The composite tensile strength of the basalt fiber exhibited stronger properties than other fibers • Stronger properties were demonstrated by the flexural strength of composites • The impact toughness of the composite-reinforced BF indicated the highest impact energy absorption in all fiber percentages at 50 mm length	Amuthakkannan et al. (2013)

(Continued)

TABLE 3.2 (*Continued*)
Reported Work on Basalt Fiber-Reinforced Polymer Composites

Polymer	Characteristics	Effect of Reinforcement	References
Sea sand concrete	Fatigue behavior	• Stiffness reduced and damage to the interface stiffness elevated • As it approached two-thirds of the depth of the sea, the cracks and ceased developed	Li et al. (2018)
Epoxy resin	Characteristics for concrete	• Exhibited tensile strength less than 1000 MPa • When introduced in a temperature above 600°C, the volumetric consistency and 90% of the strength were preserved	Sim et al. (2005)
Epoxy resin	Mechanical and environmental assessment	• The reinforcement of basalt fiber had a lower elastic module than the reinforcement of steel, resulting in extreme deformation at the service limit state • Under tension, BF did not show yield • BF reinforcement was sturdier than steel reinforcement	Inman et al. (2017)
Polyester	Effect of surface modifications on mechanical qualities	• Higher tensile toughness values and greater impact toughness when BF-reinforced fiber was acid-treated	Manikandan et al. (2012)
Epoxy	Structural performance	• Bilinear behavior for strain and deflection until failure	Elgabbas et al. (2016)
Vinyl ester and epoxy	Static and fatigue	• Epoxy composites had great mechanical qualities with respect to vinyl ester; in tensile, compressive and failure mode they were compact	Colombo et al. (2012)
Epoxy resin	Durability for cladding	• Increased in mechanical performances	Alaimo et al. (2016)
Polybenzoxazines	Adhesive and hybrid-bonded joining	• The addition of the rivet induced an increase in the absorption of energy and displacement at the break • Carbon fiber composite joints had higher lap-shear strength than BF composites	Wolter et al. (2019)
Vinyl ester resin	Dynamic performances	• The stiffness of the material did not impact the low delamination of BF laminates • Carbon fiber laminates had greater degraded areas due to lower energy absorption at low temperatures	Papa et al. (2019)

Epoxy	High velocity impact behavior	• BF showed higher ballistic limit velocity • Basalt composites mainly showed damage pattern by debonding, whereas the fracture was brittle in carbon configuration with visible signs of splitting	Tirillò et al. (2017)
Epoxy	Effect of thermal cycling	• By post-curing, the mechanical and thermal properties of BFRP composites were affected • Mechanical property deterioration due to residual thermal stress	Azimpour-shishevan and Akbulut (2020)
Polysiloxane resin	Effect of exposition temperature	• Processes of deterioration in the composite matrix • When exposed to 300°C, the flexural strength deteriorated • Decreasing trend in fracture toughness	Chlup et al. (2018a)
Epoxy	Development for conducting from insulating	• Balanced stability, wettability, conductivity and properties of morphology • Increased tensile strength of the individual filament	Miao et al. (2020)
Polyester	Quasi-static crush energy absorption	• Due to a buckling effect during the crushing process, unstable collapse was shown	Esnaola et al. (2015)
Bio-based epoxy resin	Load bearing capacity	• The deflections are maximum and by shear cavitation the cork core fails • Absolute filling with the vacant defects caused by using a longitudinal inlet parallel to the board axis	Torres et al. (2013)
Epoxy	Radiation shielding property	• Composite indicated high-efficiency shielding of X-rays and gamma rays • The composite mass weakening coefficient is much greater than that of aluminum in a comparatively low energy	Li et al. (2017b)
Epoxy resin	Deterioration in seawater	• The tensile and bending strengths of the samples showed a decreasing trend with treating time • An effective lowering of the Fe^{2+} content in the BF could lead to higher stability	Wei et al. (2011)
Vinyl ester resin	Fire structural resilience	• The tensile structural of the glass fiber laminate was poor when introduced to the same heat flux • Indicated lower tensile fire resilience than an equivalent glass fiber laminate	Bhat et al. (2015)
Epoxy	Strengthening concrete structures	• Subjected to fatigue, seismic and impact loading, elevated temperature, saline environment and cycles of freezing and thawing	Naser et al. (2019)

(Continued)

TABLE 3.2 (Continued)

Reported Work on Basalt Fiber-Reinforced Polymer Composites

Polymer	Characteristics	Effect of Reinforcement	References
Polypropylene	Mechanical properties and microstructure	• The addition of BF increased the tensile strength, flexural strength and toughness index dramatically • At 28 days, this bond showed a certain extent of weakening	Jiang et al. (2014)
Epoxy	Mechanical behavior	• Increased the first-crack toughness of concrete subjected to flexural loading • Increased the first-crack toughness of concrete subjected to both flexural and impact loading	Branston et al. (2016)
Epoxy	Mechanical characterization	• Showed 35%–42% higher Young's modulus increments • Great compressive toughness and flexural behavior	Lopresto et al. (2011)
Epoxy	Polymer composites	• Chemically unreactive, highly resistant to oxidation and possessed minimum thermal conductivity • The bonding between the matrix and the BF increased, which lead to the exceptional improvement of mechanical qualities	Dhand et al. (2015)
Polypropylene	Reinforcement of polymer composites	• Rupture toughness increased • Shift in disk speed was efficient fiber and gravel geometry procedure	Czigány et al. (2005)

Abbreviations: BF, basalt fiber; BFRP, basalt fiber-reinforced polymer; BFRTP, basalt fiber-reinforced thermoplastic epoxy.

investigation into long-term creep action of BFRP bars, Sokairge et al. (2020) found the creep behavior under normal conditions, including creeping rupture stress, creep strain and residual properties of BFRP bars as an option to other types of FRP bars in pre-stressing applications, taking into account the effect of the fiber content and bar diameter. For each 6 mm of diameter and 10 mm of diameter with a length of 1000 mm, five loads reflecting different persistent stress ratios to maximum strength were suggested. The results revealed that BFRP bars with diameters of 6 and 10 mm, tensile strength and elasticity modules were partly impacted by their creep. In other words, the residual elasticity modulus decreased by about 3% contrasted with the mean elasticity modulus of both diameters, and the mean residual tensile strength was reduced by about 5% compared with the average tensile strength of both diameters. These tests verified that BFRP bars are commended in pre-stressing applications because a comparable inferred creep rupture stress is contrasted to AFRP bars after a million hours. In a study investigated by Wang et al. (2020) on static and fatigue behavior of BF-reinforced thermoplastic epoxy composites, it was reported that the thermoplastic epoxy resin had several benefits of thermoplastic polymers like decent backup processing efficiency and better fiber interface properties. These components of liquid epoxy resin were tested with improved fatigue loading gear and an in situ SEM for quasi-static and fatigue tests. Comparison with thermosetting epoxy BFRP, the static strength and fatigue life of BF-reinforced thermoplastic epoxy polymer BFRTP were near that of thermosetting epoxy BFRP at high stress levels. However, the fatigue life of the former is much higher than the latter at low stress levels. This findings of this research provided insights into how fiber cooperation can be well preserved and fibers cannot easily split. The BFRTP can maintain a better fatigue performance.

Benefits such as high resistance to corrosion, affordable price and environment-friendly characteristics make BFRP tendons a suitable alternative to metal strengthening reinforcement. In an investigation conducted by Xu et al. (2019) on tensile mechanical qualities of BFRP tendons at low-to-moderate strain rates, it was shown in Figure 3.5 that mechanical characteristics of BFRP tendons are sensitive to strain during tensile evaluation. In contrast with quasi-static tensile evaluation, the stiffness was greatly improved by the strain rates in dynamic tensile evaluation. However, the maximum and rupture strains showed comparatively minimal differences in increased strain rate for dynamic tensile evaluation. The research also showed that it is easier to use the two-parameter Weibull distribution to describe the structural engineering mechanical qualities of the tendon BFRP.

Chlup et al. (2020) conducted an experiment on fracture tolerance of partly pyrolyzed polysiloxane pre-ceramic polymer matrix composites reinforced by unidirectional BF. The study showed that the disadvantage of unidirectional composites with a resilient directionality of characteristic, i.e., more significant characteristics such as high fracture resilient and being perpendicular to the fibers, was followed by quite poor fiber characteristic where there was no activation of the toughening effect. The first type of matrix was formed at a temperature of 650°C with partial pyrolysis of pre-ceramic polysiloxane resin, whereas the second type of matrix was made of cured polysiloxane and/or epoxy resin and used as guidance material. The most resistant to crack propagation (delamination) was the epoxy resin (EPC) material, preceded

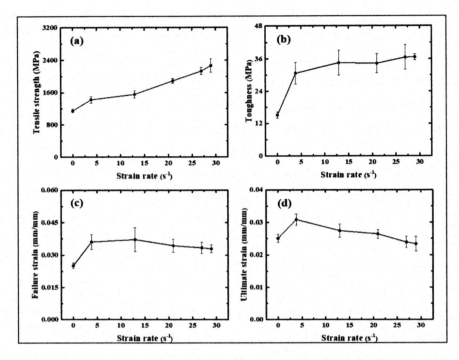

FIGURE 3.5 The consequence of strain-rate variation on the mechanical properties of BFRP tendons under tensile testing. (a) Tensile toughness (MPa) versus strain rate (s^{-1}). (b) Toughness (MPa) versus strain rate (s^{-1}). (c) Rupture strain and versus strain rate (s^{-1}). (d) Ultimate strain versus strain rate (s^{-1}). (Adapted with copyright permission from Xu et al. 2019.)

only by the polymethylsiloxane (MSC) cured material, although the MSCpyr material had slightly less tolerance. It can be inferred that even the characteristics of the in-plan room temperature fracture of pyrolyzed polymethylsiloxane (MSCpyr) material are considerably lower and can benefit from the out-of-plan fracture tolerance.

In civil infrastructure applications, the strengths of basalt composites have long been exploited. A study on FRP composites enhancing RC structures by Naser, Hawileh and Abdalla (2019) analyzed the application of FRP systems in RC structural members and emphasized the performance of FRPs (including bonding agents) under severe conditions such as elevated temperature, saline environment and cycles of freezing and thawing. Using sufficient adhesive, FRP strips or rebars are linked into "grooves" or slits cut into concrete cover. The adhesive in the groove ensures that the concrete is well secured to the FRP strip or rod to serve as an important aspect of tensile or shear reinforcement. FRP stiffness tends to experience negligible losses of up to about 400°C (above which it decreases rapidly), and CFRP and GFRP lose at 250°C and 325°C, respectively, about 50% of their original power. It should eventually be noted that FRPs have a tremendous ability for continuous integration into the reinforcement of RC systems. Such materials have excellent characteristics; therefore, they can be used in a number of building applications. In a study on fatigue attitude of sea sand concrete beams reinforced with BFRP bars conducted by Li et al. (2018), due to the deterioration of steel in challenging operating environments, the reliability of RC is still a consideration. The use of sea sand concrete FRP bars removes the corrosion concerns, tackles the scarcity of natural river sand and is in line with resource conservation. Two sizes of BFRP-reinforced sea sand concrete beams were tested for fatigue for research purposes. The low load was put at zero, the nominal load was set at 0.5–0.6 and the maximum power (FU) set at 0.7 and 10 Hz was used for four-point bending. In the experimental program, two BFRP-reinforced concrete beams as leverage and four BFRP-reinforced concrete beams for the fatigue test were used, and a standard RC beam was used for contrast. The main study found that the rigidity of BFRP-reinforced concrete beams deteriorated, and the interface stiffness damage improved as the load level and cycles rose. The exact amount of load applied escalated the damage sustained by BFRP, allowing the concrete beam of sea sand to fail prematurely. Sim, Park and Moon (2005) studied the features of BF as an enhancing component for concrete structures. They found that BF typically has greater tensile toughness than E-glass fibers, greater strain of failure than carbon fibers, high chemical attack, excellent effect load and temperature resistance without the harmful emission of fumes. Previous work by Dias and Thaumaturgo (2005) showed how BF-reinforced geopolymer concrete can withstand heavy loads. When adding 0.5 to 1.0% of basalt, the geopolymeric concrete exhibited an increase in fracture toughness compared with concretes.

3.3.2 THERMAL PROPERTIES

There are few studies that claim an extrusion technology produces BF composites. According to Czigány (2005), the temperature of the extrusion has the greatest effect on composite properties. Also, if the temperature increased from 180°C to 240°C, the tensile strength from 35 to 42 MPa and the elasticity modulus showed improved length and fiber matrix interfacial adhesion. In fact, BF obtained from basalt rock, which is mainly located at an overground, exuberant volcanic rock, has some outstanding properties due to the circumstances of its formation. On the other hand, due to its high elasticity modulus and high thermal resilience, the fibers made from it have considerable heat and acoustic resistance capacity and are excellent isolators of vibration. In the last decade, ceramic and BFs were used to produce hybrid friction materials. A study conducted by Öztürk, Arslan and Öztürk (2007) on reinforced hybrid friction materials of ceramic and BFs on hot wear performance stated that the materials created by merging two or more dissimilar types of fibers in a typical matrix are hybrid composites. They provide a number of features that cannot be accomplished with a particular form of reinforcement. For the purpose of analysis, the content of ceramic fiber retained the same at 10 vol%, and the content of BF was changed from 0 to 40 vol%. Mechanical properties, friction and wear performance of friction materials were evaluated using a pin-on disc-style system in contrast with a cast iron counterface at sliding speeds of 3.2–12.8 m/s, disc temperatures of 100°C –350°C and applied loads of 312.5–625N. Further evaluation exposed that the quality of fibers has a big influence on the composites' mechanical and tribological features. With increased additional BF content, the friction coefficient of the hybrid friction materials was increased. The wear tests showed that the friction coefficient decreased with rising load and speed, but increased up to 300°C with increasing disc temperature. Thus, this study showed that disc temperature subsequent to sliding velocity was the most significant factor influencing wear rate. The materials with greater particular wear rates yielded comparatively rougher particles of wear. They also concluded that composites of basalt fiber have outstanding wear properties.

A recent study by Zhu et al. (2014) reviewed flame retardancy capabilities at elevated temperature by applying various heat resilience vinyl and epoxy resins. They discovered that even at elevated temperatures of up to 100°C, the thermal resistance increased. The enhanced thermal consistency of the BFRP bars up to 100°C is due to the impregnation of, and adequate compatibility between, heat-resistant resins with BFs. BFs are substantially cheaper than carbon fibers and have better resistance to temperature because they are developed by a molten rock drawing process at 1400°C–1500°C. Previous research on the effect of thermal behavior on tensile failure of BFs conducted by Militký, Kovačič and Rubnerová (2002) established that BFs may be used for the production of goods that are resilient to extreme temperatures and chemically inactive. To validate whether this is true or not, properties were tested after 50, 100, 200 and 300°C were tempered. Electron microscopy scanning detected structural differences in fibers. Further investigation hypothesized that fracture happens due to fiber volume non-homogeneities, possibly of the minor mineral crystallites. The fibrous piece study that formed during basalt weave abrasion was identified. Hence, it can be summarized that the management of BFs must be conducted with caution.

Last but not least, BF is a popular fiber that has been emerging in recent years as it has gained more and more interest in the heat resistance market (Wei, Cao and Song 2010). The basalt fiber working temperature range is –260°C to 700°C, which is greater than glass fiber, which is 60°C till 450°C (Liu et al. 2018). Over the last 2 years, Liu et al. (2018) invented BF filter bags that could be used for a lengthy span of time under a massive temperature of 380°C and effectively resolve issues in glass industry kilns, such as high flue gas temperatures, smoother texture and powder dust viscosity. BF output is significantly responsible for the chemical composition of unprocessed resources and the method of manufacturing. The heat resistance rises up with an increase in the silicate glass fiber SiO_2 and Al_2O_3 content (i.e., high silica glass fiber, great toughness glass fiber and quartz fiber), all of which consist of strong heat resilience due to large SiO_2 fiber intensity. Monofilament tensile toughness was tested at ambient temperature for BFs prepared from basalts with different levels of SiO_2 and Al_2O_3. For correlation to the tensile strength at ambient temperature, the tensile toughness of BFs heated at 400°C and 500°C was measured. After 400°C and 500°C heat treatment, the tensile toughness of each specimen is minimum at ambient temperature, and after 500°C heat treatment, the tensile strength decreases drastically. This implies that the heat resilience of fibers can be enhanced by increasing the SiO_2 and Al_2O_3 content of BFs.

3.4 APPLICATIONS

Numerous authors have written about the various benefits of BFs in composites and high-performance applications in the past. In ecologically pure basalt, there are a wide variety of uses. This section identifies the major applications of BFs in different industries.

3.4.1 LAMINATES AND PRE-PREGS

In civil engineering applications, FRPs are often used due to their benefits over conventional materials, such as high toughness, lightness and corrosion resilience (Firmo, Correia and França 2012). As a potential substitute for conventional glass and carbon fibers, BF has recently received a great deal of interest (Dorigato and Pegoretti 2012). BFs are distinguished by high tolerance to alkaline conditions, whereas strong acids have shown comparatively less stability. High abrasion properties distinguish BF due to the increased hardness around 5 to 9 on Mohr's readiness scale. In fact, BF can be introduced for hours at 1100°C–1200°C without any physical harm due to good thermal properties. Because of these properties, for many technical applications, BF has been attractive, like geopolymer concretes, pressure pipes, fibrous insulators, protective clothing and fire-blocking material. BFs have been suggested in recent years in conjunction with different polymer matrices for the preparation of structural composites, such as unsaturated polyester, vinyl ester, epoxy, phenol formaldehyde, polyimide, polysiloxane, polypropylene, polycarbonate, poly (ethylene terephthalate), poly(butylene terephthalate), polyamide, starch resin and polylactic acid (Dorigato and Pegoretti 2012). According to the study by Papa et al. (2019), the alternative may be BF laminates, incorporating the environmental and mechanical issues. For painting applications, the improved top-ground layer characteristics of basalt plastics make them a wiser selection. By adding silane coupling agents that stimulate the interfacial properties between the polymer matrix and BFs, aided by intensified bending properties, layer protection for BFs has been intensified. For die-casting, winding, vacuum molding and autoclave direct pressing, pre-pregs of BFs with altered polyester resins are acceptable. BF laminates synthesized using resin transfer molding are often utilized in printable circuit boards and electrical circuits as composite panels to possess greater insulation (Dhand et al. 2015).

3.4.2 TRANSPORTATION

Currently, FRPs normally strengthened by glass fibers are implemented for retrofitting concrete, retrofitting steel, seismic retrofitting of bridge abutments, bridge structures for specific applications and internal strengthening concrete. Any of the bridges were designed completely or partly with FRP. FRP's advantages are fantastic, as FRP provides the benefits of quicker build time, higher strength, lighter weight and better life span of the environment. Melted basalt rock extruded BF has at least a 16% larger modulus, equal tensile toughness and greater base tolerance compared with E-glass fiber; outstanding interfacial shear toughness and is already commercially accessible. Composite rebars of BF, which usually consist of 80% fiber and 20% resin

TABLE 3.3
Comparative Analysis Properties of Filaments

Properties	Units	Basalt Filaments	E-glass	Silica Filament
Thermal				
Maximum application temperature	°C	982	650	1100
Sustained operating temperature	°C	820	480	1000
Thermal conductivity	W/m·K	0.031–0.038	0.034–0.04	0.035–0.04
Melting temperature	°C	1450	1120	1550
Thermal expansion coefficient	ppm/°C	8.0	5.4	0.05
Physical/mechanical				
Density	g/cm^3	2.75	2.55	2.15
Filament diameter	Mm	9–23	9–13	9–15
Tensile strength	MPa	4840	3450	4750
Compression	Psi	550.000	440.000	510.00
Elastic modulus	GPa	89	77	66
Elongation at break	%	3.15	4.7	1.2
Absorption of humidity (65% RH)	%	0.1	0.1	0.1
Stability at tension (20°C)	%	100	100	100
Stability at tension (400°C)	%	82	52	80
Chemical resistance (%)				
weight loss after				
3 h boiling in:	%	0.2	0.7	0.05
H_2O	%	5.0	6.0	5.0
2N N_2OH (sodium hydroxide)	%	2.2	38.9	15.7

Abbreviations: RH, relative humidity.

binder, will theoretically substitute steel anywhere there are oxidation concerns, such as saltwater penetration, acid-base disrupt, ocean atmosphere etc. Furthermore, In addition, basalt rebars have a capacity of one-third that of steel, a ductility that is thought to be three times that of steel and a thermal expansion coefficient that is very close to that of concrete. In implementations and simulations, researchers have found that BFs significantly influence concrete toughness in that BF altered the dramatic and brittle deterioration of normal concrete to ductile deterioration because the slow withdrawal output of the fiber enhanced energy extraction (Table 3.3).

Use in transportation requires knowledge of the material durability under dissimilar environments in addition to the mechanical qualities of the as produced composites. This analysis primarily researches the resistance to saltwater penetration, water absorption, temperature and water cycling of the BFRP composites.

3.5 CONCLUSIONS

In this chapter, scientific findings on the usage of BFs to strengthen composite materials showed that these have been used primarily to manufacture solid and lightweight materials for laminates, pre-pregs and transportation. Basalt was considered to possess greater qualities brought along in traditional form. BFs are currently almost as beneficial as carbon fibers, but they are environmentally friendly, less harmful, and a source of renewable energy. In addition, basalt is chemically unreactive, extremely corrosion resilient, and has very low thermal conductivity, proof that it is preferable to any other reinforcement currently accessible. The analysis focuses primarily on its superior physical and thermal chemical qualities, as opposed to glass and carbon fibers measured by various researchers. Finally, the chapter illustrates specific basalt attributes in the type of technologies commonly used in modern industries. Studies have identified that by combining the surface of BFs with binding substances such as silanes, the binding between the matrix and the BF is enhanced, leading to a notable boost in mechanical qualities. Using this principle, countless studies have extensively enhanced BFs in distinct organic-inorganic and cement substances and have shown remarkable industrial purposes. Also examined was the ability of basalt to withstand chemical attacks. Alkaline assaults are the most corrosive of the compounds, and some efforts to avoid degradation of the fibers are now in progress, but success is still a long way off. Basalt fillers have currently shown to be promising in many computer parts that produce these corrosive chemicals. The use of basalt in the future can also minimize costs for industrial use, improving basalt and composite studies in the long term. The interfacial area of basalt-reinforced composites tends to involve alteration earlier for use in continuing implementation requiring water contact. The results of this chapter benchmark the composites produced for a durability study, and the consequences of exposing basalt-reinforced composites to several environments.

REFERENCES

Abral, Hairul, Jeri Ariksa, Melbi Mahardika, Dian Handayani, Ibtisamatul Aminah, Neny Sandrawati, Angga Bahri Pratama, Nural Fajri, S.M. Sapuan, and R.A. Ilyas. 2020. "Transparent and Antimicrobial Cellulose Film from Ginger Nanofiber." *Food Hydrocolloids* 98 (January): 105266. https://doi.org/10.1016/j.foodhyd.2019.105266

Abral, Hairul, Jeri Ariksa, Melbi Mahardika, Dian Handayani, Ibtisamatul Aminah, Neny Sandrawati, S.M. Sapuan, and R.A. Ilyas. 2019. "Highly Transparent and Antimicrobial PVA Based Bionanocomposites Reinforced by Ginger Nanofiber." *Polymer Testing* 81 (January): 106186. https://doi.org/10.1016/j.polymertesting.2019.106186

Abral, Hairul, Melati Krista Chairani, Muhammad Dinul Rizki, Melbi Mahardika, Dian Handayani, Eni Sugiarti, Ahmad Novi Muslimin, S.M. Sapuan, and R.A. Ilyas. 2021. "Characterization of Compressed Bacterial Cellulose Nanopaper Film after Exposure to Dry and Humid Conditions." *Journal of Materials Research and Technology* 11 (March–April): 1–25. https://doi.org/10.1016/j.jmrt.2021.01.057

Afroz, Mahzabin, Indubhushan Patnaikuni, and Srikanth Venkatesan. 2017. "Chemical Durability and Performance of Modified Basalt Fiber in Concrete Medium." *Construction and Building Materials* 154: 191–203. https://doi.org/10.1016/j.conbuildmat.2017. 07.153

Aisyah, H. A., M. T. Paridah, S. M. Sapuan, A. Khalina, O. B. Berkalp, S. H. Lee, C. H. Lee, et al. 2019. "Thermal Properties of Woven Kenaf/Carbon Fibre-Reinforced Epoxy Hybrid Composite Panels." *International Journal of Polymer Science* 2019 (December): 1–8. https://doi.org/10.1155/2019/5258621

Alaimo, Giuseppe, Antonino Valenza, Daniele Enea, and Vincenzo Fiore. 2016. "The Durability of Basalt Fibres Reinforced Polymer (BFRP) Panels for Cladding." *Materials and Structures* 49 (6): 2053–2064. https://doi.org/10.1617/s11527-015-0633-3

Alsubari, S., M.Y.M. Zuhri, S.M. Sapuan, M.R. Ishak, R.A. Ilyas, and M.R.M. Asyraf. 2021. "Potential of Natural Fiber Reinforced Polymer Composites in Sandwich Structures: A Review on Its Mechanical Properties." *Polymers* 13 (3): 423. https://doi.org/10.3390/polym13030423

Amuthakkannan, P., V. Manikandan, J.T. Winowlin Jappes, and M. Uthayakumar. 2013. "Effect of Fibre Length and Fibre Content on Mechanical Properties of Short Basalt Fibre Reinforced Polymer Matrix Composites." *Materials Physics and Mechanics* 16 (2): 107–117.

Asrofi, Mochamad, Sujito, Edi Syafri, S.M. Sapuan, and R.A. Ilyas. 2020. "Improvement of Biocomposite Properties Based Tapioca Starch and Sugarcane Bagasse Cellulose Nanofibers." *Key Engineering Materials* 849 (June): 96–101. https://doi.org/10.4028/www.scientific.net/KEM.849.96

Asyraf, M.R.M., M. Rafidah, M.R. Ishak, S.M. Sapuan, R.A. Ilyas, and M.R. Razman. 2020a. "Integration of TRIZ, Morphological Chart and ANP Method for Development of FRP Composite Portable Fire Extinguisher." *Polymer Composites* 41 (7): 2917–2932. https://doi.org/10.1002/pc.25587

Asyraf, M.R.M., M.R. Ishak, S.M. Sapuan, N. Yidris, and R.A. Ilyas. 2020b. "Woods and Composites Cantilever Beam: A Comprehensive Review of Experimental and Numerical Creep Methodologies." *Journal of Materials Research and Technology* 9 (3): 6759–6776. https://doi.org/10.1016/j.jmrt.2020.01.013

Asyraf, M.M.R., M. Ridzwan Ishak, S.M. Sapuan, N. Yidris, R.M. Shahroze, A.N. Johari, M. Rafidah, and R.A. Ilyas. 2020c. "Creep Test Rig for Cantilever Beam: Fundamentals, Prospects and Present Views." *Journal of Mechanical Engineering and Sciences* 14 (2): 6869–6887. https://doi.org/10.15282/jmes.14.2.2020.26.0538

Atiqah, A., M. Jawaid, S.M. Sapuan, M.R. Ishak, M.N.M. Ansari, and R.A. Ilyas. 2019. "Physical and Thermal Properties of Treated Sugar Palm/Glass Fibre Reinforced Thermoplastic Polyurethane Hybrid Composites." *Journal of Materials Research and Technology* 8 (5): 3726–3732. https://doi.org/10.1016/j.jmrt.2019.06.032

Ayu, Rafiqah S., Abdan Khalina, Ahmad Saffian Harmaen, Khairul Zaman, Tawakkal Isma, Qiuyun Liu, R. A. Ilyas, and Ching Hao Lee. 2020. "Characterization Study of Empty Fruit Bunch (EFB) Fibers Reinforcement in Poly(Butylene) Succinate (PBS)/Starch/Glycerol Composite Sheet." *Polymers* 12 (7): 1571. https://doi.org/10.3390/polym12071571

Azammi, A.M. Noor, R.A. Ilyas, S.M. Sapuan, Rushdan Ibrahim, M.S.N. Atikah, Mochamad Asrofi, and A. Atiqah. 2019. "Characterization Studies of Biopolymeric Matrix and Cellulose Fibres Based Composites Related to Functionalized Fibre-Matrix Interface." In *Interfaces in Particle and Fibre Reinforced Composites*, 1st ed., 1–68. London: Woodhead Publishing. https://doi.org/10.1016/B978-0-08-102665-6

Azimpour-shishevan, Farzin, and Hamit Akbulut. 2020. "Effect of Thermal Cycling on Mechanical and Thermal Properties of Basalt Fibre-Reinforced Epoxy Composites." *Bulletin of Materials Science* 4: 88. https://doi.org/10.1007/s12034-020-2059-y

Baihaqi, N.M.Z. Nik, A. Khalina, N. Mohd Nurazzi, H.A. Aisyah, S.M. Sapuan, and R.A. Ilyas. 2021. "Effect of Fiber Content and Their Hybridization on Bending and Torsional Strength of Hybrid Epoxy Composites Reinforced with Carbon and Sugar Palm Fibers." *Polimery* 66 (1): 36–43.

Banibayat, Pouya, and Anil Patnaik. 2014. "Variability of Mechanical Properties of Basalt Fiber Reinforced Polymer Bars Manufactured by Wet-Layup Method." *Materials and Design* 56: 898–906. https://doi.org/10.1016/j.matdes.2013.11.081

Berozashvili, M. 2001. "Continuous Reinforcing Fibers Are Being Offered for Construction, Civil Engineering and Other Composites Applications." *Advanced Material Composite News, Composite Worldwide* 6: 5–6.

Basalt Fiber-Reinforced Polymer Composites

Bhat, T., V. Chevali, X. Liu, S. Feih, and A. P. Mouritz. 2015. "Fire Structural Resistance of Basalt Fibre Composite." *Composites Part A: Applied Science and Manufacturing* 71: 107–115. https://doi.org/10.1016/j.compositesa.2015.01.006

Branston, John, Sreekanta Das, Sara Y. Kenno, and Craig Taylor. 2016. "Mechanical Behaviour of Basalt Fibre Reinforced Concrete." *Construction and Building Materials* 124: 878–886. https://doi.org/10.1016/j.conbuildmat.2016.08.009

Callister, Jr, William D. and David G. Rethwisch. 2003. *Materials Science and Engineering: An Introduction*, 6th ed. Milton, Queensland, Australia: John Wiley and Sons Australia, Ltd.

Chen, Wensu, Hong Hao, Michael Jong, Jian Cui, Yanchao Shi, Li Chen, and Thong M. Pham. 2017. "Quasi-Static and Dynamic Tensile Properties of Basalt Fibre Reinforced Polymer." *Composites Part B: Engineering* 125: 123–133. https://doi.org/10.1016/j.compositesb.2017.05.069

Chlup, Zdeněk, Martin Černý, Adam Strachota, Hynek Hadraba, Petr Kácha, and Martina Halasová. 2018a. "Effect of the Exposition Temperature on the Behaviour of Partially Pyrolysed Hybrid Basalt Fibre Composites." *Composites Part B: Engineering* 147 (August): 122–27. https://doi.org/10.1016/j.compositesb.2018.04.021

Chlup, Zdeněk, Martin Černý, Petr Kácha, Hynek Hadraba, and Adam Strachota. 2020. "Fracture Resistance of Partially Pyrolysed Polysiloxane Preceramic Polymer Matrix Composites Reinforced by Unidirectional Basalt Fibres." *Journal of the European Ceramic Society* 40 (14): 4879–4885. https://doi.org/10.1016/j.jeurceramsoc.2020.01.047

Colombo, C., L. Vergani, and M. Burman. 2012. "Static and Fatigue Characterisation of New Basalt Fibre Reinforced Composites." *Composite Structures* 94 (3): 1165–1174. https://doi.org/10.1016/j.compstruct.2011.10.007

Czigány, Tibor. 2005. "Basalt Fiber Reinforced Hybrid Polymer Composites." *Materials Science Forum* 473–474 (January): 59–66. https://doi.org/10.4028/www.scientific.net/MSF.473-474.59

Czigány, Tibor, János Vad, and Kornél Pölöskei. 2005. "Basalt Fiber as a Reinforcement of Polymer Composites." *Periodica Polytechnica Mechanical Engineering* 49 (1): 3–14.

Dhand, Vivek, Garima Mittal, Kyong Yop Rhee, Soo-Jin Park, and David Hui. 2015. "A Short Review on Basalt Fiber Reinforced Polymer Composites." *Composites Part B: Engineering* 73 (May): 166–180. https://doi.org/10.1016/j.compositesb.2014.12.011

Dias, Dylmar Penteado, and Clelio Thaumaturgo. 2005. "Fracture Toughness of Geopolymeric Concretes Reinforced with Basalt Fibers." *Cement and Concrete Composites* 27 (1): 49–54. https://doi.org/10.1016/j.cemconcomp.2004.02.044

Dorigato, A., and A. Pegoretti. 2012. "Fatigue Resistance of Basalt Fibers-Reinforced Laminates." *Journal of Composite Materials* 46 (15): 1773–1785. https://doi.org/10.1177/0021998311425620

Elgabbas, Fareed, Patrick Vincent, Ehab A. Ahmed, and Brahim Benmokrane. 2016. "Experimental Testing of Basalt-Fiber-Reinforced Polymer Bars in Concrete Beams." *Composites Part B: Engineering* 91 (April): 205–218. https://doi.org/10.1016/j.compositesb.2016.01.045

Esnaola, A., I. Ulacia, L. Aretxabaleta, J. Aurrekoetxea, and I. Gallego. 2015. "Quasi-Static Crush Energy Absorption Capability of E-Glass/Polyester and Hybrid E-Glass-Basalt/Polyester Composite Structures." *Journal of Materials & Design* 76 (July): 18–25. https://doi.org/10.1016/j.matdes.2015.03.044

Fernando, D., A. Frangi, P. Kobel. 2016. "Behaviour of Basalt Fibre Reinforced Polymer Strengthened Timber Laminates under Tensile Loading." *Engineering Structures* 117: 437–456. https://doi.org/10.1016/j.engstruct.2016.03.009

Fiore, V., G. Di Bella, and A. Valenza. 2011. "Glass–Basalt/Epoxy Hybrid Composites for Marine Applications." *Materials & Design* 32 (4): 2091–2099. https://doi.org/10.1016/j.matdes.2010.11.043

Firmo, João P., João R. Correia, and P. França. 2012. "Fire Behaviour of Reinforced Concrete Beams Strengthened with CFRP Laminates: Protection Systems with Insulation of the Anchorage Zones." *Composites Part B: Engineering* 43 (3): 1545–1556. https://doi.org/10.1016/j.compositesb.2011.09.002

Ilyas, R.A., and S.M. Sapuan. 2020a. "Biopolymers and Biocomposites: Chemistry and Technology." *Current Analytical Chemistry* 16 (5): 500–503. https://doi.org/10.2174/157341101605200603095311

Ilyas, R.A., and S.M. Sapuan. 2020b. "The Preparation Methods and Processing of Natural Fibre Bio-Polymer Composites." *Current Organic Synthesis* 16 (8): 1068–1070. https://doi.org/10.2174/1570179416082001201005616

Ilyas, R.A., S.M. Sapuan, M.S.N. Atikah, M.R.M. Asyraf, S. Ayu. Rafiqah, H.A. Aisyah, N Mohd Nurazzi, and M.N.F. Norrrahim. 2021. "Effect of Hydrolysis Time on the Morphological, Physical, Chemical, and Thermal Behavior of Sugar Palm Nanocrystalline Cellulose (Arenga Pinnata (Wurmb.) Merr)." *Textile Research Journal* 91 (1–2): 152–167. https://doi.org/10.1177/0040517520932393

Ilyas, R.A., S.M. Sapuan, A. Atiqah, R. Ibrahim, H. Abral, M.R. Ishak, E.S. Zainudin, et al. 2020a. "Sugar Palm (Arenga Pinnata [Wurmb.] Merr) Starch Films Containing Sugar Palm Nanofibrillated Cellulose as Reinforcement: Water Barrier Properties." *Polymer Composites* 41 (2): 459–467. https://doi.org/10.1002/pc.25379

Ilyas, R.A, S.M. Sapuan, R. Ibrahim, H. Abral, M.R. Ishak, E.S. Zainudin, M. Asrofi, et al. 2019a. "Sugar Palm (Arenga Pinnata (Wurmb.) Merr) Cellulosic Fibre Hierarchy: A Comprehensive Approach from Macro to Nano Scale." *Journal of Materials Research and Technology* 8 (3): 2753–2766. https://doi.org/10.1016/j.jmrt.2019.04.011

Ilyas, R.A., S.M. Sapuan, R. Ibrahim, H. Abral, M.R. Ishak, E.S. Zainudin, M.S.N. Atikah, et al. 2019b. "Effect of Sugar Palm Nanofibrillated Cellulose concentrations on Morphological, Mechanical and Physical Properties of Biodegradable Films Based on Agro-Waste Sugar Palm (Arenga Pinnata (Wurmb.) Merr) Starch." *Journal of Materials Research and Technology* 8 (5): 4819–4830. https://doi.org/10.1016/j.jmrt.2019.08.028

Ilyas, R.A., S.M. Sapuan, R. Ibrahim, H. Abral, M.R. Ishak, E.S. Zainudin, A. Atiqah, et al. 2020b. "Thermal, Biodegradability and Water Barrier Properties of Bio-Nanocomposites Based on Plasticised Sugar Palm Starch and Nanofibrillated Celluloses from Sugar Palm Fibres." *Journal of Biobased Materials and Bioenergy* 14 (2): 234–248. https://doi.org/10.1166/jbmb.2020.1951

Ilyas, R.A., S.M. Sapuan, R. Ibrahim, M.S.N. Atikah, A. Atiqah, M.N.M. Ansari, and M.N.F. Norrrahim. 2019c. "Production, Processes and Modification of Nanocrystalline Cellulose from Agro-Waste: A Review." In *Nanocrystalline Materials*, 3–32. London: IntechOpen. https://doi.org/10.5772/intechopen.87001

Ilyas, R.A., S.M. Sapuan, and M.R. Ishak. 2018a. "Isolation and Characterization of Nanocrystalline Cellulose from Sugar Palm Fibres (Arenga Pinnata)." *Carbohydrate Polymers* 181 (February): 1038–1051. https://doi.org/10.1016/j.carbpol.2017.11.045

Ilyas, R.A., S.M. Sapuan, M.R. Ishak, and E.S. Zainudin. 2017. "Effect of Delignification on the Physical, Thermal, Chemical, and Structural Properties of Sugar Palm Fibre." *BioResources* 12 (4): 8734–8754. https://doi.org/10.15376/biores.12.4.8734-8754

Ilyas, R.A., S.M. Sapuan, M.R. Ishak, and E.S. Zainudin. 2018b. "Development and Characterization of Sugar Palm Nanocrystalline Cellulose Reinforced Sugar Palm Starch Bionanocomposites." *Carbohydrate Polymers* 202 (December): 186–202. https://doi.org/10.1016/j.carbpol.2018.09.002

Ilyas, R.A., S.M. Sapuan, M.R. Ishak, and E.S. Zainudin. 2019d. "Sugar Palm Nanofibrillated Cellulose (Arenga Pinnata (Wurmb.) Merr): Effect of Cycles on Their Yield, Physic-Chemical, Morphological and Thermal Behavior." *International Journal of Biological Macromolecules* 123 (February): 379–388. https://doi.org/10.1016/j.ijbiomac.2018.11.124

Inman, Marianne, Eythor Rafn Thorhallsson, and Kamal Azrague. 2017. "A Mechanical and Environmental Assessment and Comparison of Basalt Fibre Reinforced Polymer (BFRP) Rebar and Steel Rebar in Concrete Beams." *Energy Procedia* 111 (March): 31–40. https://doi.org/10.1016/j.egypro.2017.03.005

Jiang, Chaohua, Ke Fan, Fei Wu, and Da Chen. 2014. "Experimental Study on the Mechanical Properties and Microstructure of Chopped Basalt Fibre Reinforced Concrete." *Materials and Design* 58: 187–193. https://doi.org/10.1016/j.matdes.2014.01.056

Jumaidin, R., R.A. Ilyas, M. Saiful, F. Hussin, and M.T. Mastura. 2019a. "Water Transport and Physical Properties of Sugarcane Bagasse Fibre Reinforced Thermoplastic Potato Starch Biocomposite." *Journal of Advanced Research in Fluid Mechanics and Thermal Sciences* 61 (2): 273–281.

Jumaidin, Ridhwan, Muhammad Afif Akmal Khiruddin, Zulhelmi Asyul Sutan Saidi, Mohd Sapuan Salit, and Rushdan Ahmad Ilyas. 2020. "Effect of Cogon Grass Fibre on the Thermal, Mechanical and Biodegradation Properties of Thermoplastic Cassava Starch Biocomposite." *International Journal of Biological Macromolecules* 146 (March): 746–755. https://doi.org/10.1016/j.ijbiomac.2019.11.011

Jumaidin, Ridhwan, Zulhelmi Asyul Sutan Saidi, Rushdan Ahmad Ilyas, Mohd Nazri Ahmad, Mohammad Khalid Wahid, Mohd Yuhazri Yaakob, Nurul Ain Maidin, Mohd Hidayat Ab Rahman, and Mohd Hairizal Osman. 2019b. "Characteristics of Cogon Grass Fibre Reinforced Thermoplastic Cassava Starch Biocomposite: Water Absorption and Physical Properties." *Journal of Advanced Research in Fluid Mechanics and Thermal Sciences*, 62 (1): 43–52.

Khandelwal, Saurabh, and Kyong Yop Rhee. 2020. "Recent Advances in Basalt-Fiber-Reinforced Composites: Tailoring the Fiber-Matrix Interface." *Composites Part B: Engineering* 192 (July) 108011. https://doi.org/10.1016/j.compositesb.2020.108011

Ku, H., H. Wang, N. Pattarachaiyakoop, and M. Trada. 2011. "A Review on the Tensile Properties of Natural Fiber Reinforced Polymer Composites." *Composites Part B: Engineering* 42 (4): 856–873. https://doi.org/10.1016/j.compositesb.2011.01.010

Kumar, T. Senthil Muthu, M. Chandrasekar, K. Senthilkumar, R.A. Ilyas, S.M. Sapuan, N. Hariram, A. Varada Rajulu, N. Rajini, and S. Siengchin. 2020. "Characterization, Thermal and Antimicrobial Properties of Hybrid Cellulose Nanocomposite Films with in-Situ Generated Copper Nanoparticles in Tamarindus Indica Nut Powder." *Journal of Polymers and the Environment* 29: 1134–1142. https://doi.org/10.1007/s10924-020-01939-w

Li, Chenchen, Danying Gao, Yinglai Wang, and Jiyu Tang. 2017a. "Effect of High Temperature on the Bond Performance between Basalt Fibre Reinforced Polymer (BFRP) Bars and Concrete." *Construction and Building Materials* 141: 44–51. https://doi.org/10.1016/j.conbuildmat.2017.02.125

Li, Ran, Yizhuo Gu, Gaolong Zhang, Zhongjia Yang, Min Li, and Zuoguang Zhang. 2017b. "Radiation Shielding Property of Structural Polymer Composite: Continuous Basalt Fiber Reinforced Epoxy Matrix Composite Containing Erbium Oxide." *Composites Science and Technology* 143 (May): 67–74. https://doi.org/10.1016/j.compscitech.2017.03.002

Li, Lijuan, Bin Hou, Zhongyu Lu, and Feng Liu. 2018. "Fatigue Behaviour of Sea Sand Concrete Beams Reinforced with Basalt Fibre-Reinforced Polymer Bars." *Construction and Building Materials* 179 (August): 160–171. https://doi.org/10.1016/j.conbuildmat.2018.05.218

Liu, Jianxun, Jianping Yang, Meirong Chen, Liang Lei, and Zhishen Wu. 2018. "Effect of SiO_2, Al_2O_3 on Heat Resistance of Basalt Fiber." *Thermochimica Acta* 660 (December 2017): 56–60. https://doi.org/10.1016/j.tca.2017.12.023

Lopresto, V., C. Leone, and I. De Iorio. 2011. "Mechanical Characterisation of Basalt Fibre Reinforced Plastic." *Composites Part B: Engineering* 42 (4): 717–723. https://doi.org/10.1016/j.compositesb.2011.01.030

Manikandan, V., J.T. Winowlin Jappes, S.M. Suresh Kumar, and P. Amuthakkannan. 2012. "Investigation of the Effect of Surface Modifications on the Mechanical Properties of Basalt Fibre Reinforced Polymer Composites." *Composites Part B: Engineering* 43 (2): 812–818. https://doi.org/10.1016/j.compositesb.2011.11.009

Meenakshi, C.M., and A. Krishnamoorthy. 2018. "Preparation and Mechanical Characterization of Flax and Glass Fiber Reinforced Polyester Hybrid Composite Laminate by Hand Lay-up Method." *Materials Today: Proceedings* 5 (13): 26934–26940.

Miao, Yu-chen, Dan Xing, Xiong-yu Xi, Xiu Yue, Yong-xiao Bai, and Peng-cheng Ma. 2020. "Development of Conducting Basalt Fi Bre with Polymer-Based Nanocomposite Sizing." *Materials Today Communications* 23 (April): 101170. https://doi.org/10.1016/j.mtcomm.2020.101170

Middleton, Bethany. 2016. "Composites: Manufacture and Application. Design and Manufacture of Plastic Components for Multifunctionality." In *Design and Manufacture of Plastic Components for Multifunctionality*, 53–101. Oxford, UK: Elsevier Inc. https://doi.org/10.1016/B978-0-323-34061-8/00003-X

Militký, Jiří, Vladimír Kovačič, and Jitka Rubnerová. 2002. "Influence of Thermal Treatment on Tensile Failure of Basalt Fibers." *Engineering Fracture Mechanics* 69 (9): 1025–33. https://doi.org/10.1016/S0013-7944(01)00119-9

Nagavally, Rahul Reddy. 2017. "Composite Materials - History, Types, Fabrication Techniques, Advantages, and Applications." *International Journal of Mechanical And Production Engineering* 5 (9): 82–87.

Naser, M.Z., R.A. Hawileh, and J.A. Abdalla. 2019. "Fiber-Reinforced Polymer Composites in Strengthening Reinforced Concrete Structures: A Critical Review." *Engineering Structures* 198 (June): 109542. https://doi.org/10.1016/j.engstruct.2019.109542

Nazrin, A., S.M. Sapuan, M.Y. M. Zuhri, R.A. Ilyas, R. Syafiq, and S.F.K. Sherwani. 2020. "Nanocellulose Reinforced Thermoplastic Starch (TPS), Polylactic Acid (PLA), and Polybutylene Succinate (PBS) for Food Packaging Applications." *Frontiers in Chemistry* 8 (213): 1–12. https://doi.org/10.3389/fchem.2020.00213

Ngo, Tri-Dung. 2018. "Natural Fibers for Sustainable Bio-Composites." In *Natural and Artificial Fiber-Reinforced Composites as Renewable Sources*, i:13. InTech. https://doi.org/10.5772/intechopen.71012

Norizan, Mohd Nurazzi, Khalina Abdan, R.A. Ilyas, M.H. Zin, C. Muthukumar, S.A. Rafiqah, and H.A. Aisyah. 2020. "Effect of Fiber Orientation and Fiber Loading on the Mechanical and Thermal Properties of Sugar Palm Yarn Fiber Reinforced Unsaturated Polyester Resin Composites." *Polimery* 65 (2): 34–43. https://doi.org/10.14314/polimery.2020.2.5

Nurazzi, N. Mohd, A. Khalina, S.M. Sapuan, and R.A. Ilyas. 2019. "Mechanical Properties of Sugar Palm Yarn/Woven Glass Fiber Reinforced Unsaturated Polyester Composites : Effect of Fiber Loadings and Alkaline Treatment." *Polimery* 64 (10): 12–22. https://doi.org/10.14314/polimery.2019.10.3

Nurazzi, N. Mohd, A. Khalina, S.M. Sapuan, R.A. Ilyas, S.A. Rafiqah, and Z.M. Hanafee. 2020. "Thermal Properties of Treated Sugar Palm Yarn/Glass Fiber Reinforced Unsaturated Polyester Hybrid Composites." *Journal of Materials Research and Technology* 9 (2): 1606–1618. https://doi.org/10.1016/j.jmrt.2019.11.086

Omran, Abdoulhdi A. Borhana, Abdulrahman A.B.A. Mohammed, S.M. Sapuan, R.A. Ilyas, M.R.M. Asyraf, S.S. Rahimian Koloor, and M. Petrů. 2021. "Micro- and Nanocellulose in Polymer Composite Materials: A Review." *Polymers* 13 (2): 231. https://doi.org/10.3390/polym13020231

Öztürk, Bülent, Fazli Arslan, and Sultan Öztürk. 2007. "Hot Wear Properties of Ceramic and Basalt Fiber Reinforced Hybrid Friction Materials." *Tribology International* 40 (1): 37–48. https://doi.org/10.1016/j.triboint.2006.01.027

Padalu, Pravin Kumar Venkat Rao, Yogendra Singh, and Sreekanta Das. 2019. "Out-of-Plane Flexural Strengthening of URM Wallettes Using Basalt Fibre Reinforced Polymer Composite." *Construction and Building Materials* 216: 272–295. https://doi.org/10.1016/j.conbuildmat.2019.04.268

Papa, I., A. Langella, and V. Lopresto. 2019a. "Dynamic Performances of Basalt Fibre Laminates at Room and Low Temperatures." *Composite Structures* 220 (April): 652–661. https://doi.org/10.1016/j.compstruct.2019.04.059

Ramraji, K., K. Rajkumar, M. Dhananchezian, and P. Sabarinathan. 2019. "Key Experimental Investigations of Cutting Dimensionality by Abrasive Water Jet Machining on Basalt Fiber/Fly Ash Reinforced Polymer Composite." *Materials Today: Proceedings* 22: 1351–1359. https://doi.org/10.1016/j.matpr.2020.01.428

Rozilah, A., C.N. Aiza Jaafar, S.M. Sapuan, I. Zainol, and R.A. Ilyas. 2020. "The Effects of Silver Nanoparticles Compositions on the Mechanical, Physiochemical, Antibacterial, and Morphology Properties of Sugar Palm Starch Biocomposites for Antibacterial Coating." *Polymers* 12 (11): 2605. https://doi.org/10.3390/polym12112605

Sabaruddin, F.A., M.T. Paridah, S.M. Sapuan, R.A. Ilyas, S.H. Lee, K. Abdan, N. Mazlan, A.S.M. Roseley, and H.P.S. Abdul Khalil. 2020. "The Effects of Unbleached and Bleached Nanocellulose on the Thermal and Flammability of Polypropylene-Reinforced Kenaf Core Hybrid Polymer Bionanocomposites." *Polymers* 13 (1): 116. https://doi.org/10.3390/polym13010116

Saheb, D.N., and J.P. Jog. 1999. "Natural Fiber Polymer Composites: A Reivew." *Advances in Polymer Technology* 18 (4): 351–363.

Santosh Gangappa, Goudar, and S. Sripad Kulkarni. 2020. "Experimentation and Validation of Basalt & Jute Fiber Reinforced in Polymer Matrix Hybrid Composites." *Materials Today: Proceedings*, 38 (5): 2372–2379. https://doi.org/10.1016/j.matpr.2020.07.081

Sapuan, S.M., H.S. Aulia, R.A. Ilyas, A. Atiqah, T.T. Dele-Afolabi, M.N. Nurazzi, A.B.M. Supian, and M.S.N. Atikah. 2020. "Mechanical Properties of Longitudinal Basalt/Woven-Glass-Fiber-Reinforced Unsaturated Polyester-Resin Hybrid Composites." *Polymers* 12 (10): 2211. https://doi.org/10.3390/polym12102211

Sawyer, Daniel J. 2003. "Bioprocessing– No Longer a Field of Dreams." *Macromolecular Symposia* 201 (1): 271–282. https://doi.org/10.1002/masy.200351130

Shi, Jianzhe, Xin Wang, Zhishen Wu, and Zhongguo Zhu. 2017. "Fatigue Behavior of Basalt Fiber-Reinforced Polymer Tendons under a Marine Environment." *Construction and Building Materials* 137: 46–54. https://doi.org/10.1016/j.conbuildmat.2017.01.063

Shishevan, Farzin Azimpour, Hamid Akbulut, and M. A. Mohtadi-Bonab. 2017. "Low Velocity Impact Behavior of Basalt Fiber-Reinforced Polymer Composites." *Journal of Materials Engineering and Performance* 26 (6): 2890–2900. https://doi.org/10.1007/s11665-017-2728-1

Sim, Jongsung, Cheolwoo Park, and Do Young Moon. 2005. "Characteristics of Basalt Fiber as a Strengthening Material for Concrete Structures." *Composites Part B: Engineering* 36 (6–7): 504–512. https://doi.org/10.1016/j.compositesb.2005.02.002

Sokairge, Hesham, Fareed Elgabbas, Ahmed Rashad, and Hany Elshafie. 2020. "Long-Term Creep Behavior of Basalt Fiber Reinforced Polymer Bars." *Construction and Building Materials* 260 (November): 120437. https://doi.org/10.1016/j.conbuildmat.2020.120437

Suresh Kumar, C., Mohamad Fotouhi, Milad Saeedifar, and V. Arumugam. 2019. "Acoustic Emission Based Investigation on the Effect of Temperature and Hybridization on Drop Weight Impact and Post-Impact Residual Strength of Hemp and Basalt Fibres Reinforced Polymer Composite Laminates." *Composites Part B: Engineering* 173 (May): 106962. https://doi.org/10.1016/j.compositesb.2019.106962

Syafiq, R., S.M. Sapuan, M.Y.M. Zuhri, R.A. Ilyas, A. Nazrin, S.F.K. Sherwani, and A. Khalina. 2020. "Antimicrobial Activities of Starch-Based Biopolymers and Biocomposites

Incorporated with Plant Essential Oils: A Review." *Polymers* 12 (10): 2403. https://doi.org/10.3390/polym12102403

Syafri, Edi, Sudirman, Mashadi, Evi Yulianti, Deswita, Mochamad Asrofi, Hairul Abral, S.M. Sapuan, R.A. Ilyas, and Ahmad Fudholi. 2019. "Effect of Sonication Time on the Thermal Stability, Moisture Absorption, and Biodegradation of Water Hyacinth (Eichhornia Crassipes) Nanocellulose-Filled Bengkuang (Pachyrhizus Erosus) Starch Biocomposites." *Journal of Materials Research and Technology* 8 (6): 6223–6231. https://doi.org/10.1016/j.jmrt.2019.10.016

Tehrani Dehkordi, Majid, Hooshang Nosraty, Mahmood Mehrdad Shokrieh, Giangiacomo Minak, and Daniele Ghelli. 2013. "The Influence of Hybridization on Impact Damage Behavior and Residual Compression Strength of Intraply Basalt/Nylon Hybrid Composites." *Materials and Design* 43: 283–290. https://doi.org/10.1016/j.matdes.2012.07.005

Tirillò, J., L. Ferrante, F. Sarasini, L. Lampani, E. Barbero, S. Sánchez-Sáez, T. Valente, and P. Gaudenzi. 2017. "High Velocity Impact Behaviour of Hybrid Basalt-Carbon/Epoxy Composites." *Composite Structures* 168 (May): 305–312. https://doi.org/10.1016/j.compstruct.2017.02.039

Torres, J.P., R. Hoto, and J. Andrés. 2013. "Manufacture of Green-Composite Sandwich Structures with Basalt Fiber and Bioepoxy Resin." *Advances in Materials Science and Engineering* 2013: 214506.

Wang, Xin, Xing Zhao, Siqi Chen, and Zhishen Wu. 2020. "Static and Fatigue Behavior of Basalt Fiber-Reinforced Thermoplastic Epoxy Composites." *Journal of Composite Materials* 54 (18): 2389–2398. https://doi.org/10.1177/0021998319896842

Wang, Xin, Xing Zhao, and Zhishen Wu. 2019. "Fatigue Degradation and Life Prediction of Basalt Fiber-Reinforced Polymer Composites after Saltwater Corrosion." *Materials and Design* 163: 107529. https://doi.org/10.1016/j.matdes.2018.12.001

Wang, Yanlei, Yongshuai Wang, Baolin Wan, Baoguo Han, Gaochuang Cai, and Ruijuan Chang. 2018. "Strain and Damage Self-Sensing of Basalt Fiber Reinforced Polymer Laminates Fabricated with Carbon Nanofibers/Epoxy Composites under Tension." *Composites Part A: Applied Science and Manufacturing* 113 (June): 40–52. https://doi.org/10.1016/j.compositesa.2018.07.017

Wei, Bin, Hailin Cao, and Shenhua Song. 2010. "Environmental Resistance and Mechanical Performance of Basalt and Glass Fibers." *Materials Science and Engineering A* 527 (18–19): 4708–4715. https://doi.org/10.1016/j.msea.2010.04.021

Wei, Bin, Hailin Cao, and Shenhua Song. 2011. "Degradation of Basalt Fibre and Glass Fibre/Epoxy Resin Composites in Seawater." *Corrosion Science* 53 (1): 426–431. https://doi.org/10.1016/j.corsci.2010.09.053.

Wolter, N., V.C. Beber, M. Brede, and K. Koschek. 2019. "Adhesively- and Hybrid-Bonded Joining of Basalt and Carbon Fibre Reinforced Polybenzoxazine-Based Composites." *Composite Structures* 236 (March): 111800. https://doi.org/10.1016/j.compstruct.2019.111800

Xu, Xufeng, Prashant Rawat, Yanchao Shi, and Deju Zhu. 2019. "Tensile Mechanical Properties of Basalt Fiber Reinforced Polymer Tendons at Low to Intermediate Strain Rates." *Composites Part B* 177 (September): 107442. https://doi.org/10.1016/j.compositesb.2019.107442

Yu, Xiao, Bukui Zhou, Feng Hu, Yi Zhang, Xiangyun Xu, Chengfei Fan, Wei Zhang, Houwen Jiang, and Pengqing Liu. 2020. "Experimental Investigation of Basalt Fiber-Reinforced Polymer (BFRP) Bar Reinforced Concrete Slabs under Contact Explosions." *International Journal of Impact Engineering* 144 (October): 103632. https://doi.org/10.1016/j.ijimpeng.2020.103632

Yuan, Cheng, Wensu Chen, Thong M. Pham, and Hong Hao. 2019. "Effect of Aggregate Size on Bond Behaviour between Basalt Fibre Reinforced Polymer Sheets and Concrete."

Composites Part B: Engineering 158 (February): 459–474. https://doi.org/10.1016/j.compositesb.2018.09.089

Zhao, Xing, Xin Wang, Zhishen Wu, and Jin Wu. 2020. "Experimental Study on Effect of Resin Matrix in Basalt Fiber Reinforced Polymer Composites under Static and Fatigue Loading." *Construction and Building Materials* 242 (May): 118121. https://doi.org/10.1016/j.conbuildmat.2020.118121

Zhou, Ao, Renyuan Qin, Cheuk Lun Chow, and Denvid Lau. 2020. "Bond Integrity of Aramid, Basalt and Carbon Fiber Reinforced Polymer Bonded Wood Composites at Elevated Temperature." *Composite Structures* 245 (April): 112342. https://doi.org/10.1016/j.compstruct.2020.112342

Zhu, Hong, Gang Wu, Lei Zhang, Jianfeng Zhang, and David Hui. 2014. "Experimental Study on the Fire Resistance of RC Beams Strengthened with Near-Surface-Mounted High-Tg BFRP Bars." *Composites Part B: Engineering* 60: 680–687. https://doi.org/10.1016/j.compositesb.2014.01.011

4 Properties Enhancement of Poly(Lactic Acid) Using Functionalized Mineral Fillers

Keemi Lim and Wen Shyang Chow
Universiti Sains Malaysia
Gelugor, Malaysia

CONTENTS

4.1 Introduction 71
4.2 Halloysite Nanotube as a Mineral Filler for PLA... 72
    4.2.1 Halloysite Nanotube 72
    4.2.2 HNT as a Template for Immobilization of ZnO Nanoparticles............ 73
4.3 PLA Nanocomposites with ZnO-Functionalized HNT.. 74
4.4 Conclusions.. 80
Acknowledgment 80
References... 80

4.1 INTRODUCTION

Poly(lactic acid) (PLA) is undoubtedly one of the most promising candidates on the market for biodegradable polymers. It is synthesized from natural renewable resources, for example, sugar cane or corn, which are biodegradable, environmentally friendly and compostable. PLA qualities include high mechanical performance, biodegradability, biocompatibility, and no toxicity (Ghanbarzadeh & Almasi, 2013). However, the low thermal properties and slow crystallization of PLA should be solved to widen its application. Improvement of the quality and properties of PLA by introducing mineral filler is one of the viable approaches.

Halloysite nanotubes (HNTs) are presently popularized as potential nanofillers for polymers because of their natural abundance and high aspect ratio. These natural aluminosilicate nanotubes have demonstrated that they improve properties for the polymers, such as their tensile modulus, tensile strength, flexural modulus, flexural strength, and impact strength (Liu et al., 2013; Wu et al., 2013; Gorrasi et al., 2014; Stoclet et al., 2014; Chen et al., 2015; Tham et al., 2016). The good dispersibility of HNTs in the polymer matrix was associated with the special nanoscale crystal structure, rod-like geometry and low density of hydroxyl functional groups.

DOI: 10.1201/9781003220947-4

In most outdoor applications, the main element in fabricating polymeric material is the ability to resist ultraviolet (UV) light. Note that UV light can cause photodegradation of the polymer and polymer composites, which could cause physical and chemical changes, e.g., reduction in molecular weight and deterioration of mechanical properties. Islam et al. (2010) and Bolio-Lopez et al. (2013) described that long exposure time to UV radiation extensively reduces the molecular weight, stress, and strain at break, thus affecting the aesthetic appeal of PLA films. Numerous studies of PLA-based clay nanocomposites reveal that oxidative degradation of these materials is more significant compared with pristine PLA. Some studies proposed that fast degradation could be attributed to the catalytic effect of transition metal impurities of clay nanofillers (Bocchini et al., 2010; Bocchini & Frache, 2013; Gaaz et al., 2017a). Thus, the selection of suitable filler for PLA is essential when the composite is used for an outdoor application and there is possible exposure to UV degradation. In addition, the hybridization of filler could be a feasible method to enhance the UV stability of the PLA composites.

Among the metal oxide nanofillers, zinc oxide (ZnO) nanoparticles have gained considerable attention among researchers due to their biocompatibility, cost-effectiveness, and flexibility in surface modification (Díez-Pascual and Díez-Vicente, 2014). Manipulating ZnO into the polymeric matrix or as an additive to a coating has substantially increased the shelf-life and improved the photostability of the packaged product due to ZnO's excellent UV absorption ability. Furthermore, ZnO has been considered as a potential candidate as a reinforcing nanofiller for polymers (both thermoplastic and thermoset). ZnO possesses high thermal conductivity, low coefficient of thermal expansion, and excellent mechanical properties, which greatly enhance the mechanical and thermal properties of PLA (Pantani et al., 2013; Shankar et al., 2018).

HNT surface modification is one of the strategies to improve compatibility and interfacial interaction with polymeric materials. The functional group at the exterior surface of HNTs can facilitate chemical interaction with the guest molecules through van der Waals forces or hydrogen bonding. Molecule grafting onto the host site is often used to increase the loading efficiencies of the HNT (Guo et al., 2016). In light of this study, modification of HNTs by immobilizing ZnO nanoparticles on the tubular nanotubes was investigated. ZnO nanoparticles are used to increase the reinforcement and UV protection properties of the HNT (Li et al., 2015). Some of the polymeric materials will undergo photodegradation when they are exposed to UV radiation (Tocháček & Vrátníčková, 2014). Thus, surface modification of HNTs (ZnO-functionalized HNT) could be used to develop a UV-resistant PLA nanocomposite that is suitable for outdoor applications.

4.2 HALLOYSITE NANOTUBE AS A MINERAL FILLER FOR PLA

4.2.1 Halloysite Nanotube

Halloysite (with the molecular structure $Al_2(OH)_4Si_2O_5 \cdot nH_2O$) is a natural mineral found in weathered volcanic rocks and soils (Yuan et al., 2015). These aluminosilicate minerals are formed by wrapping $SiO_2:Al_2O_3$ clay layers driven by a misfit between tetrahedral and octahedral sheets, allowing the layers to form into a tubular-shaped

Properties Enhancement of Poly(Lactic Acid)

structure (Joussein et al., 2005). Generally, tubular-shaped halloysite is composed of two distinct basal surfaces separated by a monolayer of water molecules.

HNT crystal structure is ideally comprised of a 1:1 stoichiometric ratio bilayered array consisting of tetrahedral silicate, Si-O-Si surface on the outer layers, whereas the internal surface is made up of gibbsite octahedral layers (Al(OH)$_3$) (Zahidah et al., 2017). In principle, halloysite has two different polymorphs: (1) hydrated halloysite, which has a layer periodicity of 10 Å, and (2) dehydrated halloysite, which has an interlayer spacing of 7 Å. The most common form is the hydrated halloysite (layer periodicity of 10 Å), wherein water molecules are held weakly between the interlayer spacing and are easily transformed to irreversible halloysite (layer periodicity of 7 Å) when heated (Guimaraes et al., 2010; Lvov & Abdullayev, 2013). Interestingly with its differences in structural and adsorption properties, the inner wall consists of Al-OH, which is positively charged, whereas the outer wall is comprised of silica layers, which are weakly negatively charged (Duarte et al., 2012). This surface charge enables selective loading of negatively charged molecules loaded into the inner lumen of the nanotubes (Abdullayev et al., 2012). In general, the length of HNTs varies from 150 nm to 2 μm with its outside diameter range from 50 to 100 nm, and the internal lumen diameter ranges from 10 to 20 nm (Liu et al., 2014; Gaaz et al., 2017b).

Therefore, with its unique and outstanding properties, HNTs have been the focus of many research studies. Some of the advantages of HNTs include (1) non-toxic and biocompatible, (2) high surface area, (3) excellent dispersion capability, (4) good entrapping molecule power on specific molecules, and (5) good thermal stability (Kamble et al., 2012). Also, because of their low −OH density on the external surface, a weak tube-tube interaction of HNTs is created. Consequently, this creates a greater possibility for a large contact area between the tubes, subsequently favoring a uniformly single-tube dispersion of HNT nanofiller in the matrix of polymer-HNT nanocomposite (Du et al., 2010; Pal et al., 2012; Kubade & Kshirsagar, 2015). Furthermore, the low content of the hydroxyl group on the HNT surface, which consists of siloxane, aluminols, and silanols located at the edges of the nanotube, often makes the HNT slightly hydrophobic. This characteristic facilitates the dispersion of HNT in the non-polar polymers during melt compounding (Jia et al., 2009). Furthermore, with their good biocompatibility, HNTs can be exploited as promising fillers in biotechnology applications such as water decontamination, anticorrosive coatings, and active packaging (Thakur et al., 2017). However, HNTs, like other clays, have several drawbacks, such as low surface reactivity and low cationic exchange capacity. Therefore, various surface treatments have been investigated by researchers to enhance the properties of the HNT.

4.2.2 HNT as a Template for Immobilization of ZnO Nanoparticles

ZnO is a versatile inorganic material. It has the two most common crystalline forms, i.e., hexagonal wurtzite and cubic zinc blende. In both structures the zinc and oxide centers are tetrahedral, which is the fundamental attribute of structural geometry for zinc (Zn). At ambient pressure and temperature, zinc oxide in the form of wurtzite (B4) crystal structure is most stable (Coleman & Jagadish, 2006). The unique properties of ZnO (e.g., high mechanical and thermal stability and high electron mobility) make it suitable for various applications, such as electronics, optics, biomedical, cosmetics, and food packaging (Sabir et al. 2014; Agarwal et al., 2017). Furthermore, the UV resistance, antimicrobial behavior, and photocatalytic properties of polymeric materials are influenced by adding nano-sized ZnO (Uikey & Vishwakarma, 2016).

Surface modification of HNTs using nano-sized metal oxide is utilized to improve the self-cleaning behavior attributed to their unique surface characteristics and excellent gas barrier properties (Bratovčić et al., 2015). Herein, HNTs are used as a support to immobilize ZnO nanoparticles to achieve greater reinforcement and UV protection for the polymer. Accordingly, HNT-based immobilization techniques have several benefits. Shu et al. (2017b) have reported that utilization of HNTs can facilitate the dispersion of ZnO because of their physicochemical properties, such as their tubular structure, high specific surface area, and hydrophobicity. Also, the HNT-based immobilization strategy also furnishes material with good mechanical and thermally stable properties (Rawtani & Agrawal, 2012). This subsequently favors the nanocomposite with increments in modulus and tensile strength, good thermal stability, barrier and optical properties (Kotal & Bhowmick, 2015).

According to Huang et al. (2013), nano-sized ZnO is immobilized on the HNT surface through covalent bonding via the active Zn-terminated ZnO. This is because ZnO possesses unique bifunctional structures, in which it can react with the HNT's silanol group, as well as the polymer's functional group (Li et al., 2015). With the presence of a free hydroxyl group on the surface of HNT, this interaction sequentially fosters novel nanocomposites with functionalized Zn^{2+} on the negatively charged hydroxyl surface of the HNT.

ZnO-functionalized HNT has attracted attention because of its outstanding properties, including good UV blocking without impairing the host polymer's transparency during processing (Murariu et al., 2011). Cheng and Sun (2015) reported a facile impregnation-loaded method to assemble the ZnO nanoparticles on the HNT. A significant absorption band on the visible region (300 and 400 nm) on the UV-visible spectra was observed, and this is attributed to the typical UV absorption characteristic of ZnO. According to Peng et al. (2017), ZnO-functionalized HNT is successful because of the nanotubes' surface hydroxyl groups and the synergistic effects between ZnO and HNT. Note that the Zn^{2+} ions are adsorbed on the negatively charged HNT surface, followed by the nucleation and growth of ZnO on the HNT surface during calcination.

Along with its UV-filtering properties, the ZnO-treated HNT on polymer nanocomposite demonstrated good mechanical performance. De Silva et al. (2015) revealed that modification of HNTs by encapsulating ZnO nanoparticles into the nanotubes exhibited better performance as a filler to reinforce polymer nanocomposites when compared with an untreated HNT.

4.3 PLA NANOCOMPOSITES WITH ZnO-FUNCTIONALIZED HNT

This chapter highlights the significant finding of the PLA/ZnO-functionalized HNT nanocomposites. The ZnO-functionalized HNT nanofiller was prepared using a solvent-free method. First, the zinc acetate dihydrate $[Zn(O_2CCH_3)_2(H_2O)_2]$ was dissolved in distilled water. Then, the HNT was added to the solution, and the mixture (ratio of HNT:$Zn(O_2CCH_3)_2(H_2O)_2$ is 1:2) was stirred overnight. Further, the

Properties Enhancement of Poly(Lactic Acid) 75

FIGURE 4.1 TEM image of HNT.

precipitates were washed several times with distilled water and ethanol. The filtered products were dried in an oven (temperature = 60°C; drying time = 4 hours), followed by a calcination process (temperature = 500°C; duration = 2 hours). The HNT-reinforced and ZnO-functionalized HNT-reinforced PLA were prepared using an internal mixer (compounding temperature = 170°C, time = 10 minutes, rotor speed = 80 rpm) followed by compression molding.

The examination of the nanostructure and morphology of the HNT allows us to understand the difference between untreated HNT and ZnO-treated HNT. Transmission electron microscopy (TEM) is a good technique to analyze the morphology of the HNT. Figure 4.1 shows the TEM image of the HNT nanofiller. The HNT displayed a hollow tubular-shaped structure. Figure 4.2 reveals that there are

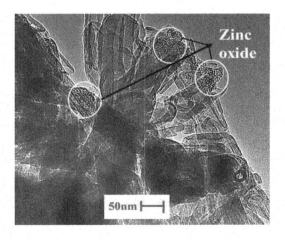

FIGURE 4.2 TEM image of ZnO-functionalized HNT.

some hexagonal-shaped ZnO particles found on the HNT surface. This indicates that the nano-sized ZnO is deposited successfully on the HNT surface. In other words, HNT serves as a template for the ZnO nanoparticle deposition.

The mechanical property of a polymer nanocomposite is one of the important criteria for industrialization and commercialization purposes. Different polymer nanocomposites require different priorities in certain mechanical properties. For example, a polymer nanocomposite foam requires good compressive strength, whereas a polymer nanocomposite scaffold needs high strength. PLA can be used for medical devices, food packaging and thermoformed products; thus, its stiffness, strength, and elongation at break (EB) should be considered for the design of the PLA nanocomposite materials.

Figure 4.3(a) shows the tensile modulus of the HNT-reinforced and ZnO-functionalized HNT-reinforced PLA nanocomposites. PLA/HNT3 and PLA/HNT5 represent the PLA containing 3 wt% and 5 wt% HNT, respectively. The adding of HNT increases the tensile modulus of the PLA. This is expected because of the reinforcing ability and stiffness enhancement contributed by the HNT. The PLA/HNT-ZnO3 and PLA/HNT-ZnO5 nanocomposites represent the PLA filled with 3 wt% ZnO-functionalized HNT and 5 wt% ZnO-functionalized HNT, respectively. The tensile modulus of PLA/HNT-ZnO3 nanocomposite is comparable to the PLA/HNT3 counterparts. The tensile modulus of PLA/HNT-ZnO5 nanocomposite is higher than that of the PLA/HNT5 nanocomposite. The modulus enhancement is associated with the co-reinforcing effects of both HNT and ZnO. According to Lizundia et al. (2016), ZnO nanoparticles can act as good reinforcing fillers and increase the stiffness of the materials.

The brittleness, low EB, and low flexibility of PLA is always a concern for the development of PLA-based material. The toughness of PLA can be improved by adding a flexible polymer (polymer blending strategy), copolymerization with polymer with a low glass transition temperature (copolymerization strategy) and incorporation of elastomer/rubber. Adding filler/nanofiller often reduces the EB of PLA, except for some cases in nano-calcium carbonate and HNT, in which the EB of the PLA was maintained or slightly increased. Figure 4.3(b) shows the EB of the HNT-reinforced and ZnO-functionalized HNT-reinforced PLA nanocomposites. The EB of the PLA nanocomposites is slightly affected by the HNT amount. The EB of the PLA nanocomposites containing 5 wt% of HNT and ZnO-functionalized HNT is slightly lower compared with pure PLA. Often, this is associated with the agglomeration of the nanofiller or limited de-agglomeration of nanofiller in the polymer matrix (Marra et al., 2017). In this case study, the addition of 5 wt% HNT (treated or untreated) could be excessive and make the dispersibility of the HNT difficult, increase the viscosity during melt-processing and cause agglomeration in the PLA matrix. Nevertheless, the EB of the PLA nanocomposites consisting of 3 wt% HNT (untreated and ZnO treated) is slightly higher than the unfilled PLA.

Figure 4.3(c) shows the tensile strength of HNT-reinforced and ZnO-functionalized HNT-reinforced PLA nanocomposites. The tensile strength of the unfilled PLA is approximately 40.9 MPa. Adding ZnO-functionalized HNT into PLA increases the tensile strength of the nanocomposites. The tensile strength of the commercially available polystyrene packaging material is about 40 MPa (Dorgan et al., 2000).

Properties Enhancement of Poly(Lactic Acid)

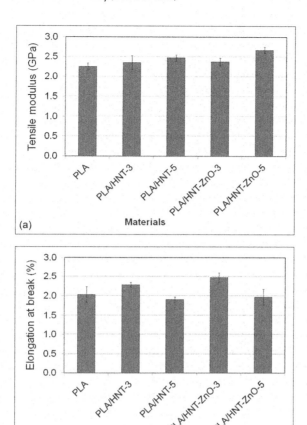

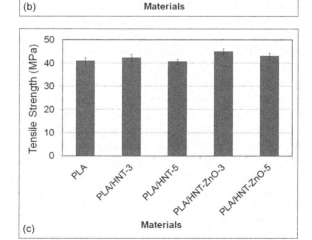

FIGURE 4.3 (a) Tensile modulus of the HNT-reinforced and ZnO-functionalized HNT-reinforced PLA nanocomposites. (b) Elongation at break of the HNT-reinforced and ZnO-functionalized HNT-reinforced PLA nanocomposites. (c) Tensile strength of the HNT-reinforced and ZnO-functionalized HNT-reinforced PLA nanocomposites.

Thus, the PLA nanocomposites containing ZnO-functionalized HNT are able to achieve the basic requirement for the tensile properties of the packaging materials. The final properties of polymer nanocomposites are governed by the intrinsic properties of the polymer, the types of nanofiller, the treatment of the nanofiller, the interfacial adhesion between the polymer and the nanofiller, the compatibility of the polymer and the nanofiller, and the dispersion of the nanofiller in the polymeric matrix. The improvement of the PLA/HNT nanocomposites could be tailored by monitoring the interfacial adhesion between the PLA and HNT. A better and efficient load transfer could always raise the reinforcement effectiveness for the PLA/HNT nanocomposites (Wang et al., 2011; Li et al., 2017; Shu et al., 2017a; Mizielińska et al., 2018). The high surface area of HNT could serve as a template to immobilize the ZnO nanoparticle and thus increase the interaction between the nanofiller with the polymer.

The thermal stability of a polymer nanocomposite is an essential property because it involves the processing ability and service environment of the final products. The assessment of the thermal stability and decomposition of polymeric materials can be obtained from the thermogravimetric analyzer (TGA). Figure 4.4(a) and (b) shows the TGA and derivative TGA (DTG) curves of PLA, HNT-reinforced and ZnO-functionalized HNT-reinforced PLA nanocomposites. The main thermal characteristics assessed are T_5 (the temperature recorded at 5% weight loss), T_d (the end decomposition temperature), and T_{max} (the maximum temperature recorded from the DTG curves). The enhancement of PLA thermal stability is one of the main concerns. Often, the thermal stability of PLA can be enhanced by using filler/nanofiller, thermal stabilizer or blended with high thermal stable polymers. In this case study, the role of HNT and ZnO in enhancing the thermal stability of the PLA was investigated. The T_5 and T_d of the PLA are approximately 299°C and 361°C, respectively. The thermal decomposition of PLA is mainly associated with the chain depolymerization (Restrepo et al., 2017).

The T_5, T_d and T_{max} of the PLA were increased by adding HNT (both treated and untreated). The thermal stability improvement is caused by three factors: (1) the HNT and ZnO are highly thermally stable, (2) good interfacial interaction between PLA and ZnO-functionalized HNT and (3) the heat barrier effects of the HNT (Abbasian et al., 2013; Saadattalab et al., 2016). The HNT and ZnO can withstand high temperatures and thus delay the thermal decomposition of the PLA. Often, the thermal stabilities of polymer nanocomposites can be enhanced by controlling the interfacial bonding between the polymer and nanofiller. Nanofiller can sometimes function as a physical barrier to mass transport, consequently retarding the volatile by-products escape during the thermal decomposition.

The UV protection property of PLA is one of the interesting aspects that can be further developed. HNT-ZnO hybrid filler can be used to improve the UV-shielding behavior of PLA nanocomposite. Figure 4.5 shows the UV-visible spectra of HNT-reinforced and ZnO-functionalized HNT-reinforced PLA nanocomposites. Note that the UV light transmittance (in the region between 300 and 400 nm) of PLA decreases in the presence of the HNT and ZnO-functionalized HNT nanofiller. This gives us a hint that the HNT is capable of providing UV resistance and inhibiting the transmittance of UVB. Referring to the UV-visible spectra of ZnO-functionalized

Properties Enhancement of Poly(Lactic Acid)

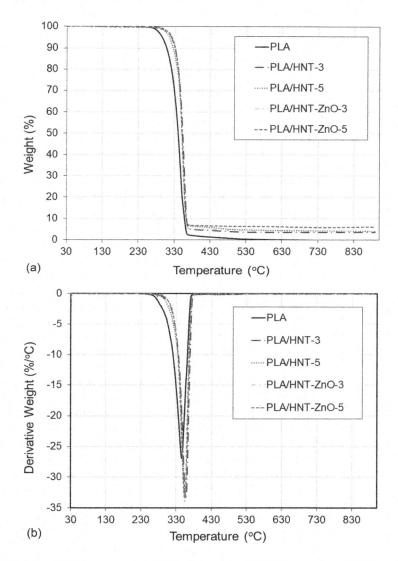

FIGURE 4.4 (a) TGA curves of the HNT-reinforced and ZnO-functionalized HNT-reinforced PLA nanocomposites. (b) DTG curves of the HNT-reinforced and ZnO-functionalized HNT-reinforced PLA nanocomposites.

HNT-reinforced PLA, there is a small absorption band observable at approximately 370 nm in the UVA region. The ZnO has a band gap at approximately 3.37 eV, which corresponds to 376 nm. This indicates that nano-sized ZnO is capable of absorbing or blocking UV radiation. In this study, the PLA nanocomposites consisting of ZnO-functionalized HNT exhibited better UV-shielding properties compared with pure PLA.

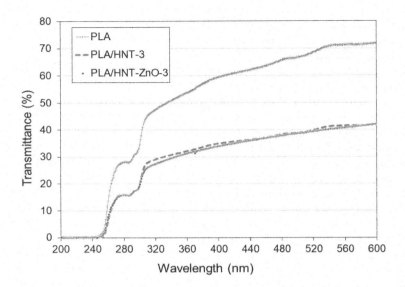

FIGURE 4.5 UV-Vis spectra of the pure PLA, HNT-reinforced and ZnO-functionalized HNT-reinforced PLA nanocomposites.

4.4 CONCLUSIONS

In this chapter, we discuss the potential of using mineral fillers to enhance the properties of PLA. The ZnO-functionalized HNT nanofiller was successfully fabricated via a solvent-free approach. The tensile strength and tensile modulus of ZnO-functionalized HNT-reinforced PLA nanocomposites are higher than that of pure PLA. The thermal stabilities of both HNT-reinforced and ZnO-functionalized HNT-reinforced PLA nanocomposites are higher compared with the pure PLA. The UV-visible spectroscopy results demonstrated that the PLA nanocomposites exhibited higher UV protection ability than that of the PLA. Overall, the ZnO-functionalized HNT-reinforced PLA nanocomposites demonstrated good mechanical, thermal and UV resistance properties, which can widen the outdoor application of PLA nanocomposites. The mineral filler plays an essential role in enhancing the properties of PLA.

ACKNOWLEDGMENT

The authors would like to thank Universiti Sains Malaysia for Research University Grant (1001/PBAHAN/8014024).

REFERENCES

Abbasian, Mojtaba, Nafiseh Khakpour Aali, and Solmaz Esmaeily Shoja. "Synthesis of poly(methyl methacrylate)/zinc oxide nanocomposite with core-shell morphology by atom transfer radical polymerization." *Journal of Macromolecular Science, Part A* 50, no. 9 (2013): 966–975. https://doi.org/10.1080/10601325.2013.813814

Abdullayev, Elshad, Anupam. Joshi, Wenbo Wei, Yafei Zhao, and Yuri Lvov. "Enlargement of halloysite clay nanotube lumen by selective etching of aluminum oxide." *ACS Nano* 6, no. 8 (2012): 7216–7226. https://doi.org/10.1021/nn302328x

Agarwal, H., S. Venkat Kumar, and S. Rajeshkumar. "A review on green synthesis of zinc oxide nanoparticles–An eco-friendly approach." *Resource-Efficient Technologies* 3, no. 4 (2017): 406–413. https://doi.org/10.1016/j.reffit.2017.03.002

Bocchini, S., and A. Frache. "Comparative study of filler influence on polylactide photo-oxidation." *Express Polymer Letters* 7, no. 5 (2013): 431–442. https://doi.org/10.3144/expresspolymlett.2013.40

Bocchini, Sergio, Kikku Fukushima, Alessandro Di Blasio, Alberto Fina, Alberto Frache, and Francesco Geobaldo. "Polylactic acid and polylactic acid-based nanocomposite photooxidation." *Biomacromolecules* 11, no. 11 (2010): 2919–2926. https://doi.org/10.1021/bm1006773

Bolio-López, G. I., L. Veleva, A. Valadez-González, and P. Quintana-Owen. "Weathering and biodegradation of polylactic acid composite reinforced with cellulose whiskers." *Revista Mexicana de Ingeniería Química* 12, no. 1 (2013): 143–153. https://www.redalyc.org/pdf/620/62028007014.pdf

Bratovčić, Amra, Amra Odobašić, S. Ćatić, and Indira Šestan. "Application of polymer nanocomposite materials in food packaging." *Croatian Journal of Food Science and Technology* 7, no. 2 (2015): 86–94. https://doi.org/10.17508/CJFST.2015.7.2.06

Chen, Hao, Hua Yan, Zhenzhao Pei, Junyong Wu, Rongrong Li, Yanxian Jin, and Jie Zhao. "Trapping characteristic of halloysite lumen for methyl orange." *Applied Surface Science* 347 (2015): 769–776. https://doi.org/10.1016/j.apsusc.2015.04.167

Cheng, Zhi-Lin, and Wei Sun. "Preparation of N-doped ZnO-loaded halloysite nanotubes catalysts with high solar-light photocatalytic activity." *Water Science and Technology* 72, no. 10 (2015): 1817–1823. https://doi.org/10.2166/wst.2015.403

Coleman, Victoria A., and C. Jagadish. "Basic properties and applications of ZnO." In *Zinc Oxide Bulk, Thin Films and Nanostructures*, pp. 1–20. Elsevier Science Ltd, 2006. https://doi.org/10.1016/B978-008044722-3/50001-4

De Silva, Rangika T., Pooria Pasbakhsh, Sui Mae Lee, and Aw Yoong Kit. "ZnO deposited/encapsulated halloysite–poly (lactic acid)(PLA) nanocomposites for high performance packaging films with improved mechanical and antimicrobial properties." *Applied Clay Science* 111 (2015): 10–20. https://doi.org/10.1016/j.clay.2015.03.024

Díez-Pascual, Ana M., and Angel L. Díez-Vicente. "Poly(3-hydroxybutyrate)/ZnO bion-anocomposites with improved mechanical, barrier and antibacterial properties." *International Journal of Molecular Sciences* 15, no. 6 (2014): 10950–10973. https://doi.org/10.3390/ijms150610950

Dorgan, John R., Hans Lehermeier, and Michael Mang. "Thermal and rheological properties of commercial-grade poly(lactic acid)s." *Journal of Polymers and the Environment* 8, no. 1 (2000): 1–9. https://doi.org/10.1023/A:1010185910301

Du, Mingliang, Baochun Guo, and Demin Jia. "Newly emerging applications of halloysite nanotubes: a review." *Polymer International* 59, no. 5 (2010): 574–582. https://doi.org/10.1002/pi.2754

Duarte, Hélio A., Maicon P. Lourenço, Thomas Heine, and Luciana Guimarães. "Clay mineral nanotubes: stability, structure and properties." *Stoichiometry and Materials Science-When Numbers Matter* 11 (2012): 3–25.

Gaaz, Tayser Sumer, Abu Bakar Sulong, Abdul Amir H. Kadhum, Ahmed A. Al-Amiery, Mohamed H. Nassir, and Ahed Hameed Jaaz. "The impact of halloysite on the thermo-mechanical properties of polymer composites." *Molecules* 22, no. 5 (2017a): 838–848. https://doi.org/10.3390/molecules22050838

Gaaz, Tayser Sumer, Abdul Amir H. Kadhum, Patina Kiah Anak Michael, Ahmed A. Al-Amiery, Abu Bakar Sulong, Mohamed H. Nassir, and Ahed Hameed Jaaz. "Unique halloysite nanotubes–polyvinyl alcohol–polyvinylpyrrolidone composite complemented with physico–chemical characterization." *Polymers* 9, no. 6 (2017b): 207–212. https://doi.org/10.3390/polym9060207

Ghanbarzadeh, Babak, and Hadi Almasi. "Biodegradable polymers." In *Biodegradation-Life of Science*, edited by Rolando Chamy, 141–174. Croatia: InTech Open, 2013. http://dx.doi.org/10.5772/56230

Gorrasi, Giuliana, Roberto Pantani, Marius Murariu, and Philippe Dubois. "PLA/halloysite nanocomposite films: water vapor barrier properties and specific key characteristics." *Macromolecular Materials and Engineering* 299, no. 1 (2014): 104–115. https://doi.org/10.1002/mame.201200424

Guimaraes, Luciana, Andrey N. Enyashin, Gotthard Seifert, and Hélio A. Duarte. "Structural, electronic, and mechanical properties of single-walled halloysite nanotube models." *The Journal of Physical Chemistry C* 114, no. 26 (2010): 11358–11363. https://doi.org/10.1021/jp100902e

Guo, Baochun, Atsushi Takahara, Eduardo Ruiz Hitzky, Bing Zhang, Giuseppe Lazzara, Rawil F. Fakhrullin, Dmitry Shchukin et al. *Functional Polymer Composites with Nanoclays*, 157–181. Cambridge: Royal Society of Chemistry. RSC Smart Materials. 2016.

Huang, Xing, Meng Wang, Lidong Shao, Marc-Georg Willinger, Chun-Sing Lee, and Xiang-Min Meng. "Polarity-free epitaxial growth of heterostructured ZnO/ZnS core/shell nanobelts." *The Journal of Physical Chemistry Letters* 4, no. 5 (2013): 740–744. https://doi.org/10.1021/jz4001533

Islam, Mohammad Saiful, Kim L. Pickering, and Nic J. Foreman. "Influence of accelerated ageing on the physico-mechanical properties of alkali-treated industrial hemp fibre reinforced poly (lactic acid) (PLA) composites." *Polymer Degradation and Stability* 95, no. 1 (2010): 59–65. https://doi.org/10.1016/j.polymdegradstab.2009.10.010

Jia, Zhixin, Yuanfang Luo, Baochun Guo, Bingtao Yang, Mingliang Du, and Demin Jia. "Reinforcing and flame-retardant effects of halloysite nanotubes on LLDPE." *Polymer-Plastics Technology and Engineering* 48, no. 6 (2009): 607–613. https://doi.org/10.1080/03602550902824440

Joussein, E., S. Petit, J. Churchman, B. Theng, D. Righi, and B. Delvaux. "Halloysite clay minerals—a review." *Clay Minerals* 40, no. 4 (2005): 383–426. https://doi.org/10.1180/0009855054040180

Kamble, Ravindra, Manasi Ghag, Sheetal Gaikawad, and Bijoy Kumar Panda. "Halloysite nanotubes and applications: A review." *Journal of Advanced Scientific Research* 3, no. 2 (2012): 25–29.

Kotal, Moumita, and Anil K. Bhowmick. "Polymer nanocomposites from modified clays: Recent advances and challenges." *Progress in Polymer Science* 51 (2015): 127–187. https://doi.org/10.1016/j.progpolymsci.2015.10.001

Kubade, Pravin, and Ravindranath Kshirsagar. "Current research trends in modification/interaction of halloysite nanotube filled polymer blends and its composites: A review." *International Journal of Science and Research (IJSR)* 4, no. 12 (2015), 1766–1772.

Li, Jinze, Mingjun Zhou, Zhefei Ye, Huiqin Wang, Changchang Ma, Pengwei Huo, and Yongsheng Yan. "Enhanced photocatalytic activity of gC$_3$N$_4$–ZnO/HNT composite heterostructure photocatalysts for degradation of tetracycline under visible light irradiation." *RSC Advances* 5, no. 111 (2015): 91177–91189. https://doi.org/10.1039/C5RA17360D

Li, Wenhui, Lin Li, Yun Cao, Tianqing Lan, Haiyan Chen, and Yuyue Qin. "Effects of PLA film incorporated with ZnO nanoparticle on the quality attributes of fresh-cut apple." *Nanomaterials* 7, no. 8 (2017): 207–213. https://doi.org/10.3390/nano7080207

Liu, Mingxian, Zhixin Jia, Demin Jia, and Changren Zhou. "Recent advance in research on halloysite nanotubes-polymer nanocomposite." *Progress in Polymer Science* 39, no. 8 (2014): 1498–1525. https://doi.org/10.1016/j.progpolymsci.2014.04.004

Properties Enhancement of Poly(Lactic Acid) 83

Liu, Mingxian, Yun Zhang, and Changren Zhou. "Nanocomposites of halloysite and polylactide." *Applied Clay Science* 75 (2013): 52–59. https://doi.org/10.1016/j.clay.2013.02.019

Lizundia, Erlantz, Leyre Pérez Álvarez, Míriam Sáenz Pérez, David Patrocinio, José Luis Vilas, and Luis Manuel León. "Physical aging and mechanical performance of poly (l-lactide)/ZnO nanocomposites." *Journal of Applied Polymer Science* 133, no. 45 (2016): 43619–43626. https://doi.org/10.1002/app.43619

Lvov, Yuri, and Elshad Abdullayev. "Functional polymer–clay nanotube composites with sustained release of chemical agents." *Progress in Polymer Science* 38, no. 10–11 (2013): 1690–1719. https://doi.org/10.1016/j.progpolymsci.2013.05.009

Marra, Antonella, Gennaro Rollo, Sossio Cimmino, and Clara Silvestre. "Assessment on the effects of ZnO and coated ZnO particles on iPP and PLA properties for application in food packaging." *Coatings* 7, no. 2 (2017): 29–37. https://doi.org/10.3390/coatings7020029

Mizielińska, Małgorzata, Urszula Kowalska, Michał Jarosz, Patrycja Sumińska, Nicolas Landercy, and Emmanuel Duquesne. "The effect of UV aging on antimicrobial and mechanical properties of PLA films with incorporated zinc oxide nanoparticles." *International Journal of Environmental Research and Public Health* 15, no. 4 (2018): 794–811. https://doi.org/10.3390/ijerph15040794

Murariu, Marius, Awa Doumbia, Leila Bonnaud, Anne–Laure Dechief, Yoann Paint, Manuela Ferreira, Christine Campagne, Eric Devaux, and Philippe Dubois. "High-performance polylactide/ZnO nanocomposites designed for films and fibers with special end-use properties." *Biomacromolecules* 12, no. 5 (2011): 1762–1771. https://doi.org/10.1021/bm2001445

Pal, Parthajit, Mrinal Kanti Kundu, Swinderjeetsingh Kalra, and Chapal Kumar Das. "Mechanical and crystalline behavior of polymeric nanocomposites in presence of natural clay." *Open Journal of Applied Sciences* 2, no. 4 (2012): 277–282. doi:10.4236/ojapps.2012.24041

Pantani, Roberto, Giuliana Gorrasi, Giovanni Vigliotta, Marius Murariu, and Philippe Dubois. "PLA-ZnO nanocomposite films: Water vapor barrier properties and specific end-use characteristics." *European Polymer Journal* 49, no. 11 (2013): 3471–3482. https://doi.org/10.1016/j.eurpolymj.2013.08.005

Peng, Hongxia, Xiaohe Liu, Wei Tang, and Renzhi Ma. "Facile synthesis and characterization of ZnO nanoparticles grown on halloysite nanotubes for enhanced photocatalytic properties." *Scientific Reports* 7, no. 1 (2017): 1–10. https://doi.org/10.1038/s41598-017-02501-w

Rawtani, Deepak, and Y. K. Agrawal. "Multifarious applications of halloysite nanotubes: a review." *Reviews on Advanced Materials Science* 30, no. 3 (2012): 282–295. Corpus ID: 2764475

Restrepo, I., N. Benito, C. Medinam, R. V. Mangalaraja, P. Flores, and S. Rodriguez-Llamazares. "Development and characterization of polyvinyl alcohol stabilized polylactic acid/ZnO nanocomposites." *Materials Research Express* 4, no. 10 (2017): 105019–105028. https://doi.org/10.1088/2053-1591/aa8b8d

Saadattalab, Vahid, Alireza Shakeri, and Hamid Gholami. "Effect of CNTs and nano ZnO on physical and mechanical properties of polyaniline composites applicable in energy devices." *Progress in Natural Science: Materials International* 26, no. 6 (2016): 517–522. https://doi.org/10.1016/j.pnsc.2016.09.005

Sabir, Sidra, Muhammad Arshad, and Sunbal Khalil Chaudhari. "Zinc oxide nanoparticles for revolutionizing agriculture: synthesis and applications." *The Scientific World Journal* 2014 (2014): 1–8. https://doi.org/10.1155/2014/925494

Shankar, Shiv, Long-Feng Wang, and Jong-Whan Rhim. "Incorporation of zinc oxide nanoparticles improved the mechanical, water vapor barrier, UV-light barrier, and antibacterial properties of PLA-based nanocomposite films." *Materials Science and Engineering: C* 93 (2018): 289–298. https://doi.org/10.1016/j.msec.2018.08.002

Shu, Zhan, Yi Zhang, Jing Ouyang, and Huaming Yang. "Characterization and synergetic antibacterial properties of ZnO and CeO_2 supported by halloysite." *Applied Surface Science* 420 (2017a): 833–838. https://doi.org/10.1016/j.apsusc.2017.05.219

Shu, Zhan, Yi Zhang, Qian Yang, and Huaming Yang. "Halloysite nanotubes supported Ag and ZnO nanoparticles with synergistically enhanced antibacterial activity." *Nanoscale Research Letters* 12, no. 1 (2017b): 1–7. https://doi.org/10.1186/s11671-017-1859-5

Stoclet, Grégory, Michel Sclavons, Benoît Lecouvet, Jacques Devaux, Pascal Van Velthem, Adrian Boborodea, S. Bourbigot, and N. Sallem-Idrissi. "Elaboration of poly(lactic acid)/ halloysite nanocomposites by means of water assisted extrusion: structure, mechanical properties and fire performance." *RSC Advances* 4, no. 101 (2014): 57553–57563. https://doi.org/10.1039/C4RA06845A

Thakur, Vijay Kumar, Manju Kumari Thakur, and Michael R. Kessler, eds. *Handbook of Composites from Renewable Materials, Nanocomposites: Science and Fundamentals.* Vol. 7, pp. 249–269. Beverly, MA: Scrivener Publishing LLC, 2017.

Tham, Wei Ling, Wen Shyang Chow, Beng Teik Poh, and Zainal Arifin Mohd Ishak. "Poly (lactic acid)/halloysite nanotube nanocomposites with high impact strength and water barrier properties." *Journal of Composite Materials* 50, no. 28 (2016): 3925–3934. https://doi.org/10.1177%2F0021998316628972

Tocháček, Jiří, and Zlata Vrátníčková. "Polymer life-time prediction: The role of temperature in UV accelerated ageing of polypropylene and its copolymers." *Polymer Testing* 36 (2014): 82–87. https://doi.org/10.1016/j.polymertesting.2014.03.019

Uikey, Prateek, and Kirti Vishwakarma. "Review of zinc oxide (ZnO) nanoparticles applications and properties." *International Journal of Emerging Technology in Computer Science & Electronics* 21, no. 2 (2016): 239–242.

Wang, H. W., H. W. Zhou, R. D. Peng, and Leon Mishnaevsky Jr. "Nanoreinforced polymer composites: 3D FEM modeling with effective interface concept." *Composites Science and Technology* 71, no. 7 (2011): 980–988. https://doi.org/10.1016/j.compscitech.2011.03.003

Wu, Wei, Xianwu Cao, Yijun Zhang, and Guangjian He. "Polylactide/halloysite nanotube nanocomposites: Thermal, mechanical properties, and foam processing." *Journal of Applied Polymer Science* 130, no. 1 (2013): 443–452. https://doi.org/10.1002/app.39179

Yuan, Peng, Daoyong Tan, and Faïza Annabi-Bergaya. "Properties and applications of halloysite nanotubes: recent research advances and future prospects." *Applied Clay Science* 112 (2015): 75–93. https://doi.org/10.1016/j.clay.2015.05.001

Zahidah, Khairina Azmi, Saeid Kakooei, Mokhtar Che Ismail, and Pandian Bothi Raja. "Halloysite nanotubes as nanocontainer for smart coating application: A review." *Progress in Organic Coatings* 111 (2017): 175–185. https://doi.org/10.1016/j.porgcoat.2017.05.018

5 Ageing of Mineral-Reinforced Polymer Composites

Emel Kuram
Gebze Technical University
Gebze, Turkey

CONTENTS

5.1 Introduction 85
5.2 Compounding and Processing 86
5.3 Applications 90
5.4 Ageing (Weathering) 90
    5.4.1 Natural Ageing 91
    5.4.2 Accelerated Ageing 94
        5.4.2.1 UV Ageing 94
        5.4.2.2 Thermal Ageing 99
        5.4.2.3 Water Ageing 101
        5.4.2.4 E-Beam Irradiation 105
        5.4.2.5 Cyclic Ageing 105
5.5 Conclusions 107
Acknowledgments 108
References 108

5.1 INTRODUCTION

Various factors such as heat, irradiation, mechanical stress, microbes, ozone and ultraviolet (UV) light degrade the polymeric materials. Degradation is promoted by humidity, oxygen and strain and causes brittleness and cracking. Inorganic fillers are incorporated into the polymeric materials to eliminate these drawbacks (Bandyopadhyay and Bhowmick 2006). To improve mechanical properties of polymeric materials alumina (Al_2O_3), clay, mica, silica (SiO_2), silicon nitride (Si_3N_4), titanium dioxide (TiO_2) and zinc oxide (ZnO) are added to polymeric materials (Xu et al. 2020).

Mineral-reinforced polymer composites have been extensively employed in the aerospace, automobile and building industries because they are low cost, light weight and have excellent rigidity and high mechanical strength. However, mineral-reinforced polymer composites are exposed to harsh environments such as moisture,

DOI: 10.1201/9781003220947-5

temperature and UV irradiation during their service life, which leads to reduction of the polymer lifetime. Therefore, the performance of mineral-reinforced polymer composites employed in these harsh environments has gained the attention of researchers. For this reason, in this chapter, the studies about processing, applications and ageing of various minerals such as calcium carbonate-, glass bead-, glass fiber-, talc- and wollastonite-reinforced polymer composites were compiled. Also, the effects of ageing on the properties of mineral-reinforced polymer composites were presented.

5.2 COMPOUNDING AND PROCESSING

Addition of mineral fillers in polymers is commonly used in the plastic industry to decrease the amount of commodity polymers in fabricated goods. These fillers not only provide cost reduction in plastic products but also enhance the durability, hardness, rigidity and strength of plastics. Al_2O_3, calcium carbonate ($CaCO_3$), clay, glass bead, glass fiber, kaolin, mica, silica, silicon nitride, talc, TiO_2, wollastonite and ZnO are added to polymeric materials as fillers. $CaCO_3$, kaolin and talc give good mechanical properties and stability to polymers (Leong et al. 2006). Glass fiber is employed to enhance the mechanical performance of polymeric materials (Zhou et al. 2019). Exterior durability of white poly(vinyl chloride) (PVC) parts, such as a window profile, must resist gloss retention, strength retention and yellowing. TiO_2 absorbs UV light, protecting the polymer from UV degradation, which causes light scattering of visible light for opacity and masks the discoloration of the polymer (i.e., PVC) (Gao et al. 2008). The addition of silver protects the materials against microbial attack (Tomacheski et al. 2018a). Silver nanoparticles (AgNp) and TiO_2 are employed as antimicrobial additives because of their capability to kill bacteria such as *Escherichia coli* and *Staphylococcus aureus*. Moreover, TiO_2 has a UV-blocking mechanism (Tomacheski et al. 2018b). Wollastonite is competitive with other mineral fillers such as glass fiber in enhancing the rigidity and strength of polyamide (Järvelä et al. 1987). Basalt fiber is cheaper than carbon fiber and possesses comparable and even higher tensile properties than glass fiber (Ma et al. 2018). The properties of mineral fillers are summarized in Table 5.1.

Mineral-reinforced polymer composites can be developed by melt compounding. High-density polyethylene (HDPE) and $CaCO_3$ at a concentration of 50 wt% were blended by an extruder with a 24 length/diameter (L/D) ratio at the screw speed of 45 rpm (Valadez-González and Veleva 2004). The silane coupling agent was blended with red pottery clay (RPC) at a mass ratio of 4:100 with a mixer at 60°C. HDPE, maleic anhydride-grafted polyethylene (PE-g-MA), paraffin lubricant and wood fiber were blended at the ratios of 58, 3, 1 and 38%, respectively. Then, five mixtures were prepared and modified RPC with a silane coupling agent (mRPC) was incorporated into the preceding blend at the ratios of 0, 3, 5, 7 and 10%. Five mixtures were fed into a mixer for 15 minutes. Specimens were extruded with a twin-screw extruder (Li et al. 2017). Low-density polyethylene (LDPE) and clay were mixed by a single-screw extruder with a temperature of 160°C and at the screw speed of 60 rpm (Morlat-Therias et al. 2008). Initially, LDPE was blended with 5% PE-g-MA by using a twin-screw extruder at the operating temperature of 120,

TABLE 5.1
The Properties of Mineral Fillers

Minerals	Bulk Density (g/cm³)	Density (g/cm³)	Mohr's Hardness	Particle Size (μm)	References
CaCO$_3$	0.52	2.7	3	1.4–100.0	Valadez-González and Veleva (2004); Leong et al. (2006); Butylina et al. (2012)
Glass bead	~1	NA	NA	5–30	Chylińska et al. (2020)
Glass fiber	NA	NA	NA	17	Zhou et al. (2019)
Kaolin	NA	NA	NA	1.7	Leong et al. (2006)
Perlite	1.0–1.3	NA	NA	<20–100	Chylińska et al. (2020)
Sillikolloid	0.25	NA	NA	1.5–6.0	Chylińska et al. (2020)
Talc	0.75	2.75	1	2.88–37.40	Leong et al. (2006); Jahani and Ehsani (2009); Butylina et al. (2012); Linares et al. (2019)
Wollastonite (CaSiO$_3$)	0.29–0.40	2.94	4.5	9.8–36.6	Järvelä et al. (1987); Butylina et al. (2012, 2015)

Abbreviations: NA, not available.

150 and 190 from hopper to die and a screw speed of 60 rpm. Then, PE-g-MA and clay (2, 3, 5 and 7 wt%) were mixed and extruded again (Kumanayaka et al. 2010). Composites of LDPE, clay and PE-g-MA or zinc-neutralized carboxylate ionomer as compatibilizers were prepared by melt blending with a twin-screw extruder by employing two-stage blending. First, a master batch of compatibilizers (PE-g-MA or zinc-neutralized carboxylate ionomer) and clay (60/40) were blended with a twin-screw extruder operating at a screw speed of 50 rpm and the temperature profile from 180°C to 190°C. The clay was incorporated through a side feeder. Then, the desired content of compatibilizer, master batch and virgin PE were mixed at 100 rpm and a temperature from 190 to 200°C for the one-stage blending. After that the specimens were pelletized and blended again with the extruder in a two-stage blending with 200 rpm and a temperature profile from 190°C to 200°C (Sánchez-Valdés et al. 2008). PE and clay composites in the existence or absence of the compatibilizer (PE-g-MA) were prepared by melt extrusion employing a co-rotating intermeshing twin-screw extruder (D = 19 mm, L/D = 35) at the temperature profile of 120, 140, 160, 170, 180 and 180°C (die), with a screw speed of 250 rpm. The extrudates were cooled with water and granulated before extrusion again in a single-screw extruder at the temperature profile of 120, 140, 160 and 190°C and a screw speed of 70 rpm (Dintcheva et al. 2009). LDPE and organo-modified montmorillonite (OMMT) were extruded with a co-rotating twin-screw extruder at the rotational speed of 200 rpm and the temperature profile of 120, 130, 140, 150, 160, 170 and 180°C (Dintcheva et al. 2012). Polyamide 6 (PA6) with 0.5 wt% antioxidant and clay at a concentration of 5 wt% were prepared with a single-screw extruder. The temperature profiles from hopper to die zones of extruder were set as 210, 220, 230

and 240°C and screw speed was selected as 7 rpm (Kiliaris et al. 2009). PA6 and wollastonite were compounded by using twin-screw extruder (Järvelä et al. 1987). Then 9.5 wt% clay and 28.5 wt% PE-g-MA was mixed for 2 minutes with an internal mixer at 90 rpm and 200°C. Then polypropylene (PP) was added for 18 minutes (Gutiérrez et al. 2010). T30 (70 wt% PP and 30 wt% untreated talc), UCC30 (70 wt% PP and 30 wt% untreated $CaCO_3$), T15UCC15 (70 wt% PP, 15 wt% untreated talc and 15 wt% untreated $CaCO_3$), K30 (70 wt% PP and 30 wt% untreated kaolin) and T15K15 (70 wt% PP, 15 wt% untreated talc and 15 wt% untreated kaolin) composites were prepared with a twin-screw extruder at the temperature of 160, 170, 180 and 190°C from hopper to die zones and at a speed of 25 rpm (Leong et al. 2006). Isotactic PP films including 2.5, 5 and 10 wt% mineral filler (glass bead, perlite and sillikolloid) were fabricated with the use of a co-rotating twin-screw extruder with a screw speed of 300 s^{-1} and at the temperature range of 190°C–195°C. Then, the achieved granules were exposed to extrusion employing a single-screw extruder with a screw speed of 75 s^{-1} and at the temperature range of 225°C–245°C (Chylińska et al. 2020). PP and long glass fiber (40 wt%) were mixed with a twin-screw extruder at 180°C–210°C. OMMT, intumescent flame retardant (IFR) and long glass fiber-reinforced PP (LGFPP) composite with 60 wt% of PP, 20 wt% of long glass fiber, 19 wt% of IFR and 1 wt% of OMMT were blended utilizing a twin-screw extruder (D = 40 mm, L/D = 40). Temperatures from the hopper to die were 180°C–210°C (Zhou et al. 2019). Reactive mixing of epoxy resin (2.5, 5 and 10 wt%) with PP and talc (20, 30 and 40%) was performed with a co-rotating twin-screw extruder (D = 25 mm, L/D = 40) at the screw speed of 750 rpm and at the temperature profile of 170, 170, 180, 185, 190, 200, 195, 195, 195, 190 and 190°C from the hopper to the die. The antioxidant and PP granules were fed into main hopper of extruder. Epoxy resin was premixed with polyester resin by using a mixer (Jahani and Ehsani 2009). Wood (41.5 wt%), PP (30 wt%), wollastonite (20 wt%), additives (coupling agent maleated polypropylene [MAPP] 3 wt%), lubricant (3 wt%) and pigment (carbon black [CB] master-batch or synthetic iron oxide [Fe_2O_3, 2.5 wt%]) were compounded by employing a counterrotating twin-screw extruder. The barrel temperatures were 170°C–190°C, the melt temperature at the die was 170°C and the screw speed was 13 rpm (Butylina et al. 2015). Polyetheretherketone (PEEK) and TiO_2 (1, 3, and 5 volume [v]%) were blended with a single-screw extruder at a temperature of 390°C (Bragaglia et al. 2020). PVC resin (100 phr), acrylic polymer impact modifier (6 phr), acrylic polymer processing aid (2 phr), $CaCO_3$ (5 phr), calcium stearate (1 phr), organic tin (1.5 phr) and PE wax (1 phr) were mixed with various amounts (0, 1, 3, 5, 8 and 10 phr) of TiO_2 on a two-roll mill at the temperature of 180°C (Xu et al. 2018). TiO_2 (3 wt%)-reinforced poly(3-hydroxybutyrate-*co*-3-hydroxyvalerate) (PHBV) composites were prepared by melt mixing at 120°C and using a screw speed of 30 rpm for 10 minutes (Antunes et al. 2020). Blends of PHBV and poly(butylene adipate-*co*-terephthalate) (PBAT) reinforced with OMMT were processed at 165°C and 45 rpm for 13 minutes (Bittmann et al. 2018). Silver ions (bentonite organo-modified with silver denoted as Ag⁺_bentonite, supported in phosphate glass, denoted as Ag⁺_phosphate) and silver nanoparticles adsorbed on fumed silica (AgNp_silica)-based additives at the proportions of 2.0, 0.3 and 0.05% were mixed with white mineral oil (36% naphthenic and 64% paraffinic), PP and

Ageing of Mineral-Reinforced Polymer Composites

styrene-ethylene/butylene-styrene (SEBS; ethylene/butylene 32/68, 32% styrene) at a proportion of 50/20/30, respectively. The composites were compounded employing a co-rotating twin-screw extruder (D = 16 mm, L/D = 40) with a temperature profile from 170°C to 190°C at the screw speed of 300 rpm. An antioxidant was incorporated at a ratio of 0.1% to eliminate thermal degradation during processing (Tomacheski et al. 2018a). Thermoplastic elastomer (TPE) compounds (depended on white mineral oil [36% naphthenic and 64% paraffinic]), PP and SEBS in the ratio of 50/20/30 including silver nanoparticles (AgNp; 0.05%), TiO_2 (4.0%) and an antioxidant to prevent thermal degradation during processing were blended employing a co-rotating twin-screw extruder (D = 16 mm, L/D = 40) with temperature profile from 170°C to 190°C at a screw speed of 300 rpm (Tomacheski et al. 2018b).

Epoxy resin and different weight percentages (1 and 2 wt%) of clay were prepared by employing the magnetic mixing method. Clay dispersed in part A (diglycidyl ether of bisphenol A [DGEBA], aliphatic diglycidyl ether and epoxy toughener) of epoxy resin with a magnetic stirrer for 2 hours. Then the modified part A was mixed with part B (hardener) of epoxy resin at a ratio of 10:3 utilizing a high-speed mechanical stirrer at 800 rpm for 5 minutes (Zainuddin et al. 2009). MMT clay (loading of 1, 2 and 3 wt%) was dispersed into part A of the DGEBA epoxy resin employing a magnetic stirrer. A stoichiometry quantity of part B (hardener) was incorporated to epoxy/clay in a mass ratio of 100:30 and stirred utilizing a mechanical stirrer at approximately 800 rpm for 5–10 minutes (Tcherbi-Narteh et al. 2014). OMMT (0, 1, 2, 3 and 4 wt%) and ZnO (0, 1, 2, 3 and 4 wt%) were dispersed into unsaturated polyester (UP) and vinyl ester (VE) resins. ZnO/OMMT/UP or ZnO/OMMT/VE was mixed with a mechanical mixer for 30 minutes for each mixture (Xu et al. 2020).

Mineral-reinforced polymer composites also can be developed by the sol-gel technique. Acrylic rubber (ACM) and epoxidized natural rubber (ENR) were dissolved in tetrahydrofuran (THF; 5% w/v) whereas poly(vinyl alcohol) (PVA) was dissolved in boiling water (5% w/v) then cooled to room temperature. For the rubbers, tetraethoxysilane (TEOS) and water in the mole ratio of 1:2 along with concentrated hydrochloric acid (HCl) catalyst and for PVA, HCl and TEOS were incorporated into the polymer solutions under stirring conditions at 25°C (room temperature). The initial concentration of TEOS was changed as 10, 30 and 50 wt% with respect to polymer. After mixing of the catalyst, TEOS and water in ACM and ENR for 30 minutes at room temperature, curatives were incorporated and stirred for 30 minutes. For ACM, 2.5-phr ammonium benzoate (AmBz) and 1.5-phr hexamethylene-diamine carbamate (HMDC) were employed, whereas for ENR, 0.75-phr dicumyl peroxide (DCP) was used (Bandyopadhyay and Bhowmick 2006).

TiO_2 powders were dispersed in Dispex N40 solution employing a homogenizer then blended with the aqueous dispersions of the respective polymeric binders; 2 minutes of the homogenization time was used. Polymer latexes were methyl methacrylate-ethylhexyl acrylate (MM-EHA), styrene-butyl acrylate (S-BA), vinyl acetate (VA) and vinyl acetate-butyl acrylate (VA-BA) prepared by the emulsion polymerization method. TiO_2 content was kept constant as 1% w/w (Wojciechowski et al. 2015). Unvulcanized styrene butadiene rubber (SBR) deposits (neat SBR, SBR + 5 phr disazopyrazolone dye and SBR + 5 phr TiO_2) were prepared by dissolving the polymer in THF in the absence and presence of TiO_2 (Mertz et al. 2012).

5.3 APPLICATIONS

Polymer composites used outdoors must have high resistance to harsh environmental conditions, especially UV irradiation (Tcherbi-Narteh et al. 2014). Photoresistance of mineral-reinforced polymer composites is important because of their applications devices that are subjected to radiation outside. Glass bead-, perlite- and sillikolloid-reinforced isotactic PP films were manufactured for the devices in which the piezoelectric effect could be employed. The existence of glass bead, perlite and sillikolloid in isotactic PP films formed the cellular architecture, which enhanced piezoelectric properties of isotactic PP films but deteriorated photostability of PP-limiting applications of these materials outdoors or when they were subjected to UV irradiation (Chylińska et al. 2020). Wood/talc/PP composite is suitable for outdoor applications due to its relatively good mechanical properties and low sensitivity to ageing (Butylina et al. 2012). PP/talc composite films are good candidates for packaging materials because they can bear UV light for a long time without exposure to major changes, but they can be degraded in a short period under landfill conditions (Linares et al. 2019). Wood/PP composite with the addition of wollastonite and CB pigment can be employed for outdoor applications (Butylina et al. 2015). The existence of a clay causes a drop in the oxidation induction time of LDPE polymer, indicating a lower durability of the composites. This is a major drawback for outdoor applications of clay-reinforced polymer composites (Morlat-Therias et al. 2008). For outdoor applications such as exterior and interior automotive parts, it is essential that clay-reinforced composites must have both photo-oxidative and thermal stability (Dintcheva et al. 2009). PVC/TiO$_2$ composite can be utilized as a cooling material in outdoor applications because the cooling performance and high solar reflectance of composites reinforced with TiO$_2$ do not change after UV weathering (Xu et al. 2018). Specimens with AgNp gave higher antimicrobial efficacy than TiO$_2$ specimens, even after 6 months of weathering exposure. Thus, the combination of AgNp and TiO$_2$ may be utilized if the retention of mechanical properties after natural exposure is mandatory, for instance, in elastomeric parts of bicycle handlebars, diving masks and fins and hiking stick handles. The devices manufactured from TPE, mineral oil, PP and SEBS blends usually are hand-contacting surfaces, such as household and medical items, that are susceptible to the colonization of a number of non-pathogenic and pathogenic microorganisms. Regarding their resistance to weather conditions, antimicrobial additive-reinforced polymer matrices can be employed in the fabrication of sporting products, especially those subjected to UV light and water such as diving equipment (Tomacheski et al. 2018b).

5.4 AGEING (WEATHERING)

Various environmental factors, such as chemicals, heat, humidity, impurities, mechanical load, microorganisms, ozone and UV light, individually or in combinations, can degrade polymeric materials (Ray and Cooney 2012). Environmental exposure can change the mechanical performance of polymeric materials. Determining the failure of polymeric parts under service conditions is costly and time-consuming. Ageing tests (natural or accelerated ageing) are performed to determine the performance of polymeric materials under service conditions. To reduce test times and cost

Ageing of Mineral-Reinforced Polymer Composites

TABLE 5.2
Natural Ageing Conditions

Beginning Year	Exposure Time	Angle (Degrees)	References
NA	6 months	45	Leong et al. (2006)
August 2015	9 months	30	Tomacheski et al. (2018a)
August 2015	9 months	30	Tomacheski et al. (2018b)
July 1997	2 years	22	Valadez-González and Veleva (2004)
June 2011	1 year	45	Butylina et al. (2015)
July 2007	120 days	NA	Morlat-Therias et al. (2008)

Abbreviations: NA, not available.

of natural weathering, accelerated ageing methods such as UV, thermal, water and hygrothermal ageing are developed. In this section of chapter, ageing methods used in mineral-reinforced polymer composites are presented.

5.4.1 Natural Ageing

Natural ageing conditions reported in the literature are summarized in Table 5.2. Silver-reinforced TPE specimens subjected to natural weathering at an inclination of 30° to the ground were placed in the city of Campo Bom, southern Brazil over 9 months (from August 2015 to May 2016). Natural weathering caused a decrease in the mechanical properties of silver-reinforced and unreinforced TPE. After 9 months of weathering, TPE specimens were almost completely degraded and lost their anti-bacterial properties. Better biodegradation rate was obtained with specimens subjected to ageing than unexposed specimens. Melting temperature and crystallinity index before (initial) and after natural ageing are given in Table 5.3 (Tomacheski

TABLE 5.3
Melting Temperature and Crystallinity Index before (Initial) and after Natural Ageing

	Initial Properties		Properties after Natural Ageing					
	Melting Temperature $(T_m, °C)$	Crystallinity Index $(X_C, \%)$	T_m (°C)	X_C (%)	T_m (°C)	X_C (%)	T_m (°C)	X_C (%)
Samples			3 months		6 months		9 months	
Standard	154.2	39.7	153.0	42.3	152.7	45.0	152.0	46.0
Ag⁺_bentonite	152.1	45.6	153.0	42.2	152.3	39.2	151.8	35.9
Ag⁺_phosphate	153.4	44.8	153.3	41.4	152.4	41.6	153.0	42.7
AgNp_silica	152.5	42.5	153.0	41.8	152.1	40.7	152.0	39.7

Source: Tomacheski et al. (2018a).

TABLE 5.4

Melting Temperature, Melting Enthalpy, Crystallinity Index, Crystallization Temperature and Crystallization Enthalpy as a Function of Natural Exposure Time

Samples	Exposure Time (Months)	$T_{m(PP)}$ (°C)	Melting Enthalpy ($\Delta H_{m(PP)}$, J g^{-1})	$X_{c(PP)}$ (%)	Crystallization Temperature ($T_{c(PE)}$, °C)	Crystallization Enthalpy ($\Delta H_{c(PE)}$, J g^{-1})
Standard	0	153	17.4	39.6	−9.0	1.7
	3	153	18.6	42.3	−7.7	1.0
	6	153	19.7	45.0	−10.2	0.3
	9	152	20.2	46.0	NA	0.0
TiO$_2$ 4.0%	0	154	18.1	43.1	−5.8	1.7
	3	153	16.0	37.9	−5.6	1.8
	6	154	16.1	38.2	−6.2	1.4
	9	154	16.6	39.5	−6.1	1.4
AgNp 0.05%	0	152	18.5	42.2	−4.0	1.2
	3	153	18.3	41.8	−3.9	1.3
	6	152	17.8	40.7	−5.7	0.4
	9	152	17.4	39.7	NA	0.0

Source: Tomacheski et al. (2018b).

et al. 2018a). TPE compounds (depended on white mineral oil [36% naphthenic and 64% paraffinic], PP and SEBS [ethylene/butylene 32/68, 32% styrene] in the ratio of 50/20/30) including silver nanoparticles (AgNp, 0.05%), TiO$_2$ (4.0%) and an antioxidant to prevent thermal degradation during processing and a compound without antimicrobial additive (standard) were subjected to 9 months of natural weathering (from August 2015 to May 2016) in Campo Bom city, southern Brazil. After being subjected to 9 months of weathering, both AgNp-reinforced and standard specimens lost their mechanical properties, whereas the TiO$_2$ specimen had better mechanical resistance to the natural weathering due to the UV-absorbing characteristic of the TiO$_2$ additive. Melting temperature, melting enthalpy, crystallinity index, crystallization temperature and crystallization enthalpy as a function of natural exposure time are presented in Table 5.4 (Tomacheski et al. 2018b). Natural ageing tests were conducted on an HDPE/CaCO$_3$ composite subjected to the tropical humid climate of the Yucatan peninsula in Mexico (southeastern Mexico, Merida and Progreso) by determining the physical and chemical properties. It was concluded that the existence of the mineral filler modified the photodegradation of unreinforced HDPE polymer (Valadez-González and Veleva 2004). PP films with 1 and 5% w/w of talc minerals with different iron content (0.41 and 2.22% w/w) were subjected to natural ageing for 2 months during the summer season in the city of Blanca, Argentina. Whiteness and yellowness index before (initial) and after natural ageing are given in Table 5.5. Talc addition in PP caused greater degradation compared with neat PP polymer and this behavior became more pronounced with increasing iron content in

Ageing of Mineral-Reinforced Polymer Composites

TABLE 5.5

Whiteness and Yellowness Index before (Initial) and after Natural Ageing

Composites	Initial Properties		Properties after Natural Ageing	
	Whiteness Index	Yellowness Index	Whiteness Index	Yellowness Index
PP1A (PP with 1% w/w of talc mineral having iron content of 0.41% w/w)	96.6 ± 0.3	0.23 ± 0.04	94.0 ± 0.1	1.29 ± 0.02
PP1SJ (PP with 1% w/w of talc mineral having iron content of 2.22% w/w)	97.0 ± 0.2	0.17 ± 0.04	91.6 ± 0.3	2.18 ± 0.33
PP5A (PP with 5% w/w of talc mineral having iron content of 0.41% w/w)	97.9 ± 0.4	0.16 ± 0.07	91.7 ± 0.3	2.02 ± 0.26
PP5SJ (PP with 5% w/w of talc mineral having iron content of 2.22% w/w)	97.8 ± 0.4	0.08 ± 0.03	91.2 ± 1.0	2.57 ± 0.32

Source: Linares et al. (2019).

talc and concentration of talc. Yield stress, Young's modulus and elongation at break before (initial) and after natural ageing are summarized in Table 5.6 (Linares et al. 2019). The natural ageing in Finnish climatic conditions of wood/wollastonite/PP/CB and wood/wollastonite/PP/Fe_2O_3 were performed for 1 year (12 months). The addition of CB pigment and wollastonite preserved Charpy impact strength of wood/PP composite after 12 months of outdoor exposure (Table 5.7) (Butylina et al. 2015). Hybrid mineral filler (either talc-$CaCO_3$ or talc-kaolin)-reinforced PP composites

TABLE 5.6

Yield Stress, Young's Modulus and Elongation at Break before (Initial) and after Natural Ageing

Composites	Initial Properties			Properties after Natural Ageing		
	Yield Stress (MPa)	Young's Modulus (MPa)	Elongation at Break (%)	Yield Stress (MPa)	Young's Modulus (MPa)	Elongation at Break (%)
PP1A	28.3 ± 2.4	1373 ± 122	590 ± 64	31.1 ± 3.3	1911 ± 146	3.2 ± 0.4
PP1SJ	28.5 ± 2.3	1394 ± 142	688 ± 85	20.1 ± 4.9	2100 ± 185	1.5 ± 1.0
PP5A	33.9 ± 3.0	1563 ± 137	603 ± 61	22.5 ± 5.7	1843 ± 274	1.6 ± 0.5
PP5SJ	31.8 ± 3.5	1542 ± 168	747 ± 84	5.3 ± 1.9	2064 ± 280	0.3 ± 0.1

Source: Linares et al. (2019).

94   Mineral-Filled Polymer Composites

TABLE 5.7
Charpy Impact Strength before (Initial) and after Natural Ageing

	Initial Properties	Properties after Natural Ageing	
	Charpy Impact Strength (kJ/m²)	Charpy Impact Strength (kJ/m²)	
Composites		3 Months	12 Months
Wood/wollastonite/PP/CB	2.87 ± 0.17	2.79 ± 0.16	2.74 ± 0.11
Wood/wollastonite/PP/Fe$_2$O$_3$	2.89 ± 0.12	3.00 ± 0.12	2.76 ± 0.14

Source: Butylina et al. (2015).

were exposed to natural weathering for a period of 6 months. It was found that hybrid composites had promising results in terms of mechanical property retention on natural ageing (Leong et al. 2006).

5.4.2 ACCELERATED AGEING

5.4.2.1 UV Ageing

UV ageing conditions reported in the literature are summarized in Table 5.8. The influences of accelerated weathering on chemistry, color, mechanical properties and morphology of wood/PP composites with and without mineral fillers (calcium carbonate, wollastonite and talc) were studied. Water absorption and thickness swelling as a function of UV exposure time are given in Table 5.9. It was found that UV

TABLE 5.8
UV Ageing Conditions

Irradiance (W/m²)	Exposure Time (h)	References
0.8	90 days	Xu et al. (2020)
72–85	2000	Butylina et al. (2012)
350	720	Chylińska et al. (2020)
0.78	225	Linares et al. (2019)
0.89	500, 1000, 1500, 2000, 2500, 3000	Li et al. (2017)
0.68	7, 14 days	Kumanayaka et al. (2010)
0.77	NA	Bragaglia et al. (2020)
0.51	200, 400, 600	Xu et al. (2018)
0.76	500, 1000, 2000	Antunes et al. (2020)
0.68	15 days	Tcherbi-Narteh et al. (2014)
400	NA	Mertz et al. (2012)

Abbreviations: NA, not available.

Ageing of Mineral-Reinforced Polymer Composites

TABLE 5.9

Water Absorption and Thickness Swelling as a Function of UV Exposure Time

Composites	Exposure Time (h)	Water Absorption (%)	Thickness Swelling (%)
Wood (64%)/PP (30%)	72	4.85 ± 0.32	2.44 ± 0.37
Wood (44%)/calcium carbonate (20%)/PP (30%)	72	3.54 ± 0.50	2.06 ± 0.99
Wood (44%)/wollastonite (20%)/PP (30%)	72	3.74 ± 0.22	1.40 ± 0.61
Wood (44%)/talc (20%)/PP (30%)	72	2.94 ± 0.16	0.85 ± 0.40

Source: Butylina et al. (2012).

exposure resulted in color change and surface lightening in composites containing mineral fillers. The ageing of mineral-based polymer composites caused the easily distinguishable mineral particles on the surface. The composite including talc was more efficient in retaining the Charpy impact strength after ageing since the hydrophobic nature of talc facilitates its compatibility with the hydrophobic PP matrix (Butylina et al. 2012). Glass bead-, perlite- and sillikolloid-reinforced isotactic PP films were exposed to UV ageing for 720 hours. Photo-oxidation of isotactic PP was more effective in the existence of mineral fillers and based on the kind of the filler but not on the amount. UV exposure of mineral isotactic PP films resulted in a formation of new oxygen containing functional groups due to photo-oxidative degradation. Longer UV exposure caused significant surface oxidation and damage, which should be considered to design piezo materials (Chylińska et al. 2020). PP films with 1 and 5% w/w of talc minerals with different iron content (0.41 and 2.22% w/w) were subjected to UV ageing for 225 hours. The existence of talc resulted in greater degradation of PP polymer and degradation increased with talc concentration. Specimens having talc with higher iron were more influenced by ageing conditions because iron behaved as a promoter of the degradation process (Linares et al. 2019). HDPE/wood fiber/RPC composites were exposed to UV irradiation of 0.89 W/m^2 for a duration of 500, 1000, 1500, 2000, 2500 and 3000 hours. The flexural modulus, flexural strength and impact strength reduced after 3000 hours of UV ageing. The composite with 5% mRPC caused the smallest drop in mechanical properties after 3000 hours of ageing. The photodegradation reaction was prevented by the addition of mRPC when ageing time was higher than 2000 hours (Li et al. 2017). UV ageing of LDPE/clay composites was performed to determine photo-oxidative degradation of this composite. The addition of clay improved the degradation of LDPE (Kumanayaka et al. 2010). The rate of photo-oxidation of PE/clay composites was found to be faster than virgin PE polymers because clay has a higher degradation effect (Sánchez-Valdés et al. 2008). PHBV/TiO$_2$ composites were subjected to UV ageing up to 2000 hours of exposure time. Results after UV ageing are summarized in Tables 5.10–5.13. Only after 2000 hours of UV ageing was there a surface change for PHBV/TiO$_2$ composites.

TABLE 5.10
Differential Scanning Calorimetry (DSC) Data for PHBV/TiO$_2$ Composite after UV Ageing

	First Heating					Cooling		Second Heating
Exposure Time (h)	T_{mL} (°C)	T_{m2} (°C)	T_{m3} (°C)	Measured Melting Enthalpy (ΔH_m, J g^{-1})	Degree of Crystallinity (X_c, %)	T_C (°C)	Enthalpy of Crystallization (ΔH_C, J g^{-1})	T_g (°C)
0	80.2	92.6	NA	55.2	52.0	56.7	39.7	−43.3
500	81.1	92.6	56.3	57.7	54.3	51.9/59.5	42.9	−43.6
1000	79.8	93.3	63.8	53.7	50.6	52.3	42.1	−43.5
2000	81.1	95.9	NA	49.6	46.7	56.3	42.3	−43.0

Source: Antunes et al. (2020).

TABLE 5.11
Thermogravimetric Analysis (TGA) Data for PHBV/TiO$_2$ Composite after UV Ageing

Exposure Time (h)	Onset Decomposition Temperature of Composites of 5% Weight Losses ($T_{5\%}$, °C)	Onset Decomposition Temperature of Composites of 50% Weight Losses ($T_{50\%}$, °C)	Maximum Degradation Rate Peak ($T_{max\%}$, °C)
0	348	399	407
500	352	397	404
1000	343	393	398
2000	345	395	403

Source: Antunes et al. (2020).

TABLE 5.12
Melt Flow Index (MFI) Values for PHBV/TiO$_2$ Composite after UV Ageing

Exposure Time (h)	MFI (g/10 min)
0	4.2 ± 0.5
500	8.1 ± 0.1
1000	16.1 ± 1.5
2000	34.1 ± 4.8

Source: Antunes et al. (2020).

TABLE 5.13
Mechanical Properties of PHBV/TiO$_2$ Composite after UV Ageing

Exposure Time (h)	Strength at Break (MPa)	Elongation at Break (%)	Young's Modulus (MPa)
0	36.3 ± 0.2	672 ± 34	238 ± 8
500	27.2 ± 1.4	520 ± 44	296 ± 22
1000	21.5 ± 1.9	241 ± 26	366 ± 61
2000	7.8 ± 0.5	2.6 ± 0.1	177 ± 7

Source: Antunes et al. (2020).

TiO$_2$ protected the PHBV polymer from UV radiation, slowed down the reduction in mechanical properties and restricted the mobility of polymer chains, behaving as a nucleating agent during the crystallization process (Antunes et al. 2020). Blends of PHBV and PBAT reinforced with OMMT were exposed to UV irradiation (Bittmann et al. 2018). TiO$_2$ behaved as a UV blocker and reduced the photodegradation (limiting it only to the skin surface) of PEEK after UV ageing. It was stated that the failure mechanism and mechanical properties (elongation at break and tensile strength) of 5 v% TiO$_2$-reinforced PEEK composite did not change after UV ageing, whereas unreinforced PEEK polymer had ductility loss and embrittlement (Table 5.14) (Bragaglia et al. 2020). Nano ZnO/OMMT-modified UP and VE resin-based glass fiber-reinforced polymer (GFRP) composites were exposed to UV ageing for 90 days. All samples had mass loss under UV ageing. The incorporation of ZnO/OMMT decreased the mass loss of UP and VE-based GFRP under UV irradiation. After 90 days of UV ageing, flexural strength and interlaminar shear strength improved by 23.5 and 27.8% for ZnO/OMMT-modified VE-based GFRP compared with VE-based GFRP (Xu et al. 2020). UV irradiation of carbon fiber-reinforced epoxy composites modified with clay (loading of 1, 2 and 3 wt%) was conducted for 15 days. Reduction in the mechanical properties was found after ageing (Tables 5.15 and 5.16). Specimens containing 2 and 3 wt% clay decreased glass transition temperature (T$_g$) value after irradiation, whereas an increment was found in neat and 1 wt% clay samples. Storage modulus increased in both aged and unaged specimens with increased clay amount up to 2 wt% and decreased amount at 3 wt% (Tcherbi-Narteh et al. 2014). Thin films achieved from MM-EHA, S-BA, VA and VA-BA doped with TiO$_2$ were subjected to UV ageing for specified periods of 24, 72, 120, 144, 168, 216, 240, 288 and 336 hours. It was stated that the photodegradation of four polymeric binders was not affected significantly by the existence of a small amount (1% w/w) of TiO$_2$ (Wojciechowski et al. 2015). Neat SBR, SBR + 5 phr disazopyrazolone dye and SBR + 5 phr TiO$_2$ deposits were subjected to UV irradiation at 400 W/m^2. It was declared that disazopyrazolone dye and TiO$_2$ fillers protected the matrix from photo-oxidation. Better stabilizing effect was obtained with disazopyrazolone dye compared with TiO$_2$ (Mertz et al. 2012).

TABLE 5.14

Results before (Initial) and after UV Ageing

Composites	Exposure Time (h)	Initial Properties					Properties after UV Ageing				
		Storage Modulus (GPa)	Glass Transition Temperature (T_g, °C)	Tensile Strength (MPa)	Elastic Modulus (GPa)	Elongation at Break (%)	Storage Modulus (GPa)	Glass Transition Temperature (T_g, °C)	Tensile Strength (MPa)	Elastic Modulus (GPa)	Elongation at Break (%)
PEEK	NA	2.32	152.6	86 ± 7	1.85 ± 0.11	35 ± 5	2.47	150.0	66 ± 8	2.15 ± 0.12	15 ± 6
PEEK/TiO$_2$ (1%)	NA	2.43	153.9	91 ± 12	1.87 ± 0.13	38 ± 7	2.51	150.4	68 ± 7	2.21 ± 0.13	12 ± 4
PEEK/TiO$_2$ (3%)	NA	2.74	152.3	78 ± 8	2.03 ± 0.17	42 ± 3	2.12	150.8	62 ± 6	2.18 ± 0.13	16 ± 6
PEEK/TiO$_2$ (5%)	NA	2.83	153.6	75 ± 13	2.07 ± 0.11	40 ± 4	3.11	150.6	76 ± 9	2.12 ± 0.10	38 ± 6

Source: Bragaglia et al. (2020).

Ageing of Mineral-Reinforced Polymer Composites

TABLE 5.15

Average Compressive Modulus of Unaged and Aged Specimens (Quasi-Static)

Exposure Time (h)	Compressive Modulus (GPa)			
	0 wt%	1 wt%	2 wt%	3 wt%
0	11.20 ± 0.84	11.34 ± 0.71	13.20 ± 1.08	12.21 ± 0.83
120	8.07 ± 0.52	10.34 ± 0.89	13.80 ± 0.73	13.70 ± 1.04
240	7.62 ± 0.45	10.60 ± 0.68	13.80 ± 0.88	13.50 ± 0.97
360	7.95 ± 1.78	7.93 ± 1.11	13.12 ± 2.08	13.00 ± 3.11

Source: Tcherbi-Narteh et al. (2014).

TABLE 5.16

Average Dynamic Compressive Modulus of Unaged and Aged Specimens

Exposure Time (h)	Dynamic Compressive Modulus (GPa)			
	0 wt%	1 wt%	2 wt%	3 wt%
0	26.36 ± 5.02	34.17 ± 4.13	40.74 ± 6.03	37.15 ± 7.43
120	35.47 ± 3.46	40.55 ± 6.03	45.21 ± 4.45	37.31 ± 5.58
240	31.99 ± 3.90	32.16 ± 4.11	35.19 ± 4.08	27.25 ± 0.15
360	23.32 ± 1.93	34.62 ± 4.27	37.52 ± 2.33	31.75 ± 4.52

Source: Tcherbi-Narteh et al. (2014).

5.4.2.2 Thermal Ageing

Thermal ageing conditions reported in the literature are summarized in Table 5.17. Thermal ageing of OMMT/IFR/LGFPP composites was carried out for 50 days at 140°C. Compared with unaged specimens, flexural, notched impact and tensile strength of OMMT/IFR/LGFPP composites after 50 days of ageing were reduced by

TABLE 5.17

Thermal Ageing Conditions

Temperature (°C)	Exposure Time	References
50, 70, 90	24, 48, 72 h	Bandyopadhyay and Bhowmick (2006)
120, 150	7, 14, 21, 28, 35 days	Kiliaris et al. (2009)
60, 80, 100	NA	Gutiérrez et al. (2010)
80, 100, 120, 150	NA	Ito and Nagai (2008)

Abbreviations: NA, not available.

TABLE 5.18

Limiting Oxygen Index (LOI) Values and Underwriters Laboratories-94 (UL-94) Vertical Combustion Performances of OMMT/IFR/LGFPP Composites under Various Thermal Ageing Time

Ageing Time (Days)	0	10	30	50
LOI (%)	23.5 ± 0.1	24.7 ± 0.1	24.2 ± 0.1	23.3 ± 0.1
UL-94	V-0	V-0	V-1	V-2

Source: Zhou et al. (2019).

34.9, 57.7 and 34.9%, respectively. Results obtained from this study are presented in Tables 5.18–5.21 (Zhou et al. 2019). PP/talc composites with epoxy resin were aged at 100°C up to 700 hours (Jahani and Ehsani 2009). Thermal ageing of PA6/wollastonite composites was conducted at temperatures of 80°C, 100°C and 120°C. No important drop in tensile strength was observed at the temperature of 100°C; only a gradual drop in tensile strength was evident at the end of the longest period. At the

TABLE 5.19

Cone Calorimeter Test (CCT) Data for OMMT/IFR/LGFPP Composites under Various Thermal Ageing Times

Ageing time (days)	0	10	30	50
Initial ignition time (TTI, s)	7 ± 1	9 ± 1	11 ± 1	12 ± 2
Peak heat release rate (pHRR, kW/m^2)	233 ± 5	252 ± 3	277 ± 6	310 ± 4
Mean heat release rate (HRR, kW/m^2)	105 ± 2	110 ± 3	128 ± 1	131 ± 2
Total heat release (THR, MJ/m^2)	182.4 ± 7.5	180.6 ± 7.5	176.5 ± 7.5	175.4 ± 7.5

Source: Zhou et al. (2019).

TABLE 5.20

TGA Data for OMMT/IFR/LGFPP Composites under Various Thermal Ageing Times

Ageing Time (Days)	0	10	30	50
$T_{5\%}$ (°C)	377.1 ± 1.3	400.0 ± 2.1	397.2 ± 1.7	386.7 ± 1.5
$T_{max\%}$ (°C)	482.6 ± 0.8	489.6 ± 0.4	493.7 ± 1.1	490.1 ± 0.6
Char yield (%)	31.80 ± 0.06	30.80 ± 0.11	29.50 ± 0.04	29.70 ± 0.21

Source: Zhou et al. (2019).

TABLE 5.21

Mechanical Properties of OMMT/IFR/LGFPP Composites under Various Thermal Ageing Times

Ageing Time (Days)	0	10	30	50
Tensile strength (MPa)	127.1 ± 2.3	98.1 ± 0.8	91.9 ± 1.0	88.9 ± 2.2
Flexural strength (MPa)	94.3 ± 1.7	70.7 ± 1.1	65.1 ± 2.1	61.3 ± 1.6
Notched Izod impact strength (kJ/m²)	17.5 ± 0.3	11.3 ± 0.1	9.1 ± 0.2	7.4 ± 0.1

Source: Zhou et al. (2019).

temperature of 120°C, tensile strength decreased almost immediately, and the reduction slowed down as a function of ageing time (Järvelä et al. 1987). Clay-reinforced PA6 was exposed to thermal ageing to determine changes in mechanical properties, molecular weight and thermal properties. It was found that the addition of clay caused moderate polymer degradation with ageing. The loss of ductility with ageing was smaller for clay-reinforced PA6 composite compared with unreinforced PA6 polymer, implying that clay restricted degradation, extending durability (Kiliaris et al. 2009). Nylon 6/MMT composite became yellowish after thermal ageing (Ito and Nagai 2008). Thermal ageing at 50°C, 70°C and 90°C showed that PVA/silica composites were more resistant to deterioration compared with ACM/silica and ENR/silica composites (Table 5.22) (Bandyopadhyay and Bhowmick 2006).

5.4.2.3 Water Ageing

Water causes hydrolysis reaction of plastic or is absorbed by plastic as bound or free water. Water is absorbed by polymers, especially epoxy, nylon and polyester, thus decreasing their T_g values. Drying of polymers returns the T_g value to its original value. However, when polymers are exposed to chemical hydrolysis, T_g decreases through breaking of bonds (Harvey 2012). Water ageing of PA6/wollastonite composites was conducted by using tap water. The properties remained unchanged after 500 hours of ageing and a slight increment in impact strength was found. An evident reduction in tensile strength started at 500–1000 hours and propagated to 3000 hours, after which strength was stabilized. A similar result was obtained for impact strength, although the drop was not as great as in tensile strength (Järvelä et al. 1987). Wood/wollastonite/PP/CB and wood/wollastonite/PP/Fe₂O₃ were immersed in water for 28 days. The incorporation of CB pigment and wollastonite reduced the thickness swelling and water absorption of wood/PP composite (Butylina et al. 2015). PHBV/PBAT reinforced with OMMT composites was immersed in distilled water for 12 weeks. Thermal stability of PHBV/PBAT reinforced with OMMT composites reduced after moisture absorption (Bittmann et al. 2018).

The combined effect of humidity and temperature cycles (hygrothermal ageing) can result in severe deterioration of surface cracks in plastic parts. In outdoor ageing, cyclic variation of humidity results in absorption and desorption of moisture and this causes alternate shrinking and swelling of the surface. Due to changes in moisture

TABLE 5.22
Tensile Strength and Elongation at Break as a Function of Thermal Exposure Time

Composites	Ageing Time (h)	50°C		70°C		90°C	
		Tensile Strength (MPa)	Elongation at Break (%)	Tensile Strength (MPa)	Elongation at Break (%)	Tensile Strength (MPa)	Elongation at Break (%)
ACM D (0 wt%	0	1.00	800	1.00	800	1.00	800
TEOS, 0.00%	24	0.96	749	0.94	761	0.94	745
silica residue)	48	0.81	728	0.79	728	0.82	700
	72	0.65	710	0.62	718	0.80	689
ACM D30	0	3.00	760	3.00	760	3.00	760
(30 wt%	24	2.90	700	2.85	689	2.82	710
TEOS, 7.98%	48	2.61	657	2.52	632	2.30	650
silica residue)	72	2.21	619	2.10	621	1.95	610
ENR D (0 wt%	0	4.00	850	4.00	850	4.00	850
TEOS, 0.00%	24	3.10	780	3.00	720	2.76	682
silica residue)	48	2.50	710	2.20	657	1.95	525
	72	2.20	645	2.00	400	1.25	323
ENR D30	0	6.90	765	6.90	765	6.90	765
(30 wt%	24	6.60	710	6.10	687	6.12	585
TEOS, 8.15%	48	6.20	640	6.00	638	5.82	463
silica residue)	72	6.00	585	5.90	591	5.23	250
PVA (0 wt%	0	21.00	180	21.00	180	NA	NA
TEOS, 0.00%	24	21.05	98	21.10	65	NA	NA
silica residue)	48	21.09	59	21.00	32	NA	NA
	72	21.08	45	15.23	25	NA	NA
PVA30 (30 wt%	0	38.00	75	38.00	75	NA	NA
TEOS, 8.25%	24	38.12	42	38.00	51.20	NA	NA
silica residue)	48	38.10	28	38.05	22.08	NA	NA
	72	38.50	21	35.60	9.23	NA	NA

Abbreviations: NA, not available.
Source: Bandyopadhyay and Bhowmick (2006).

amount and temperature in the plastic and due to the existence of flaws, the cyclic dimensional alternations are not uniform in a plane parallel to the surface or in the direction normal to the sheet. Thus, they result in a nonuniform, variable stress that causes fatigue (McKeen 2014). The environmental temperature affects the rate of ageing more than the humidity (Valadez-González and Veleva 2004).

The influences of alkali and water solutions on ageing during 45, 90, 135 and 180 days and the temperature (20°C and 40°C) on the surface morphology, tensile properties and weight gain of basalt fabric-reinforced epoxy composite were determined. Weight gain of basalt-reinforced epoxy composites after 45 days of immersion

TABLE 5.23
Weight Gain of Basalt-Reinforced Epoxy Composites after 45 Days of Immersion in Percentage (%)

Temperature (°C)	Solution	Weight Gain (%)
20	Alkali	2.49
	Water	1.87
40	Alkali	0.94
	Water	0.77

Source: Ma et al. (2018).

in percentage is summarized in Table 5.23. Reduction in the tensile strength was obtained with the increment of exposure temperature of alkali and water solutions. The strength drop at alkali solution was found to be larger than that at water solution. However, the modulus was unaffected by ageing conditions of alkali and water solutions, even slightly improved after ageing (Ma et al. 2018).

Rubber-modified, mineral (calcium silicate and fumed silica)-reinforced epoxy resin depended on the DGEBA cured with dicyandiamide was aged in deionized water or 5% w/w sodium chloride (NaCl) solution at the constant temperature of $65 \pm 1°C$ (Ivanova et al. 2001). Nano ZnO/OMMT-modified UP and VE resin-based GFRP composites were exposed to hygrothermal ageing at 30°C, 50°C and 60°C for 90 days. Experimental values for moisture uptake (%) are summarized in Table 5.24. Long-term durability prediction was carried out with the Arrhenius model. This is expressed by Equation (1) (Xu et al. 2020):

$$L = Ce^{\left(\frac{B}{T}\right)}$$

(5.1)

TABLE 5.24
Experimental Values for Moisture Uptake (%)

Ageing Time (Days)	30°C	50°C	60°C
0	0	0	0
15	0.023	0.384	0.378
30	0.045	0.680	0.669
45	0.078	0.850	0.902
60	0.083	0.961	1.039
75	0.085	0.981	1.160
90	0.095	0.975	1.187

Source: Xu et al. (2020).

where L is lifetime, T is the temperature in Kelvin, and B and C are the model parameters to be determined. When Equation (1) is inverted, Equation (2) is obtained (Xu et al. 2020):

$$\ln L = \ln C + \frac{B}{T} \qquad (5.2)$$

Equation (2) represents a straight line in the slope-intercept form, where B is the slope of the line, $\ln C$ is the intercept and the variable on the horizontal axis is the inverse of temperature. Equation (2) can be written as Equation (3) (Xu et al. 2020):

$$y = a\left(\frac{1}{T}\right) + b \qquad (5.3)$$

Relationships between ultimate flexural strength and shear strength retention with time for VE-based GFRP under hygrothermal ageing are presented in Tables 5.25 and 5.26, respectively (Xu et al. 2020).

After 90 days of hygrothermal ageing at 30°C, 50°C and 60°C, flexural strength improved by 23.2, 25.7 and 26.5%, respectively, and interlaminar shear strength improved by 30.1, 27.0 and 27.2%, respectively, for ZnO/OMMT-modified VE-based GFRP compared with VE-based GFRP (Xu et al. 2020). Accelerated ageing of GFRP (composed of 28% VE resin and 72% glass fiber) bars embedded in concrete beams was conducted by immersing in tap water at 23°C and alkaline solution at 60°C for an exposure time of 6, 12 and 18 months. After immersion, tensile strength of GFRP bars decreased. The retention of tensile strength was 75.4–79.7% after 18 months of alkaline solution. Almost no significant reduction was found in elastic modulus regardless of exposure environment and period (He et al. 2017).

TABLE 5.25

Relationship Between Ultimate Flexural Strength Retention and Time for VE-Based GFRP under Hygrothermal Ageing

Ageing Time (Days)	Relationship Between Percent Retention and 1/T	Ageing Time (Days)	Relationship Between Percent Retention and 1/T
30	$y = 103.72 - 0.97\left(\dfrac{1000}{T}\right)$	180	$y = 30.35 + 10.91\left(\dfrac{1000}{T}\right)$
60	$y = 75.34 + 3.63\left(\dfrac{1000}{T}\right)$	365	$y = 1.41 + 15.6\left(\dfrac{1000}{T}\right)$
90	$y = 58.74 + 6.32\left(\dfrac{1000}{T}\right)$	730	$y = -26.98 + 20.19\left(\dfrac{1000}{T}\right)$
120	$y = 46.96 + 8.23\left(\dfrac{1000}{T}\right)$	1825	$y = -64.49 + 26.27\left(\dfrac{1000}{T}\right)$
150	$y = 37.82 + 9.7\left(\dfrac{1000}{T}\right)$	3650	$y = -92.88 + 30.86\left(\dfrac{1000}{T}\right)$

Source: Xu et al. (2020).

Ageing of Mineral-Reinforced Polymer Composites

TABLE 5.26

Relationship Between Shear Strength Retention and Time for VE-Based GFRP under Hygrothermal Ageing

Ageing Time (Days)	Relationship Between Percent Retention and 1/T	Ageing Time (Days)	Relationship Between Percent Retention and 1/T
30	$y = 99.98 - 0.06\left(\dfrac{1000}{T}\right)$	180	$y = -38.12 + 35.59\left(\dfrac{1000}{T}\right)$
60	$y = 46.56 + 13.73\left(\dfrac{1000}{T}\right)$	365	$y = -92.6 + 49.65\left(\dfrac{1000}{T}\right)$
90	$y = 15.31 + 21.8\left(\dfrac{1000}{T}\right)$	730	$y = -146.02 + 63.44\left(\dfrac{1000}{T}\right)$
120	$y = -6.86 + 27.52\left(\dfrac{1000}{T}\right)$	1825	$y = -216.65 + 81.67\left(\dfrac{1000}{T}\right)$
150	$y = -24.06 + 31.96\left(\dfrac{1000}{T}\right)$	3650	$y = -270.65 + 95.46\left(\dfrac{1000}{T}\right)$

Source: Xu et al. (2020).

For cold (−18°C) dry/wet ageing, epoxy/clay composites were placed in a box with/ without water and put in a deep freezer for 15, 45 and 90 days. For hot dry ageing, epoxy/ clay composites were put in an oven at temperatures of 60°C and 80°C for 15, 45 and 90 days. For hot wet ageing, epoxy/clay composites were put in a hot water glass containers kept at temperatures of 60°C and 80°C for 15, 45 and 90 days. The mechanical properties (flexural modulus and flexural strength) deteriorated with the increment in the ageing time. The 2 wt% clay-reinforced epoxy composite increased flexural strength and flexural modulus (7 and 38% at room temperature, 20 and 29% at hot [80°C] wet ageing for 90 days) compared with neat epoxy (Table 5.27) (Zainuddin et al. 2009).

5.4.2.4 E-Beam Irradiation

The e-beam irradiation of OMMT-reinforced LDPE films was carried out at the pulse current of 470 mA, pulse frequency of 400 Hz and dose of 25 kGy. Total doses of 25, 50, 75, 100, 125, 150, 200 and 250 kGy were applied to samples. The presence of OMMT and e-beam irradiation caused reduction in the photo-oxidation resistance of LDPE films. Elastic modulus increased and elongation at break decreased with the presence of OMMT and increment in the dose (Dintcheva et al. 2012).

5.4.2.5 Cyclic Ageing

Wood/wollastonite/PP/CB and wood/wollastonite/PP/Fe$_2$O$_3$ were subjected to three cycles, namely immersion in water at the temperature of 23°C for 70 ± 1 hours, freezing at −20°C for 24 hours and drying at 70°C for 70 ± 1 hours. The addition of CB pigment and wollastonite retained Charpy impact strength of wood/PP composite after cyclic ageing (Table 5.28) (Butylina et al. 2015).

Combined actions of heat, water and room temperature called thermal + water + air ageing of glass fiber-reinforced poly(oxymethylene) (POM) were determined.

TABLE 5.27
Flexural Strength and Flexural Modulus as a Function of Water Exposure Time

Materials	Conditions	Flexural Strength (MPa)			Flexural Modulus (GPa)		
		15 Days	45 Days	90 Days	15 Days	45 Days	90 Days
Epoxy	Hot (60°C) dry ageing	91 ± 1.58	83 ± 1.56	81 ± 0.58	2.59 ± 0.05	2.47 ± 0.03	2.31 ± 0.06
	Hot (60°C) wet ageing	80 ± 1.11	78.6 ± 1.27	78 ± 1.18	2.53 ± 0.02	2.34 ± 0.03	2.28 ± 0.05
	Hot (80°C) dry ageing	82.3 ± 1.63	80 ± 0.83	77.6 ± 1.03	2.39 ± 0.07	2.37 ± 0.07	2.34 ± 0.08
	Hot (80°C) wet ageing	79.5 ± 1.56	75 ± 1.03	74 ± 0.58	2.23 ± 0.02	2.18 ± 0.05	2.14 ± 0.05
	Cold (−18°C) dry ageing	86 ± 1.80	84 ± 1.32	77.6 ± 1.55	2.59 ± 0.05	2.54 ± 0.05	2.34 ± 0.06
	Cold (−18°C) wet ageing	84 ± 1.53	80 ± 0.96	76 ± 0.63	2.45 ± 0.06	2.34 ± 0.06	2.21 ± 0.03
1% reinforced epoxy composite	Hot (60°C) dry ageing	91 ± 1.60	87 ± 1.33	86 ± 1.18	2.7 ± 0.02	2.65 ± 0.08	2.59 ± 0.04
	Hot (60°C) wet ageing	84 ± 0.86	83.5 ± 0.58	77.6 ± 1.22	2.7 ± 0.05	2.46 ± 0.03	2.37 ± 0.07
	Hot (80°C) dry ageing	87 ± 1.70	84.3 ± 1.65	82.3 ± 1.57	2.63 ± 0.07	2.46 ± 0.06	2.39 ± 0.07
	Hot (80°C) wet ageing	83 ± 1.30	81.6 ± 1.06	78 ± 1.00	2.47 ± 0.03	2.34 ± 0.02	2.23 ± 0.02
	Cold (−18°C) dry ageing	89 ± 1.41	89 ± 1.60	84 ± 1.71	2.57 ± 0.1	2.56 ± 0.05	2.54 ± 0.03
	Cold (−18°C) wet ageing	85 ± 1.20	83.4 ± 0.42	81 ± 1.58	2.54 ± 0.05	2.43 ± 0.07	2.31 ± 0.05
2% reinforced epoxy composite	Hot (60°C) dry ageing	111 ± 1.60	103 ± 1.27	102.8 ± 1.20	3.03 ± 0.1	2.99 ± 0.05	2.97 ± 0.04
	Hot (60°C) wet ageing	97 ± 1.03	95 ± 0.58	94 ± 1.00	2.93 ± 0.07	2.91 ± 0.03	2.86 ± 0.05
	Hot (80°C) dry ageing	98 ± 1.34	94 ± 1.40	89 ± 1.84	2.96 ± 0.07	2.87 ± 0.05	2.87 ± 0.07
	Hot (80°C) wet ageing	91 ± 0.71	89.7 ± 1.05	87 ± 1.22	2.81 ± 0.04	2.8 ± 0.05	2.8 ± 0.05
	Cold (−18°C) dry ageing	104 ± 1.20	99.3 ± 1.88	96 ± 1.33	2.97 ± 0.02	2.97 ± 0.08	2.97 ± 0.04
	Cold (−18°C) wet ageing	92 ± 1.60	90.4 ± 1.02	91 ± 1.05	2.91 ± 0.05	2.87 ± 0.02	2.86 ± 0.02

Source: Zainuddin et al. (2009).

Ageing of Mineral-Reinforced Polymer Composites

TABLE 5.28

Charpy Impact Strength before (Initial) and after Cyclic Ageing

Composites	Initial Properties Charpy Impact Strength (kJ/m²)	Properties after Cyclic Ageing Charpy Impact Strength (kJ/m²)
Wood/wollastonite/PP/CB	2.87 ± 0.17	2.75 ± 0.14
Wood/wollastonite/PP/Fe$_2$O$_3$	2.89 ± 0.12	2.47 ± 0.09

Source: Butylina et al. (2015).

Specimens were heated to 100°C and kept in the oven for 7 days, cooled down to room temperature, then put into water at room temperature for 7 days and finally taken from the water and kept at room temperature for 7 days. It was concluded that thermal + water + air ageing did not further degrade glass fiber-reinforced POM composite in compared with only water ageing (Kuram 2019).

5.5 CONCLUSIONS

Mineral-reinforced polymer composites have been employed for several applications because they are low cost, light weight and have excellent rigidity and high mechanical strength. However, mineral-reinforced polymer composites are subjected to harsh environments such as heat, mechanical stress, microbes, moisture, ozone and UV irradiation during their service life, which causes reduction in the polymer lifetime. Therefore, in this chapter, the studies about processing, applications and the effects of ageing on the properties of various minerals such as calcium carbonate, glass bead, glass fiber, talc and wollastonite-reinforced polymer composites were reported. The following results were obtained from the literature studies:

- The presence of glass bead, perlite and sillikolloid in PP films deteriorated photostability of PP limiting applications of these materials outdoors or when they were exposed to UV radiation. Wood/talc/PP, wood/PP composite with the addition of wollastonite and CB pigment and PVC/TiO$_2$ composites were found to be suitable for outdoor applications.
- The addition of talc in PP resulted in greater degradation during natural ageing. The incorporation of CB pigment and wollastonite preserved Charpy impact strength of wood/PP composite after natural exposure and cyclic ageing. Natural weathering caused reduction in the mechanical properties of silver-reinforced and unreinforced TPE.
- It was found that UV exposure resulted in color change and surface lightening in wood/PP composites with calcium carbonate, wollastonite and talc. The composite with talc was more efficient in retaining the Charpy impact strength after UV ageing. The addition of clay improved the degradation of LDPE. TiO$_2$ behaved as a UV blocker and reduced the photodegradation of PEEK and PHBV after UV ageing.

- The addition of clay caused moderate PA6 degradation with thermal ageing. Nylon 6/MMT composite became yellowish after thermal ageing.
- The incorporation of CB pigment and wollastonite reduced the thickness swelling and water absorption of wood/PP composite. Thermal stability of PHBV/PBAT reinforced with OMMT composites reduced after moisture absorption.
- The presence of OMMT e-beam irradiation caused reduction in the photo-oxidation resistance of LDPE films.
- It was concluded that thermal + water + air ageing did not further degrade glass fiber-reinforced POM composite with respect to only water ageing.

ACKNOWLEDGMENTS

Saying "Thank You" seems so inadequate, but I cannot find the right words to express my feelings, so I will stick with these two simple words. I thank my doctor interventional neurologist Assoc. Prof. Hasan Huseyin Karadeli who gave me a second life after my brain operation in August 2019. If it had not been for his operation and treatment, I would not have been able to do all the things I can do now. I dedicate this chapter to my family and Assoc. Prof. Hasan Huseyin Karadeli.

REFERENCES

Antunes, A., A. Popelka, O. Aljarod, M.K. Hassan, P. Kasak, and A.S. Luyt. 2020. "Accelerated Weathering Effects on Poly(3-Hydroxybutyrate-*co*-3-Hydroxyvalerate) (PHBV) and PHBV/TiO$_2$ Nanocomposites." *Polymers* 12:1743. https://doi.org/10.3390/polym12081743

Bandyopadhyay, A., and A.K. Bhowmick. 2006. "Low and High Temperature Degradation of Polymer/In Situ Silica Hybrid Nanocomposites." *Plastics, Rubber and Composites* 35:210–8. https://doi.org/10.1179/174328906X128180

Bittmann, B., R. Bouza, L. Barral, R. Bellas, and A. Cid. 2018. "Effect of Environmental Factors on Poly(3-Hydroxybutyrate-*co*-3-Hydroxyvalerate)/Poly(butylene Adipate-*co* Terephthalate)/Montmorillonite Nanocomposites with Antimicrobial Agents." *Polymer Composites* 39:915–23. https://doi.org/10.1002/pc.24018

Bragaglia, M., V. Cherubini, and F. Nanni. 2020. "PEEK-TiO$_2$ Composites with Enhanced UV Resistance." *Composites Science and Technology* 199:108365. https://doi.org/10.1016/j.compscitech.2020.108365

Butylina, S., M. Hyvärinen, and T. Kärki. 2012. "Accelerated Weathering of Wood-Polypropylene Composites Containing Minerals." *Composites: Part A* 43:2087–94. https://doi.org/10.1016/j.compositesa.2012.07.003

Butylina, S., M. Hyvärinen, and T. Kärki. 2015. "Weathering of Wood-Polypropylene and Wood-Wollastonite-Polypropylene Composites Containing Pigments in Finnish Climatic Conditions." *Pigment & Resin Technology* 44:313–21. https://doi.org/10.1108/PRT-08-2014-0066

Chylińska, M., H. Kaczmarek, D. Moszyński, B. Królikowski, and J. Kowalonek. 2020. "Surface Studies of UV Irradiated Polypropylene Films Modified with Mineral Fillers Designed as Piezoelectric Materials." *Polymers* 12:562. https://doi.org/10.3390/polym12030562

Dintcheva, N.T., S. Al-Malaika, and F.P. La Mantia. 2009. "Effect of Extrusion and Photo-Oxidation on Polyethylene/Clay Nanocomposites." *Polymer Degradation and Stability* 94:1571–88. https://doi.org/10.1016/j.polymdegradstab.2009.04.012

Ageing of Mineral-Reinforced Polymer Composites 109

Dintcheva, N.T., S. Alessi, R. Arrigo, G. Przybytniak, and G. Spadaro. 2012. "Influence of the e-Beam Irradiation and Photo-Oxidation Aging on the Structure and Properties of LDPE-OMMT Nanocomposite Films." *Radiation Physics and Chemistry* 81:432–6. https://doi.org/10.1016/j.radphyschem.2011.12.018

Gao, A.X., J.D. Bolt, and A.A. Feng. 2008. "Role of Titanium Dioxide Pigments in Outdoor Weathering of Rigid PVC." *Plastics, Rubber and Composites* 37:397–402. https://doi.org/10.1179/174328908X356545

Gutiérrez, G., F. Fayolle, G. Régnier, and J. Medina. 2010. "Thermal Oxidation of Clay-Nanoreinforced Polypropylene." *Polymer Degradation and Stability* 95:1708–15. https://doi.org/10.1016/j.polymdegradstab.2010.05.020

Harvey, J.A. 2012. "Chemical and Physical Aging of Plastics. Handbook of Environmental Degradation of Materials. In *Elsevier Science & Technology Books*, M. Kutz, editor, 195–211.

He, X.J., L. Dai, and W.R. Yang. 2017. "Durability and Degradation Mechanism of GFRP Bars Embedded in Concrete Beams with Cracks." *Plastics, Rubber and Composites* 46:17–24. https://doi.org/10.1080/14658011.2016.1245807

Ito, M., and K. Nagai. 2008. "Evaluation of Degradation on Nylon-6 and Nylon-6/Montmorillonite Nanocomposite by Color Measurement." *Journal of Applied Polymer Science* 108:3487–94. https://doi.org/10.1002/app.27954

Ivanova, K.I., R.A. Pethrick, and S. Affrossman. 2001. "Hygrothermal Aging of Rubber-Modified and Mineral-Filled Dicyandiamide-Cured DGEBA Epoxy Resin. II. Dynamic Mechanical Thermal Analysis." *Journal of Applied Polymer Science* 82:3477–85. https://doi.org/10.1002/app.2209

Jahani, Y., and M. Ehsani. 2009. "The Effects of Epoxy Resin Nano Particles on Shrinkage Behavior and Thermal Stability of Talc-Filled Polypropylene." *Polymer Bulletin* 63:743–54. https://doi.org/10.1007/s00289-009-0145-9

Järvelä, P.K., P.A. Järvelä, J.C. Le Bell, and P. Törmälä. 1987. "Effect of Humidity and Temperature on the Properties of Wollastonite Filled Polyamide 6." *Composites Evaluation* 222–8. https://doi.org/10.1016/B978-0-408-02569-0.50031-3

Kiliaris, P., C.D. Papaspyrides, and R. Pfaendner. 2009. "Influence of Accelerated Aging on Clay-Reinforced Polyamide 6." *Polymer Degradation and Stability* 94:389–96. https://doi.org/10.1016/j.polymdegradstab.2008.11.016

Kumanayaka, T.O., R. Parthasarathy, and M. Jollands. 2010. "Accelerating Effect of Montmorillonite on Oxidative Degradation of Polyethylene Nanocomposites." *Polymer Degradation and Stability* 95:672–6. https://doi.org/10.1016/j.polymdegradstab.2009.11.036

Kuram, E. 2019. "Thermal and Water Ageing Effect on Mechanical, Rheological and Morphological Properties of Glass-Fibre-Reinforced Poly(oxymethylene) Composite." *Proceedings of the Institution of Mechanical Engineers, Part E: Journal of Process Mechanical Engineering* 233:211–24. https://doi.org/10.1177/0954408918770059

Leong, Y.W., M.B. Abu Bakar, Z.A. Mohd. Ishak, and A. Ariffin. 2006. "Filler Treatment Effects on the Weathering of Talc-, CaCO$_3$- and Kaolin-Filled Polypropylene Hybrid Composites." *Composite Interfaces* 13:659–84. https://doi.org/10.1163/156855406779366840

Li, Q., X. Gao, W. Cheng, and G. Han. 2017. "Effect of Modified Red Pottery Clay on the Moisture Absorption Behavior and Weatherability of Polyethylene-Based Wood-Plastic Composites." *Materials* 10:111. https://doi.org/10.3390/ma10020111

Linares, P.B., L.A. Castillo, and S.E. Barbosa. 2019. "Pro-Degradant Effect of Talc Nanoparticles on Polypropylene Films." *Journal of Polymers and the Environment* 27:1666–76. https://doi.org/10.1007/s10924-019-01461-8

Ma, G., L. Yan, W. Shen, D. Zhu, L. Huang, and B. Kasal. 2018. "Effects of Water, Alkali Solution and Temperature Ageing on Water Absorption, Morphology and Mechanical Properties of Natural FRP Composites: Plant-Based Jute vs. Mineral-Based Basalt." *Composites Part B* 153:398–412. https://doi.org/10.1016/j.compositesb.2018.09.015

McKeen, L.W. 2014. *The Effect of Long Term Thermal Exposure on Plastics and Elastomers.* William Andrew: Norwich, NY.

Mertz, G., F. Hassouna, V. Toniazzo, A. Dahoun, and D. Ruch. 2012. "Effect of Coated Rutile TiO_2 and Disazopyrazolone Dye Additives on Unvulcanized Styrene Butadiene Rubber During Photo-Ageing." *Journal of Engineering Materials and Technology* 134:010903. https://doi.org/10.1115/1.4005418

Morlat-Therias, S., E. Fanton, J.-L. Gardette, N.T. Dintcheva, F.P. La Mantia, and V. Malatesta. 2008. "Photochemical Stabilization of Linear Low-Density Polyethylene/ Clay Nanocomposites: Towards Durable Nanocomposites." *Polymer Degradation and Stability* 93:1776–80. https://doi.org/10.1016/j.polymdegradstab.2008.07.031

Ray, S., and R.P. Cooney. 2012. "Thermal Degradation of Polymer and Polymer Composites. Handbook of Environmental Degradation of Materials." In *Elsevier Science & Technology Books,* M. Kutz, editor, 213–42.

Sánchez-Valdés, S., J.G. Martínez Colunga, M.L. López-Quintanilla, I. Yañez Flores, M.L. García-Salazar, and C. González Cantu. 2008. "Preparation and UV Weathering of Polyethylene Nanocomposites." *Polymer Bulletin* 60:829–36. https://doi.org/10.1007/s00289-008-0911-0

Tcherbi-Narteh, A., M. Hosur, and S. Jeelani. 2014. "Influence of Nanoclay on the Durability of Woven Carbon/Epoxy Composites Subjected to Ultraviolet Radiation." *Mechanics of Advanced Materials and Structures* 21:222–36. https://doi.org/10.1080/15376494.2013.834097

Tomacheski, D., M. Pittol, A.P.M. Lopes, D.N. Simões, V.F. Ribeiro, and R.M.C. Santana. 2018a. "Effects of Weathering on Mechanical, Antimicrobial Properties and Biodegradation Process of Silver Loaded TPE Compounds." *Journal of Polymers and the Environment* 26:73–82. https://doi.org/10.1007/s10924-016-0927-8

Tomacheski, D., M. Pittol, D.N. Simões, V.F. Ribeiro, and R.M.C. Santana. 2018b. "Influence of Natural Ageing on Mechanical, Thermal and Antimicrobial Properties of Thermoplastic Elastomers Containing Silver Nanoparticles and Titanium Dioxide." *Polymer Bulletin* 75:3917–34. https://doi.org/10.1007/s00289-017-2245-2

Valadez-González, A., and L. Veleva. 2004. "Mineral Filler Influence on the Photo-Oxidation Mechanism Degradation of High Density Polyethylene. Part II: Natural Exposure Test." *Polymer Degradation and Stability* 83:139–48. https://doi.org/10.1016/S0141-3910(03)00246-5

Wojciechowski, K., G.Z. Zukowska, I. Korczagin, and P. Malanowski. 2015. "Effect of TiO_2 on UV Stability of Polymeric Binder Films Used in Waterborne Facade Paints." *Progress in Organic Coatings* 85:123–30. https://doi.org/10.1016/j.porgcoat.2015.04.002

Xu, S., J. Xu, and J. Zhang. 2018. "Surface Topography and Cooling Effects in Poly(vinyl Chloride) (PVC)/Titanium Dioxide (TiO_2) Composites Exposed to UV-Irradiation." *Iranian Polymer Journal* 27:1011–22. https://doi.org/10.1007/s13726-018-0671-0

Xu, Y., Y. Fang, K. Wang, W. Liu, and H. Fang. 2020. "Improving Durability of Glass Fiber Reinforced Polymer Composites by Incorporation of ZnO/OMMT Nanoparticles Subjected to UV Radiation and Hygrothermal Aging." *Materials Research Express* 7:035301. https://doi.org/10.1088/2053-1591/ab771b

Zainuddin, S., M.V. Hosur, Y. Zhou, A. Kumar, and S. Jeelani. 2009. "Durability Studies of Montmorillonite Clay Filled Epoxy Composites Under Different Environmental Conditions." *Materials Science and Engineering A* 507:117–23. https://doi.org/10.1016/j.msea.2008.11.058

Zhou, Y., W. He, Y. Wu, D. Xu, X. Chen, M. He, and J. Guo. 2019. "Influence of Thermo-Oxidative Aging on Flame Retardancy, Thermal Stability, and Mechanical Properties of Long Glass Fiber-Reinforced Polypropylene Composites Filled with Organic Montmorillonite and Intumescent Flame Retardant." *Journal of Fire Sciences* 37:176–89. https://doi.org/10.1177/0734904119833014

6 Halloysite Nanotubes-Filled Natural Rubber Composite
Mechanical and Other Related Properties

Nabil Hayeemasae
Prince of Songkla University, Pattani Campus
Hat Yai, Thailand

Hanafi Ismail
Universiti Sains Malaysia
Nibong Tebal, Malaysia

CONTENTS

6.1 Introduction 112
6.2 Preparation of the Composites 114
6.3 Preparation of MNR 115
6.4 Testing and Characterization of the Composites 115
    6.4.1 Cure Characteristics 115
    6.4.2 Fourier-Transform Infrared Spectroscopic Analysis (FTIR) 116
    6.4.3 Swelling Resistance 116
    6.4.4 Cross-link Density 116
    6.4.5 Dynamic Property 117
    6.4.6 Mechanical Properties 117
6.5 Effects of HNT Loading on the Properties of Natural Rubber
    Composites 118
    6.5.1 Curing Characteristic 118
    6.5.2 FTIR Analysis 119
    6.5.3 Swelling Resistance and Cross-link Density 120
    6.5.4 Dynamic Properties 121
    6.5.5 Mechanical Properties 121
6.6 Effect of Maleated Natural Rubber-Compatibilized NR/HNT
    Composites 124
    6.6.1 Functionalities of Maleated Natural Rubber 124
    6.6.2 Cure Characteristics 125

DOI: 10.1201/9781003220947-6

6.6.3 Dynamic Properties 127
6.6.4 Mechanical Properties 129
6.6.5 Scanning Electron Microscopy 129
6.7 Conclusions 130
References 131

6.1 INTRODUCTION

Today, rubber technology has become an important part of the industry and can be applied to various applications (Bokobza, 2007; Frogley *et al.*, 2003). Many types of rubber have been used to produce rubber products (Mooibroek and Cornish, 2000), which can be categorized into two groups, i.e., natural rubber (NR) extracted from tree and synthetic rubber derived from petroleum products (Eirich, 1978). NR is only biomass rubber and is extracted from tropical plants, namely *Hevea brasiliensis* (Kohjiya, 2013; Sethuraj and Mathew, 1992; Webster and Baulkwill, 1989). It is a truly renewable resource as the chemical structure consistently belongs to *cis*-1,4-polyisoprene, which has the ability to rapidly deform and recover due to high elasticity. However, the essential modulus and strength of this material can be improved by addition of filler and chemical modification and blending with other polymers. This results in advantageous properties, such as abrasion resistance, good hysteresis, high tensile capability, high green strength and high tear strength (Rodgers, 2004).

Incorporation of filler into rubber matrices leads to significant improvements in the physical, mechanical and electrical properties of the cross-linked rubber composites. The reinforcing effect is mainly supported by hydrodynamic interaction between filler and rubber surfaces (Medalia and Krauss, 1994). Traditionally, the carbon black and silica have been widely used as reinforcing filler in the rubber industry, and they are made by particle aggregation that cannot be well separated via thermomechanical mixing.

Over the last year, polymer scientists have attracted considerable attention by characterizing the presence of nanofillers (Lopez-Manchado *et al.*, 2004). These nanofillers are made by a primary particle with one or a few nanometers that can be individually dispersed in the polymer matrix such as carbon nanotubes (CNTs), clay mineral, zinc nanoparticles, and silica nanoparticles (Galimberti *et al.*, 2014). Incorporation of a small number of nanofillers into the rubber matrix has drawn considerable attention (Alexandre and Dubois, 2000). Significant improvement of physical, chemical, mechanical and thermal properties (Usuki *et al.*, 1993); gas permeability (Messersmith and Giannelis, 1995) and fire retardance (Gilman *et al.*, 1997) of rubber composites can be achieved through this technique.

It is also well known that fibrous or rod-like nanoparticles are a very promising class of reinforcement materials because of their large surface areas and high aspect ratio (Thakur *et al.*, 2009; Wang *et al.*, 2004). Clay is an inorganic filler with a molecular structure of layered silicate; it can be classified into various types, i.e., hectorite, montmorillonite, smectite (Ray and Okamoto, 2003), polygorskite (Neaman and Singer, 2004), and halloysite (Du *et al.*, 2010). Recently, incorporation of halloysite nanotubes (HNTs) into a polymer matrix has drawn considerable attention because it can reinforce offer unique reinforcing effects to different polymers. Halloysite has

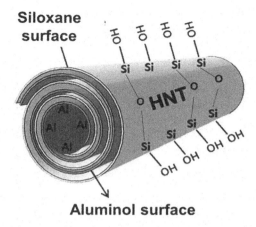

FIGURE 6.1 Schematic structure of HNT.

unique and versatile nanomaterials that are formed by surface weathering of aluminosilicate minerals ($Al_2Si_2O_5OH_4 \cdot nH_2O$), which are composed of aluminum, silicon, hydrogen and oxygen. HNT consists of ultra-tiny hollow tubes with diameters typically smaller than 100 nm, with lengths typically ranging from about 500 nm to over 1.2 microns. Figure 6.1 shows the schematic structure of an HNT, which has two different interlayer surfaces; the Al-OH group is located inside the tubes, whereas the outer surface of the HNT is covered by the siloxane group (Joussein et al., 2005; Liu et al., 2007). The lumen space inside the HNT can be intercalated and interacts with vulcanization ingredients and other materials (Pasbakhsh et al., 2010). The particles of HNT can adopt a variety of morphology, the most dominant of which is the fine, elongated tubule. The tubule may be long and thin, short and stubby or emerging from other tubes (Hedicke-Höchstötter et al., 2009; Joussein et al., 2005).

The key factors for the improving the performance of polymer-HNT nanocomposites are based on the homogeneous distribution and compatibility of HNT within the polymer matrix, and a strong interfacial adhesion between the matrix and tubular structures is of importance. As far as rubber is concerned, insufficient dispersion due to the high viscosity of the rubber and poor interaction between rubber and the HNT of nanofiller to elastomeric composites has resulted in low-performance properties. Homogeneous distribution and good compatibility of the HNT have been a potent challenge in rubber composites. Still, the major cause of concern is not only to achieve homogeneous distributions of HNT to prevent secondary agglomeration of the tubes and to disentangle the filler aggregates, but to ensure the compatibility between the rubber matrix and the inert surface of the HNT because the components have low interaction energy. Generally, there are several methods of mixing and functionalization that are commonly used in rubber nanocomposites in which the aim is only to improve the interaction of filler within the rubber matrix.

Currently, using modified NR as a compatibilizer or a matrix bearing functional groups that can interact with the reactive surfaces of inorganic fillers has been widely researched. Dileep and Avirah (2003) prepared carboxy-terminated liquid natural rubber (CTNR) by a photochemical reaction, which was then applied as a potential compatibilizer in silica-filled NR. The CTNR improved the tensile properties, aging and oil resistance due to an increase of the filler-rubber interaction in NR vulcanizates. Sengloyluan *et al.* (2014) reported the use of epoxidized natural rubber (ENR) as a compatibilizer in silica-filled NR compounds. The addition of ENR-51 at 7.5 phr shows the best overall properties with preferably the lowest filler-filler interaction as well as optimum mechanical and dynamic properties. Cataldo (2002) also reported the improved mechanical properties of silica-filled NR compounds through the use of ENR without a silane coupling agent due to the enhancement of the preferred filler-polymer interaction by a hydrogen bonding mechanism between epoxide groups of the ENR and silanol groups on the silica surface.

As the reactive surfaces of silica are quite similar to that of HNT, similar approaches were also applied for HNT-filled NR composites. Pasbakhsh *et al.* (2009) reported the use of ethylene propylene diene rubber (EPDM)-grafted maleic anhydride (MA) as a compatibilizer in HNT-filled EPDM compounds. The remarkable enhancement of mechanical properties was achieved on the addition of such a modified rubber. Recently, ENR with 50 mol% epoxide filled with HNT has been investigated by Ismail *et al.* (2013). It was observed that the tensile strength and other related properties were not enhanced by the use of ENR, assuming that excessive amounts of mole epoxy may interfere the interaction in the systems.

The aim of this study is to use HNT in the NR matrix where the modification of NR was also applied to improve the overall properties of the composites. With this idea, the interaction between certain groups available in proposed modifiers and the HNT can be extended; it is expected that improvement in compatibility and occasionally intercalation of the polymer inside HNT lumen and/or HNT interlayer to the composites would be obtained, which later results in enhancement of the reinforcing efficiency to HNT-filled NR composites.

6.2 PREPARATION OF THE COMPOSITES

The recipes for the preparation of the HNT-filled NR composites are given in Table 6.1. The HNT loading was varied to 0, 2.5, 5.0, 7.5 and 10 phr. The compounding was done by the Brabender Plasticorder at an initial mixing temperature of

TABLE 6.1

Formulation of HNT-Filled NR Composites

Raw Materials	Amount (phr)
STR 5L	100.0
Stearic acid	1.0
Zinc oxide	5.0
HNT	0–10
CBS	2.0
Sulfur	2.0

TABLE 6.2
Mixing Procedures of the Compounding Process

Operations	Time (min)
Mastication of rubber	1.0
Addition of stearic acid	0.5
Addition of zinc oxide	0.5
Addition of HNT	3.0
Addition of CBS	1.0
Addition of sulfur	1.0
Total	7.0

50°C with a rotor speed 60 rpm and later sheeted by the conventional two-roll mill to avoid premature vulcanization of excess heat generated during compounding. The mixing time and sequence were kept constant for all the mixes as given in Table 6.2. After sheeting, the sample of the respective compounds was later tested for its curing characteristics.

6.3 PREPARATION OF MNR

Grafting of MA e.g., 1–8 phr, onto NR was done by mixing the NR with MA in a Brabender Plasticorder at 145°C at a rotor speed of 60 rpm under normal atmosphere. The mixing lasted for 10 minutes. The resulting rubber was purified by reprecipitation only for the purpose of characterization by Fourier-transformed infrared spectroscopy (FTIR). The resulting maleated NR (MNR) was then purified to confirm grafting of MA onto NR. This was carried out by dissolving the rubber sample in toluene at room temperature for 24 hours and then at 60°C for 2 hours. The soluble part was collected and precipitated in acetone. The sample was dried in a vacuum oven at 40°C for 24 hours. The purified MNR was finally characterized for FTIR spectrum.

Table 6.3 lists the main ingredients used for preparing the rubber composites, in which the main matrix used was separated accordingly. The entire amount of additives was mixed in a Brabender Plastigraph® (EC Plus, Mixer W50EHT 3Z) and, just after the dumping, the compounds were passed through a two-roll mill to avoid excess heat. The compounds were then compressed into certain shapes using a hydraulic hot press, with the vulcanizing times obtained by a moving die rheometer (MDR) as described later.

6.4 TESTING AND CHARACTERIZATION OF THE COMPOSITES

6.4.1 CURE CHARACTERISTICS

Cure characteristic of NR and NR/HNT composite compounds were measured at 150°C via Rheoline Mini MDR Lite (Prescott instruments Ltd, UK) following ASTM D5289. The samples were tested at a frequency of 1.67 Hz for 20 minutes.

TABLE 6.3

Compounding Ingredients Used for Preparation of the Composites

Ingredients	Amount (phr)
NR	90
MNR[a]	10
ZnO	5
Stearic acid	1
CBS	2
Sulfur	2
HNT	10

[a] MNR used was compounded separately according to the MA content.

The testing parameters included the minimum torque (M_L), maximum torque (M_H), torque difference (M_H–M_L), scorch time (ts_2) and cure time (tc_{90}).

6.4.2 FOURIER-TRANSFORM INFRARED SPECTROSCOPIC ANALYSIS (FTIR)

The FTIR model TENSOR27 with a combination of platinum attenuated total reflection (ATR) plate (Bruker Steel Corporation, Houston, TX) was used to characterize the chemistry and chemical interaction in HNT and NR/HNT composites. The raw rubbers were dissolved in chloroform. To carry out the measurement, the dissolved rubbers were spread out to make a thin film on the KBr plate, dried and further tested. For pure HNT powder and NR/HNT composite, the samples were placed onto the smart durable single bounce diamond in the ATR cell. Each spectrum was later recorded in transmission mode by averaging 32 scans per spectrum with 4-cm^{-1} resolution from 4000 to 550 cm^{-1}.

6.4.3 SWELLING RESISTANCE

For swelling measurement, the samples with a dimension of $10 \times 10 \times 2$ mm^3 were weighted and immersed in the toluene at room temperature for 168 hours (7 days) according to ASTM D471. Then, the respective samples were taken out as swollen samples, which were later removed from the solvent at the surface by using tissue paper. The swelling resistance was expressed in terms of the swelling percentage, which was calculated as follows:

$$\text{Degree of swelling}\,(\%) = \left(\frac{W_f - W_i}{W_i} \right) \times 100 \tag{6.1}$$

6.4.4 CROSS-LINK DENSITY

The cross-link density of the samples was determined by the equilibrium toluene swelling method as described in ASTM D6814, which normally took 72 hours

Halloysite-Filled NR Composite: Mechanical and Other Related Properties   117

(Swapna *et al.*, 2014). The composite samples were cut into circular shapes and weighted before immersing in toluene. The cross-link density (ν) can be calculated using the modified Flory-Rehner equation (Ichazo *et al.*, 2011).

$$\nu = \frac{1}{2M_c} \tag{6.2}$$

$$M_c = \frac{\rho V_0 \left(V_r^{1/3} - V_r/2 \right)}{\ln\left(1 - V_r\right) + V_r + \mu V_r^2} \tag{6.3}$$

where M_c is the number-average molecular weight of the polymer chains between cross-links, μ is the polymer-solvent interaction parameter ($\mu = 0.42$ for NR-toluene), ρ is the density of the test sample, V_0 is the molar volume of solvent ($V_0 = 106.2$ cm³/mol) and V_r is the volume fraction in the swollen specimen, which can be defined (Marykutty *et al.*, 2003) as follows:

$$V_r = \frac{(D - FT)\rho^{-1}}{(D - FT)\rho^{-1} + A_0\rho_s^{-1}} \tag{6.4}$$

where T is the weight of the test sample, D is the weight of the de-swollen test sample, F is the weight fraction of insoluble components, A_0 is the weight of the absorbed solvent given for the swelling increment, ρ is the density of the test sample and ρ_s is the density of the solvent (0.886 g/cm³).

6.4.5 DYNAMIC PROPERTY

The Payne effect or filler-filler interaction of the cured NR/HNT composites was studied by using a rubber process analyzer model D-RPA 3000 (MonTech Werkstoffprüfmaschinen GmbH, Buchen, Germany). The composite sample was cured at the respective temperature given for the curing test to reach maximum torque (8 minutes) and the temperature was cooled to 60°C. The Payne effect was later performed at 60°C, frequency 10 Hz with varying strains in the range of 0.56–90%. The difference of storage moduli at low strain (0.56%) and high strain (90%) is reported.

6.4.6 MECHANICAL PROPERTIES

Mechanical properties of composite samples, including the tensile strength, elongation at break, tear strength and hardness were examined in this study. The tensile properties were conducted following to ASTM D412 standard test. The samples were cut into dumbbell shape type C. In the case of tear strength, the testing was carried out according to ASTM D624. The angle shape test sample was prepared by using Die C. The harness property of the composite samples was measured using the Toyoseiki hardness tester (Toyoseiki Co., Ltd., Japan). The samples were molded and shaped as per ASTM D2240. The measurement was later determined by means of durometer hardness with shore A-type standard.

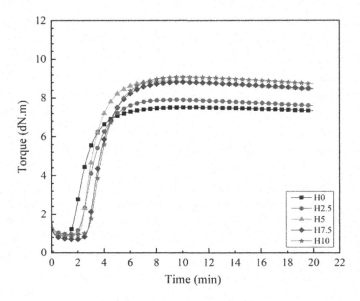

FIGURE 6.2 Curing curves of NR/HNT composites at various HNT loadings.

6.5 EFFECTS OF HNT LOADING ON THE PROPERTIES OF NATURAL RUBBER COMPOSITES

6.5.1 Curing Characteristic

Figure 6.2 shows curing curves of the NR/HNT composites. The data obtained from curing curves are tabulated in Table 6.4. The scorch time (ts_2) and curing time (tc_{90}) gradually increase and cure rate index (CRI) decreases with HNT loading. These changes are simply due to the surface chemistry of HNT. The outer surfaces of HNT are covered by silanol and siloxane functionalities. These functionalities are known to adsorb certain vulcanizing agents, particularly accelerators (López-Manchado

TABLE 6.4
The Raw Data Obtained from Curing Curves of NR/HNT Composites at Various HNT Loadings

HNT Content (phr)	ts_2 (min)	tc_{90} (min)	M_L (dN·m)	M_H (dN·m)	(M_H–M_L) (dN·m)	CRI (min^{-1})
0	1.92	4.04	0.92	8.19	7.28	47.28
2.5	2.51	4.77	0.97	8.62	7.65	44.35
5	2.68	4.96	0.88	8.65	7.77	43.92
7.5	2.82	5.14	0.78	8.76	7.99	43.10
10	3.20	5.74	0.92	9.17	8.25	39.45

et al., 2003). Hence, longer ts_2 and tc_{90} are observed when HNT is added. Rooj et al. (2010) reported that the incorporation of silicates into the rubber matrix delays the vulcanization process, which is usually ascribed to the adsorption between silicates and vulcanization additives, such as accelerators.

Maximum torque (M_H) represents the stiffness or shear modulus of the completely vulcanized specimens at the curing temperature. M_H tends to increase consistently with HNT loading. HNT is a rigid powder at the test temperature (Nabil et al., 2012) and can reduce the fraction of deformable rubber in the compounds (Ansarifar et al., 2005; Ismail et al., 2011). The addition of HNT restricts the flow of rubber in the compounds, resulting in an increase in M_H. Similar observations pertain to delta torque (M_H–M_L), which is a measure of the difference between the stiffness (or shear moduli) of the fully vulcanized and the unvulcanized specimens, taken at the lowest point of the vulcanizing curve (Berahman et al., 2016)

6.5.2 FTIR Analysis

Figure 6.3 presents the FTIR spectra in the wave number range 4000-550 cm^{-1} for HNT powder, raw NR and NR containing 2.5, 5, 7.5 and 10 phr of HNT. For HNT powder, the absorption bands around 3694 and 3622 cm^{-1} are specifically assigned to the stretching vibrations of inner surface hydroxyl groups and outer hydroxyls group

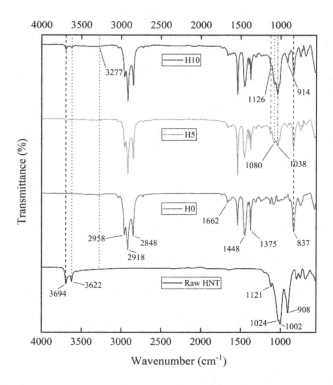

FIGURE 6.3 Infrared spectra of NR/HNT composites at various HNT loadings.

(Du et al., 2010; Kadi et al., 2012; Pasbakhsh et al., 2009, 2010; Yuan et al., 2008). The presence of these hydroxyl groups causes absorbed moisture peaks detected at 3200–3400 cm^{-1}. The distinct peak at 908 cm^{-1} is attributed to the deformation of inner hydroxyl groups of Al-OH libations, whereas the peaks at 1024 and 1002 cm^{-1} are associated with stretching of Si–O (Kadi et al., 2012).

As for the NR/HNT composites, the characteristic peaks are found at around 1662, 1448, 1375, and 837 cm^{-1}, associated with the stretching vibrations of C=C bonds, bending vibrations of CH$_2$ and CH$_3$ groups and out of plane deformations of =C–H groups, respectively. On inclusion of HNT and further increase in the HNT loading have increased the peak intensities of Si–O and Al–OH vibrations, confirming the presence of HNT in the NR matrix.

6.5.3 Swelling Resistance and Cross-link Density

Figure 6.4 shows the effect of HNT loading on the swelling percentage and cross-link density of NR composites. The solvent uptake to the sample tends to decrease with the increment of HNT loading levels. This indicates the improved interaction between NR and HNT, which decreases rubber chain mobility (Jia et al., 2016). Moreover, HNT acts as barrier preventing solvent molecules, resulting in less penetration by the solvent into the NR molecules (Ismail et al., 2013). As for cross-link density, it was found that an increase in the HNT loading resulted in a decrease of the cross-link density of NR/HNT composites. Generally, the swelling resistance has the opposite correlation to cross-link density, but this was not here. This might be due to the tubular structure of HNT that made more NR chains embedded inside the tube while HNT increased, causing a decrease of swollen rubber (V_r) and cross-link density of NR/HNT composites (Jia et al., 2016).

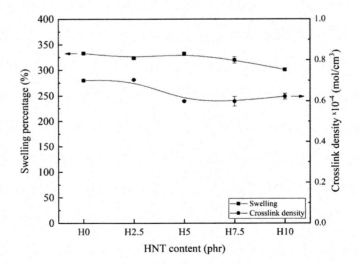

FIGURE 6.4 Swelling percentage and cross-link density of NR/HNT composites at various HNT loadings.

Halloysite-Filled NR Composite: Mechanical and Other Related Properties 121

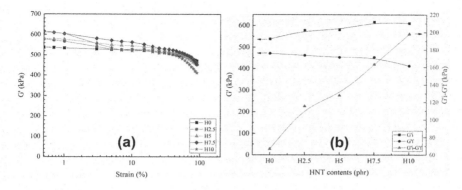

FIGURE 6.5 (a) Strain dependence on storage modulus, G' and storage modulus at strain amplitude of G'$_i$ (0.5%) and G'$_f$ (90%), and its differentiation (G'$_i$-G'$_f$) (b) of NR/HNT composites at various HNT loadings.

6.5.4 Dynamic Properties

Dynamic properties of the composites were carried out using a rubber process analyzer. This is to investigate the storage modulus and the Payne effect. Figure 6.5(a) illustrates the storage modulus and the Payne effect of NR/HNT composites. The storage modulus of gum NR showed constant values at the low strain region but slightly decreased when the strain was higher than 50%. This common phenomenon happens to the viscoelastic material due to the molecular stability of the rubber. In addition, the Payne effect (see Figure 6.5(b)) of all composites was also estimated from the differences between the storage modulus at low strain and high strain amplitude (Kaewsakul et al., 2014; Payne and Whittaker, 1971). The levels of Payne effect of unfilled NR and filled NR were found to be 66.80, 115.74, 128.02, 163.21 and 198.06 kPa, respectively. Increasing such values indicates a higher Payne effect, which is responsible for the filler-filler interaction (Rooj et al., 2013) and physical adsorption of NR onto the surface of HNT (Jia et al., 2016). A drastic change of Payne effect was observed, particularly at 7.5 and 10 phr of HNT, which is attributed to the large agglomeration of HNT in the composites.

6.5.5 Mechanical Properties

Stress-strain curves of the NR/HNT composites are shown in Figure 6.6. Typical strain-induced crystallization of raw NR and of NR containing 2.5, 5, 7.5 and 10 phr of HNT is seen in the stress-strain curves. Initially, stress increases gradually as a function of applied strain, then increases sharply due to strain-induced crystallization of NR during tensile stretching. The stress and strain values appear to differ between the raw NR and the NR/HNT composites. From the stress-strain curves, it is possible to estimate the change point of the strain for each of the samples. Clearly, the strain at the onset of the stress upturn for the NR containing HNT is much lower than that of the raw NR, and the onset strain decreases with increasing HNT loading. This observation indicates that the addition of HNT affects the stress-strain

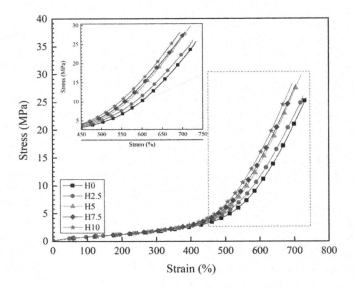

FIGURE 6.6 Stress-strain dependence of HNT-filled NR composites with different HNT loadings.

behavior of NR and lowers the strain at the onset of the stress upturn. The relationship between the mechanical strength and strain-induced crystallization behavior is discussed in a later section.

Figure 6.7 shows the tensile, tear strength and hardness properties of the NR/HNT composites. The raw data is also shown in Table 6.5. The tensile strength improves up to 5 phr of HNT, but above this level the strength is reduced. For tear property, the strength of NR/HNT composites improve slightly when HNT content was up to 5 phr as well, and then remain constant irrespective of HNT loadings. HNTs have a very high elastic modulus and aspect ratio (Du et al., 2010), so they are frequently combined with various rubbers to increase their mechanical strength as composites. The particle sizes of HNT are very small, resulting in strong interfacial and intertubular interactions in the NR matrix.

Such interactions could induce tightly immobilized NR chains and form a solid bridge between filler and rubber (Zhong et al., 2017). On stretching, the tightly immobilized part subsequently anchors and forms a proper stress transfer, leading to an enhancement of the mechanical strength. The strength enhancement could also be due to the special characteristics of HNT themselves, such as low hydroxyl content, tubular structure and unique crystal structure (Du et al., 2010). These characteristics could allow the HNT to disperse well in the NR matrix and improve the stress transfer in the NR matrix (Du et al., 2010; Ismail et al., 2008). It was already reported in the literature (Ismail et al., 2011, 2013; Rooj et al., 2010) that the enhancement of tensile strength of rubber/HNT composites contributed to a good dispersion of HNT within rubber matrix, which made strong interfacial and intertubular interaction between HNT and rubber.

Halloysite-Filled NR Composite: Mechanical and Other Related Properties

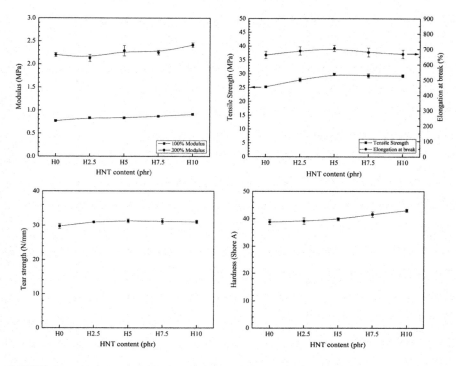

FIGURE 6.7 Modulus at 100% and 300%, tensile strength and elongation at break, tear strength and hardness of HNT-filled NR composites with different HNT loadings.

A similar trend is also seen for the elongation at break of the NR/HNT composites. The reduction in tensile strength and elongation at break with loadings beyond 5 phr of HNT is simply due to filler agglomeration (Sadequl *et al.*, 1999). When more HNTs are integrated into the NR matrix, the HNT particles tend to interact with each other. These so-called filler–filler interactions (Ismail *et al.*, 2011, 2013)

TABLE 6.5
Modulus at 100%, 300%, Tensile Strength, Elongation at Break, Tear Strength and Hardness Values of NR/HNT Composites at Various HNT Loadings

HNT Content (phr)	100% Modulus (MPa)	300% Modulus (MPa)	Tensile Strength (MPa)	Elongation at Break (%)	Tear Strength (kN/m)	Hardness (Shore A)
0	0.77 ± 0.01	2.20 ± 0.04	25.29 ± 0.31	662 ± 24	29.77 ± 0.72	38.8 ± 0.9
2.5	0.83 ± 0.02	2.13 ± 0.07	27.83 ± 0.64	689 ± 26	30.94 ± 0.15	39.2 ± 1.2
5	0.83 ± 0.02	2.29 ± 0.11	29.88 ± 0.37	706 ± 20	31.30 ± 0.55	39.8 ± 0.6
7.5	0.87 ± 0.02	2.25 ± 0.05	29.32 ± 0.74	680 ± 29	31.14 ± 0.78	41.6 ± 1.0
10	0.91 ± 0.02	2.42 ± 0.05	29.26 ± 0.51	668 ± 28	31.04 ± 0.51	43.0 ± 0.6

can be seen in the scanning electron microscopy (SEM) micrographs. The addition of HNT also results in a stress increase at 100% (M100) and 300% (M300) strains and hardness property. As more HNT get into the rubber, the elasticity of the rubber is reduced, resulting in more rigid, stiffer and harder composites (Bokobza, 2004). This observation is supported by the changes in M_H and M_H–M_L reported in the preceding section.

6.6 EFFECT OF MALEATED NATURAL RUBBER-COMPATIBILIZED NR/HNT COMPOSITES

6.6.1 FUNCTIONALITIES OF MALEATED NATURAL RUBBER

The FTIR spectrum of MNR at various MA contents is shown in Figure 6.8 where the peak assignments are listed in Table 6.6. As for the unmodified NR, the characteristic peaks are found at around 2960, 2920 and 2850 cm^{-1}, indicating the CH stretching vibrations of carbon-carbon double bond in NR. Other important peaks are at 166 and 835 cm^{-1}, associated with the stretching vibrations of C=C bonds and out-of-plane deformations of =C–H groups, respectively. When NR was grafted by MA, a broad and intense characteristic band at a wave number of 1787 cm^{-1} and a weak absorption band at 1875 cm^{-1} were observed. These bands can be assigned to grafted anhydride, which are due to symmetric (strong) and asymmetric (weak) C=O stretching vibrations of succinic anhydride rings, respectively. These bands were responsible for the presence of succinic anhydride groups grafted onto NR molecules. Moreover, there was an important peak captured at wave number of 1723 cm^{-1} due to the formation of carbonyl groups of opened ring structure succinic anhydride. This is because a high level of grafted MA tends to react with moisture during

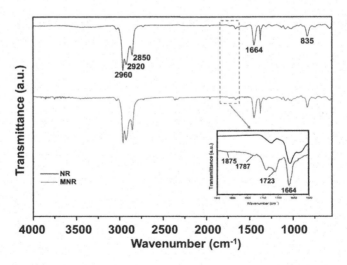

FIGURE 6.8 FTIR spectrum at wave numbers of 1900–1600 cm^{-1} of NR and MNR at 8 phr of MA.

TABLE 6.6
The Observed Peaks and Respective Assignments of MNR

Wave Numbers (cm⁻¹)	Assignments
2960	–C–H stretching vibration of carbon-carbon double bond
2920	CH$_2$ stretching vibration of –C=C–
2850	CH stretching vibration of –C=C–
1875	C=O stretch of succinic anhydride (weak)
1787	C=O stretch of polymeric anhydride (weak)
1723	C=O stretch, carbonyl group
1664	C=C stretching vibration
835	Out-of-plane bending vibration of C–H in the –CH=CH– group

drying and storage. The peaks seen in this study were quite similar to the previous results in the literature (Nakason et al., 2004; Sahakaro and Beraheng, 2008).

6.6.2 CURE CHARACTERISTICS

The curing curves of the NR/HNT in the absence and presence of MNR as a compatibilizer are shown in Figure 6.9 and the summarized results are listed in Table 6.7. The minimum torque (M$_L$) slightly decreased with the MA content in MNR, and M$_L$ is known to be a representative of a compound's viscosity. Introducing the MNR causes an increase the M$_L$. During the preparation of MNR, the maleated cross-links can be formed, which has led to increasing a gel part in MNR. This later resulted in an increase in the compound's viscosity in the composite. A similar observation was also made by Nakason et al. (2004) and Sahakaro and Beraheng (2008); they also

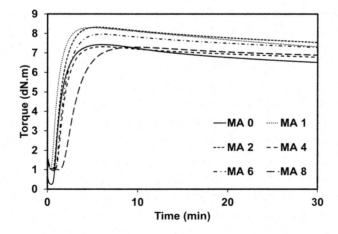

FIGURE 6.9 Curing curves of NR/HNT composites in the absence and presence of MNR as a compatibilizer.

TABLE 6.7
Curing Characteristics of NR/HNT Composites in the Absence and Presence of MNR as Compatibilizer

Compound	M_L (dN·m)	M_H (dN·m)	M_H-M_L (dN·m)	t_{S1} (min)	t_{c90} (min)	CRI (min^{-1})
MA 0	0.25	7.43	7.18	0.84	2.81	50.76
MA 1	1.03	8.31	7.28	0.62	2.24	61.73
MA 2	0.98	8.33	7.35	0.90	2.83	51.81
MA 4	0.98	7.97	6.99	1.25	3.16	52.36
MA 6	1.00	7.30	6.30	1.16	3.24	48.08
MA 8	0.95	7.33	6.38	2.09	5.20	32.15

explained the same reason behind such a finding. Further increase in MA content has given M_L more or less the same values. However, it is interesting to highlight that M_H and M_H-M_L were observed differently. Both values increased up to 2 phr of MA contained in MNR and then decreased after this level. The increments of these values indicate a higher extent of cross-linking and/or interaction between the NR and HNT. The proposed interaction between NR and HNT is illustrated in Figure 6.10. There are two possible interactions formed in the composite either through opened ring and/or cyclic structures. Grafting of the succinic anhydride groups onto NR molecules of the MNR enabled an increase in polarity of rubber and made it compatible with the HNT. Pasbakhsh *et al.* (2009) also proposed a similar interaction forming from the hydroxyl groups of HNT and succinic anhydride groups of EPDM-g-MA. Considering the decrease of M_H and M_H-M_L, it could be due to the higher level of self-cross-link (maleated cross-link) in the MNR, especially at a higher level

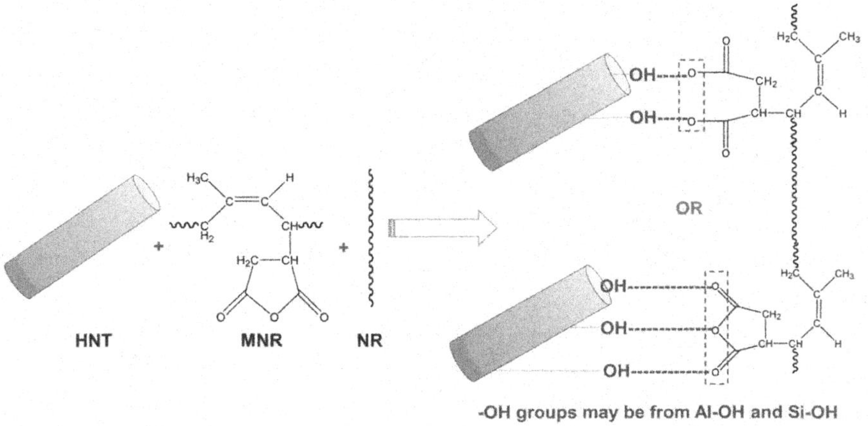

FIGURE 6.10 Possible interaction between MNR and HNT.

of MA. As more cross-link was formed, less succinic anhydride groups were available to mediate the interaction between NR and HNT.

As for the vulcanizing reaction, introducing the MNR lengthens the vulcanizing process. This was monitored through the ts$_2$ and tc$_{90}$; it is simply due the presence of acids from ring opening of succinic anhydride groups. Any chemical substance that gives the rubber compound more acidity will lead to an adsorption of accelerator and delay the reactivity of accelerators (Coran, 2003; Nabil et al., 2011).

6.6.3 DYNAMIC PROPERTIES

Dynamic properties of the composites were carried out using a rubber process analyzer to investigate the storage modulus and the Payne effect. Figures 6.11 and 6.12 illustrate the storage modulus and the Payne effect of NR/HNT composites in the absence and presence of MNR as a compatibilizer. It can be seen that the storage modulus of all compounds showed constant values at the low strain region but slightly decrease when the strain is higher than 50%. This common phenomenon happens to the viscoelastic material due to the molecular stability of the rubber. In addition to that, the Payne effects of all composites were also estimated from the difference between the storage modulus at low strain and high strain amplitude (Payne and Whittaker, 1971; Rattanasom et al., 2007). The level of Payne effect of the NR/HNT compound was found to be 231.49 where the Payne effect was comparatively reduced against the MA contents, i.e., 182.47, 157.86, 176.71, 161.14 and 135.52, respectively, for MA contents at 1–8 phr consecutively. This is a good indication that the interaction between NR and HNT was improved. The lower Payne effect is responsible because of the lower filler-filler interaction (Kaewsakul et al., 2014). This finding is in very good agreement with the state of cure observed in the previous study.

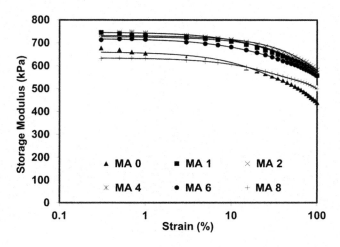

FIGURE 6.11 Storage modulus of NR/HNT composites in the absence and presence of MNR as a compatibilizer.

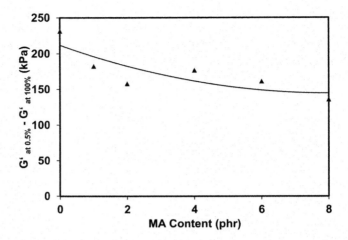

FIGURE 6.12 Payne effect of NR/HNT composites in the absence and presence of MNR as compatibilizer.

Dependence of damping characteristic (tan δ) as functions of strain is shown in Figure 6.13. Considering the composite without the addition of MNR as a compatibilizer, the highest damping value was observed. High damping indicates low elastic response over dynamic conditions. However, when the MNR was added as a compatibilizer, it is obvious that the composites exhibited low damping characteristics, suggesting that a considerable degree of mobility was exhibited. This is simply due to the better interaction between rubber and filler through the use of MNR as the main rubber matric in the system. The compatibility of non-polar rubber and HNT increases an interfacial adhesion and results in an improved elastic property of the composites.

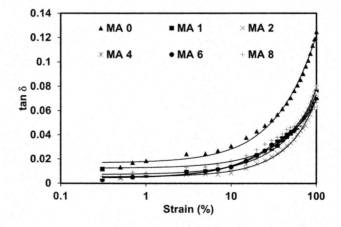

FIGURE 6.13 Damping characteristic (tan δ) of NR/HNT composites in the absence and presence of MNR as a compatibilizer.

Halloysite-Filled NR Composite: Mechanical and Other Related Properties **129**

TABLE 6.8
Mechanical of NR/HNT Composites in the Absence and Presence of MNR as Compatibilizer

Compound	Tensile Strength (MPa)	Elongation at Break (%)	M100 (MPa)	M300 (MPa)	Tear Strength (N/mm)
MA 0	18.31 ± 1.85	640.36 ± 16.67	1.00 ± 0.01	2.50 ± 0.05	31.8 ± 0.20
MA 1	20.33 ± 1.47	640.67 ± 13.13	0.98 ± 0.02	2.44 ± 0.02	34.2 ± 0.31
MA 2	22.05 ± 1.41	647.71 ± 41.42	1.00 ± 0.01	2.56 ± 0.01	35.7 ± 0.26
MA 4	21.89 ± 1.50	637.00 ± 24.99	1.00 ± 0.01	2.62 ± 0.03	35.1 ± 0.22
MA 6	18.70 ± 0.97	624.18 ± 20.42	0.95 ± 0.02	2.46 ± 0.02	35.0 ± 0.16
MA 8	17.23 ± 0.26	561.12 ± 25.37	1.08 ± 0.02	3.00 ± 0.02	34.1 ± 0.55

6.6.4 MECHANICAL PROPERTIES

To confirm more on the compatibility of NR and HNT, mechanical properties are a good indication of compatibility. Tensile properties and tear strength of the NR/HNT composites in the absence and presence of MNR as a compatibilizer are listed in Table 6.8. Tensile strength was found to be higher when MNR was added to the composite and the value increased up to 2 phr of MA content. Higher tensile strength is responsible for high levels of rubber-filler interaction. Such increment is definitely attributed to an improved degree of compatibility between rubber and HNT in the presence of MNR, which was described earlier in Figure 6.10. A further increment of MA content also leads to a reduction of tensile strength due to the formation of a maleate network as discussed earlier (Ismail *et al.*, 2005). As a result, the stress concentration point was observed at the interacting point, creating catastrophic failure in the rubber samples while stretching. This also caused the same phenomenon to the elongation at break of the composites.

The strong interaction of the NR and HNT has made the tensile modulus (stresses at 100% and 300% strains) higher especially at high concentration of MA. As more MA was grafted to the NR, a possibility of self-crosslink was formed, resulting in stiffer and harder composites. In addition to this, the tear strength was also carried out to monitor the strength of the composites. Similar optimum content of MA was also observed for the tear strength. Again, this is simply to an improvement of the compatibility between the NR and HNT, higher energy was then highly required to tear the sample.

6.6.5 SCANNING ELECTRON MICROSCOPY

The fractured samples after testing the tensile properties were used to observe the microfractured surface. The image obtained can be used to correlate with the tensile strength. The tensile fractured surfaces of the NR/HNT composites in the absence and presence of MNR as a compatibilizer are shown in Figure 6.14. Figure 6.14(a) and (b) show the tensile fractured surface of the composites with the control formulation and the use of MNR as a compatibilizer. Better dispersion of HNT was seen

130 | Mineral-Filled Polymer Composites

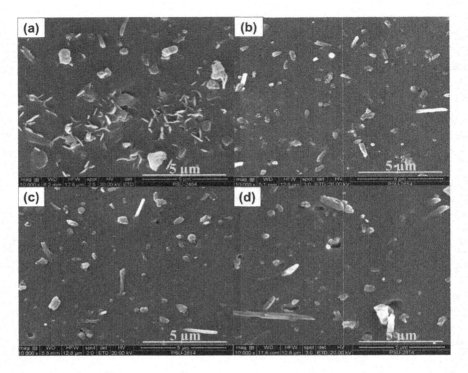

FIGURE 6.14 SEM images obtained from tensile fractured surfaces of NR/HNT composites in the absence and presence of MNR as a compatibilizer: (a) MA 2 phr, (b) MA 4 phr and (c and d) MA 8 phr (d). 10,000× magnification.

when the MNR was added to the composite. This may be attributed to an improved compatibility between NR and HNT. Higher compatibility has reduced the possibility of HNT to interact with each other. As a result, the dispersion was improved, leading to an increase in resistance to crack propagation, thus giving higher tensile strength.

However, when a higher amount of MA was used in the MNR, e.g., MA contents at 6 and 8 phr, respectively (see Figure 6.14(c) and (d)), the HNTs tended to agglomerate with each other due to their filler-filler interaction as observed from the higher Payne effect. Such agglomeration is simply due to low compatibility between NR and HNT caused by the self-cross-linked MNR. Similar observations were previously reported on changes of microfractured surfaces against the addition of other filled NR composites in the presence of a compatibilizer (Rooj et al., 2013; Waesateh et al., 2018).

6.7 CONCLUSIONS

The following conclusions can be drawn:

- The addition of HNT resulted in a delayed scorch time and curing time, and maximum torque and delta torque increased consistently with HNT loading.

Halloysite-Filled NR Composite: Mechanical and Other Related Properties 131

- The optimum tensile strength and elongation at break were exhibited at 5 phr HNT loading, due to better dispersion of HNT at this level.
- MNR also acted as a good compatibilizer to the NR/HNT composites. The overall properties of the composites were clearly enhanced when MNR was used as a compatibilizer. MNR has a very special functional group that can form hydrogen bonding with the hydroxyl groups available on the HNT inner and outer surface.
- The presence of MNR also enhanced the mechanical properties such as tensile strength, modulus and tear strength of the composites, which is verified by the reduction of Payne effect observed from the dynamic properties.

REFERENCES

Alexandre, Michael, and Philippe Dubois. 2000. "Polymer-layered silicate nanocomposites: preparation, properties and uses of a new class of materials." *Materials Science and Engineering: R: Reports* 28 (1–2): 1–63.

Ansarifar, A, A Azhar, N Ibrahim, SF Shiah, and JMD Lawton. 2005. "The use of a silanised silica filler to reinforce and crosslink natural rubber." *International Journal of Adhesion and Adhesives* 25 (1): 77–86.

Berahman, Reyhaneh, Maryam Raiati, Majid Mehrabi Mazidi, and Seyed Mohamad Reza Paran. 2016. "Preparation and characterization of vulcanized silicone rubber/halloysite nanotube nanocomposites: Effect of matrix hardness and HNT content." *Materials & Design* 104: 333–345.

Bokobza, Liliane. 2004. "The reinforcement of elastomeric networks by fillers." *Macromolecular Materials and Engineering* 289 (7): 607–621.

Bokobza, Liliane. 2007. "Multiwall carbon nanotube elastomeric composites: A review." *Polymer* 48 (17): 4907–4920.

Cataldo, Franco. 2002. "Preparation of silica-based rubber compounds without the use of a silane coupling agent through the use of epoxidized natural rubber." *Macromolecular Materials and Engineering* 287 (5): 348–352.

Coran, AY. 2003. "Chemistry of the vulcanization and protection of elastomers: A review of the achievements." *Journal of Applied Polymer Science* 87 (1): 24–30.

Dileep, U, and Avirah, SA. 2003. "Studies on carboxy-terminated natural rubber in filled NR and NR latex vulcanizates." *Iranian Polymer Journal* 12(6): 441–448.

Du, Mingliang, Baochun Guo, and Demin Jia. 2010. "Newly emerging applications of halloysite nanotubes: A review." *Polymer International* 59 (5): 574–582.

Eirich, FR. 1978. *Science and technology of rubber*, Academic Press, New York.

Frogley, Mark D., Diana Ravich, and H. Daniel Wagner. 2003. "Mechanical properties of carbon nanoparticle-reinforced elastomers." *Composites Science and Technology* 63 (11): 1647–1654.

Galimberti, Maurizio, Vineet Kumar, Michele Coombs, Valeria Cipolletti, Silvia Agnelli, Stefano Pandini, and Lucia Conzatti. 2014. "Filler networking of a nanographite with a high shape anisotropy and synergism with carbon black in poly (1, 4-cis-isoprene)– based nanocomposites." *Rubber Chemistry and Technology* 87 (2): 197–218.

Gilman, Jeffrey W., Takashi Kashiwagi, and Joseph D. Lichtenhan. 1997. "Nanocomposites: A revolutionary new flame retardant approach." *Sampe Journal* 33: 40–46.

Hedicke-Höchstötter, Katrin, Goy Teck Lim, and Volker Altstädt. 2009. "Novel polyamide nanocomposites based on silicate nanotubes of the mineral halloysite." *Composites Science and Technology* 69 (3–4): 330–334.

Ichazo, Miren N., Carmen Albano, Marianella Hernández, Jeanette González, and Jenny Peña. 2011. "Characterization of natural rubber/cassava starch/maleated natural rubber formulations." *Revista Latinoamericana de Metalurgia y Materiales* 31 (1): 71–84.

Ismail, H, Pooria Pasbakhsh, MN Ahmad Fauzi, and A Abu Bakar. 2008. "Morphological, thermal and tensile properties of halloysite nanotubes filled ethylene propylene diene monomer (EPDM) nanocomposites." *Polymer Testing* 27 (7): 841–850.

Ismail, Hanafi, Arjulizan Rusli, and Azura A. Rashid. 2005. "Maleated natural rubber as a coupling agent for paper sludge filled natural rubber composites." *Polymer Testing* 24 (7): 856–862.

Ismail, H, SZ Salleh, and Z Ahmad. 2013. "Properties of halloysite nanotube (HNT) filled SMR L and ENR 50 nanocomposites." *International Journal of Polymeric Materials and Polymeric Biomaterials* 62 (6): 314–322.

Ismail, Hanafi, Siti Zuliana Salleh, and Zulkifli Ahmad. 2011. "Curing characteristics, mechanical, thermal, and morphological properties of halloysite nanotubes (HNTs)-filled natural rubber nanocomposites." *Polymer-Plastics Technology and Engineering* 50 (7): 681–688.

Jia, Zhixin, Tiwen Xu, Shuyan Yang, Yuanfang Luo, and Demin Jia. 2016. "Interfacial mechano-chemical grafting in styrene-butadiene rubber/halloysite nanotubes composites." *Polymer Testing* 54: 29–39.

Joussein, E, S Petit, J Churchman, B Theng, D Righi, and B Delvaux. 2005. "Halloysite clay minerals—a review." *Clay Minerals* 40 (4): 383–426.

Kadi, Samir, Salima Lellou, Kheira Marouf-Khelifa, Jacques Schott, Isabelle Gener-Batonneau, and Amine Khelifa. 2012. "Preparation, characterisation and application of thermally treated Algerian halloysite." *Microporous and Mesoporous Materials* 158: 47–54.

Kaewsakul, Wisut, Kannika Sahakaro, Wilma K Dierkes, and Jacobus WM Noordermeer. 2014. "Cooperative effects of epoxide functional groups on natural rubber and silane coupling agents on reinforcing efficiency of silica." *Rubber Chemistry and Technology* 87 (2): 291–310.

Kohjiya, S. 2013. *History of natural rubber*, Kyoto University Press, Kyoto, Japan.

Liu, Mingxian, Baochun Guo, Mingliang Du, and D Jia. 2007. "Drying induced aggregation of halloysite nanotubes in polyvinyl alcohol/halloysite nanotubes solution and its effect on properties of composite film." *Applied Physics A* 88 (2): 391–395.

López-Manchado, MA, M Arroyo, B Herrero, and J Biagiotti. 2003. "Vulcanization kinetics of natural rubber–organoclay nanocomposites." *Journal of Applied Polymer Science* 89 (1): 1–15.

Lopez-Manchado, MA, B Herrero, and M Arroyo. 2004. "Organoclay–natural rubber nanocomposites synthesized by mechanical and solution mixing methods." *Polymer International* 53 (11): 1766–1772.

Marykutty, CV, G Mathew, EJ Mathew, and Sabu Thomas. 2003. "Studies on novel binary accelerator system in sulfur vulcanization of natural rubber." *Journal of Applied Polymer Science* 90 (12): 3173–3182.

Medalia, A. and Krauss, G. 1994. "Reinforcement of elastomers by particulate filler." *Science and technology of rubber*, Academic Press, San Diego, pp. 387–418.

Messersmith, Phillip B, and Emmanuel P Giannelis. 1995. "Synthesis and barrier properties of poly (ε-caprolactone)-layered silicate nanocomposites." *Journal of Polymer Science Part A: Polymer Chemistry* 33 (7): 1047–1057.

Mooibroek, H, and K Cornish. 2000. "Alternative sources of natural rubber." *Applied Microbiology and Biotechnology* 53 (4): 355–365.

Nabil, H, H Ismail, and AR Azura. 2011. "Recycled polyethylene terephthalate filled natural rubber compounds: effects of filler loading and types of matrix." *Journal of Elastomers & Plastics* 43 (5): 429–449.

Nabil, Hayeemasae, Hanafi Ismail, and Azura Abdul Rashid. 2012. "Effects of partial replacement of commercial fillers by recycled poly (ethylene terephthalate) powder on the properties of natural rubber composites." *Journal of Vinyl and Additive Technology* 18 (2): 139–146.

Nakason, C, A Kaesaman, and P Supasanthitikul. 2004. "The grafting of maleic anhydride onto natural rubber." *Polymer Testing* 23 (1): 35–41.

Neaman, Alexander, and Arieh Singer. 2004. "The effects of palygorskite on chemical and physico-chemical properties of soils: a review." *Geoderma* 123 (3–4): 297–303.

Pasbakhsh, P, H Ismail, MN Ahmad Fauzi, and A Abu Bakar. 2009. "Influence of maleic anhydride grafted ethylene propylene diene monomer (MAH-g-EPDM) on the properties of EPDM nanocomposites reinforced by halloysite nanotubes." *Polymer Testing* 28 (5): 548–559.

Pasbakhsh, Pooria, H Ismail, MN Ahmad Fauzi, and A Abu Bakar. 2010. "EPDM/modified halloysite nanocomposites." *Applied Clay Science* 48 (3): 405–413.

Payne, AR, and RE Whittaker. 1971. "Low strain dynamic properties of filled rubbers." *Rubber Chemistry and Technology* 44 (2): 440–478.

Rattanasom, N, TA Saowapark, and C Deeprasertkul. 2007. "Reinforcement of natural rubber with silica/carbon black hybrid filler." *Polymer Testing* 26 (3): 369–377.

Ray, Suprakas Sinha, and Masami Okamoto. 2003. "Polymer/layered silicate nanocomposites: a review from preparation to processing." *Progress in Polymer Science* 28 (11): 1539–1641.

Rodgers, B. 2004. *Rubber compound: chemistry and application*, Marcel Dekker, Inc., New York.

Rooj, Sandip, Amit Das, Klaus Werner Stöckelhuber, De-Yi Wang, Vassilios Galiatsatos, and Gert Heinrich. 2013. "Understanding the reinforcing behavior of expanded clay particles in natural rubber compounds." *Soft Matter* 9 (14): 3798–3808.

Rooj, Sandip, Amit Das, Varun Thakur, RN Mahaling, Anil K Bhowmick, and Gert Heinrich. 2010. "Preparation and properties of natural nanocomposites based on natural rubber and naturally occurring halloysite nanotubes." *Materials & Design* 31 (4): 2151–2156.

Sadequl, AM, BT Poh, and US Ishiaku. 1999. "Effect of filler loading on the mechanical properties of epoxidized natural rubber (ENR 25) compared with natural rubber (SMR L)." *International Journal of Polymeric Materials* 43 (3–4): 261–278.

Sahakaro, Kannika, and Sumsuriya Beraheng. 2008. "Reinforcement of maleated natural rubber by precipitated silica." *Journal of Applied Polymer Science* 109 (6): 3839–3848.

Sengloyluan, Karnda, Kannika Sahakaro, Wilma K Dierkes, and Jacques WM Noordermeer. 2014. "Silica-reinforced tire tread compounds compatibilized by using epoxidized natural rubber." *European polymer journal* 51: 69–79.

Sethuraj, MR, and Mathew, NM. 1992. *Natural rubber: biology, cultivation and technology*, Elsevier, Amsterdam.

Swapna, VP, Ranimol Stephen, T Greeshma, C Sharan Dev, and MS Sreekala. 2016. "Mechanical and swelling behavior of green nanocomposites of natural rubber latex and tubular shaped halloysite nano clay." *Polymer Composites* 37 (2): 602–611.

Thakur, Varun, Amit Das, Ram N. Mahaling, Sandip Rooj, Uwe Gohs, Udo Wagenknecht, and Gert Heinrich. 2009. "Influence of Layered Double Hydroxides on the Curing of Carboxylated Nitrile Rubber with Zinc Oxide." *Macromolecular Materials and Engineering* 294 (9): 561–569.

Usuki, Arimitsu, Yoshitsugu Kojima, Masaya Kawasumi, Akane Okada, Yoshiaki Fukushima, Toshio Kurauchi, and Osami Kamigaito. 1993. "Synthesis of nylon 6-clay hybrid." *Journal of Materials Research* 8 (5): 1179–1184.

Waesateh, Kamaruddin, Sitisaiyidah Saiwari, Hanafi Ismail, Nadras Othman, Siriwat Soontaranon, and Nabil Hayeemasae. 2018. "Features of crystallization behavior of natural rubber/halloysite nanotubes composites using synchrotron wide-angle X-ray scattering." *International Journal of Polymer Analysis and Characterization* 23 (3): 260–270.

Wang, Changchun, Zhi-Xin Guo, Shoukuan Fu, Wei Wu, and Daoben Zhu. 2004. "Polymers containing fullerene or carbon nanotube structures." *Progress in Polymer Science* 29 (11): 1079–1141.

Webster, C.C, and Baulkwill, WJ (eds.). 1989. *Rubber*, Longman Science and Technical, Harlow.

Yuan, Peng, Peter D. Southon, Zongwen Liu, Malcolm E. R. Green, James M. Hook, Sarah J. Antill, and Cameron J. Kepert. 2008. "Functionalization of Halloysite Clay Nanotubes by Grafting with γ-Aminopropyltriethoxysilane." *The Journal of Physical Chemistry C* 112 (40): 15742–15751.

Zhong, Bangchao, Zhixin Jia, Yuanfang Luo, Demin Jia, and Fang Liu. 2017. "Understanding the effect of filler shape induced immobilized rubber on the interfacial and mechanical strength of rubber composites." *Polymer Testing* 58: 31–39.

7 Halloysite Nanotubes-Filled Natural Rubber Composite

Morphology and Crystallization of the Composites

Nabil Hayeemasae
Prince of Songkla University, Pattani Campus
Hat Yai, Thailand

Hanafi Ismail
Universiti Sains Malaysia
Nibong Tebal, Malaysia

CONTENTS

7.1 Introduction 136
7.2 Preparation of the Composites.. 137
7.3 Modification of Palm Stearin 137
7.4 Preparation of NR/HNT Composites 138
7.5 Testing and Characterization of the Composites.................................. 139
    7.5.1 Measurement of Curing Characteristics.................................... 139
    7.5.2 Tensile Properties 139
    7.5.3 X-Ray Diffraction Analysis (XRD).. 139
    7.5.4 Morphological Property... 139
    7.5.5 Wide Angle X-Ray Diffraction Analysis (WAXD)..................... 139
7.6 Effects of HNT Loading.. 140
    7.6.1 X-Ray Diffraction Analysis 140
    7.6.2 Tensile Properties 141
    7.6.3 Morphological Property... 143
    7.6.4 Wide Angle X-Ray Scattering 144
7.7 Effect of Modified Palm Stearin on the Strain-Induced
Crystallization of NR/HNT Composites 147
    7.7.1 Functionalities of MPS 147
    7.7.2 Cure Characteristics 148

DOI: 10.1201/9781003220947-7

7.7.3	Interaction of MPS and Halloysite Nanotubes	149
7.7.4	XRD Study of the Composites in the Presence of MPS	150
7.7.5	Reinforcement and Strain-Induced Crystallization of the Composites	152
7.8 Conclusions		156
References		157

7.1 INTRODUCTION

The crystallization behavior of natural rubber (NR) when exposed to external stretching is well documented. Strain-induced crystallization endows NR with excellent mechanical properties and good resistance to crack growth (Kuang *et al.*, 2016; Ray and Okamoto, 2003). Despite contributing good properties, products made with NR still rely on the use of fillers to improve performance, durability and service life. In recent years, clay minerals have been extensively used in many rubbers because they provide extraordinary improvement in materials' properties such as high modulus, strength and heat resistance (Kohjiya *et al.*, 2017; Toki *et al.*, 2002).

In NR/clay composites, the presence of clay can also change the microstructure and crystallization behavior of NR. Carretero-Gonzalez *et al.* (2008) and Masa *et al.* (2015, 2016) proposed that the strain-induced crystallization of NR was enhanced due to the clay particle orientation at low strain levels, followed by crystallization of networked NR chains at higher levels of strain. As a result, the onset of strain-induced crystallization in the composites occurred at lower strains, and the rate of crystallization was greater than that of the unfilled NR.

Like other clay minerals, halloysite nanotubes (HNTs) are chemically similar to clay. HNTs have hydroxyl groups on their surfaces, but the geometry is more different than typical clays. HNTs are known to reinforce many rubbers, because of their large surface area and high aspect ratio (Berahman *et al.*, 2016; Ismail *et al.*, 2011, 2013; Rooj *et al.*, 2010). For instance, HNTs have been incorporated into NR to create nanocomposites with enhanced tensile strength and elastic modulus. The tensile strength was 15%–25% higher than that of unfilled NR, depending on the compounding formulations (Ismail *et al.*, 2011, 2013; Rooj *et al.*, 2010). The enhanced tensile strength and modulus were reported to be mainly be caused by the uniform dispersion of HNT throughout the NR matrix.

Because HNTs are tubular shaped, they are expected to enhance the alignment of NR chains during stretching more than other clays. Therefore, studying the role of HNTs in strain-induced crystallization of NR is important. In this work, correlations between the mechanical strength and crystallization behavior of NR/HNT composites are discussed. Crystallization characteristics of the composites are studied through synchrotron wide-angle X-ray scattering (WAXS). The extension apparatus is equipped to examine crystallization under strain. This enables monitoring of crystallization in real time, giving detailed and accurate scattering patterns with short exposure times. The corresponding dispersions of HNT are also analyzed using scanning electron microscopy (SEM). Finally, a schematic model representing the relationship between mechanical strength and corresponding strain-induced crystallization in NR filled with HNT is proposed.

TABLE 7.1
Formulation of HNT-Filled NR Composites

Ingredients	Amount (phr)
STR 5L	100.0
Stearic acid	1.0
Zinc oxide	5.0
CBS	2.0
HNT	0–10
Sulfur	2.0

7.2 PREPARATION OF THE COMPOSITES

The recipes for the preparation of the HNT-filled NR composites are given in Table 7.1. The HNT loading was varied to 0, 2.5, 5.0, 7.5 and 10 phr. The compounding was done by the Brabender Plasticorder at an initial mixing temperature of 50°C with a rotor speed 60 rpm and later sheeted by the conventional two-roll mill to avoid premature vulcanization of excess heat generated during compounding. The mixing time and sequence were kept constant for all the mixes as given in Table 7.2. After sheeting, the sample of the respective compounds was later tested for its curing characteristics.

7.3 MODIFICATION OF PALM STEARIN

The modification of palm stearin was done according to the optimum conditions described by Surya *et al.* (2013). It was done in a reaction kettle fitted with a stirrer at atmospheric pressure. The methanol was initially added and then mixed with sodium methoxide while stirring. The mixture of palm stearin and diethanolamine was later added to the solution and mildly stirred. Next, the mixture was heated and the reaction temperature was kept constant at 70°C for 5 hours. The resultant mixture was

TABLE 7.2
Mixing Procedures of the Compounding Process

Operations	Time (min)
Mastication of rubber	1.0
Addition of stearic acid	0.5
Addition of zinc oxide	0.5
Addition of HNT	3.0
Addition of CBS	1.0
Addition of Sulfur	1.0
Total	7.0

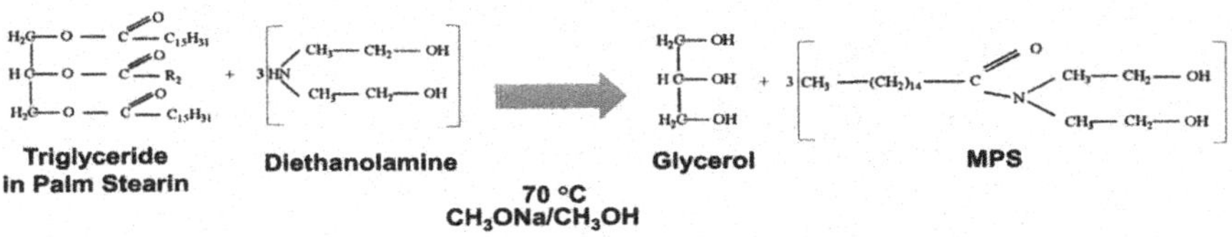

FIGURE 7.1 Proposed chemical reaction of MPS.

extracted with diethyl ether, and washed with saturated sodium chloride solution. The crude product of modified palm stearin (MPS) was finally purified with anhydrous sodium sulfate, and concentrated by a rotary evaporator. MPS was stored in a desiccator prior to characterize through Fourier-transform infrared spectroscopy (FTIR) to capture the change in functionalities. The chemical reaction during the synthesis of MPS is illustrated in Figure 7.1. The MPS appeared as a cream-colored wax and was used as a compatibilizer to improve the compatibility of NR/HNT composites.

7.4 PREPARATION OF NR/HNT COMPOSITES

Table 7.3 lists the starting materials used for compounding the compatibilized NR/HNT composites. Here, stearic acid was not used in this formulation because the MPS also contains fatty acid. The entire amounts of NR, HNT, MPS and other additives were prepared using a Brabender (Plastograph® EC Plus, Mixer W50EHT 3Z). The compounds produced are hereafter designated as MPS0, MPS0.5, MPS0.7, MPS1 and MPS2 for the composites with 0, 0.5, 0.7, 1 and 2 phr of MPS, respectively. After dumping, the compounds were passed through a tight nip (~2 mm) two-roll mill to remove excess generated heat. The compounds were then compression molded into specific shapes by a hydraulic hot press, using the curing times determined by a moving die rheometer (MDR) as described in the following section.

TABLE 7.3

Compound Formulation of the NR/HNT Composites with and without MPS

	Amount (phr)				
Ingredients	MPS 0	MPS 0.5	MPS 0.7	MPS 1	MPS 2
RSS3	100	100	100	100	100
ZnO	5	5	5	5	5
HNT	5	5	5	5	5
MPS	-	0.5	0.7	1	2
CBS	2	2	2	2	2
Sulfur	2	2	2	2	2

7.5 TESTING AND CHARACTERIZATION OF THE COMPOSITES

7.5.1 MEASUREMENT OF CURING CHARACTERISTICS

The curing characteristics of the composites were performed using an MDR (Rheoline, Mini MDR Lite) at the temperature of 150°C. It was used to determine the torque, scorch time (ts_2) and curing time (tc_{90}) according to ASTM D5289.

7.5.2 TENSILE PROPERTIES

Tensile properties of composite samples, which include the tensile strength, elongation at break and tensile modulus, were examined in this study. The tensile properties were conducted following the ASTM D412 standard test. The samples were cut into dumbbell shape type C.

7.5.3 X-RAY DIFFRACTION ANALYSIS (XRD)

The X-ray diffraction (XRD) analysis of pure HNT and NR/HNT composites was carried out by using Philips X'Pert MPD (Eindhoven, Netherlands) with CuKα radiation tube ($\lambda = 0.154$ nm) at 40 kV and a current of 30 mA, and Bruker D2 Phaser (Billerica, MA) with CuKα radiation source ($\lambda = 0.154$ nm) and a current of 10 mA. The diffraction patterns were scanned in the diffraction angle region 2θ of 5–30° along with step size of 0.05° and 3°/min of scan speed. The d-spacing of HNT layers in particles was further calculated by Bragg's equation:

$$n\lambda = 2d\sin\theta \qquad (7.1)$$

where λ is the wavelength of the X-ray, d is the interlayer distance and θ is the angle of incident X-ray radiation.

7.5.4 MORPHOLOGICAL PROPERTY

Tensile-fractured surfaces were examined via a SEM (Quanta FEG 400, FEI, Hillsboro, OR) and field emission SEM (FESEM; Supra-35VP field emission) to study the dispersion of HNT throughout NR matrix microdefects. The fractured pieces were coated with a layer of gold to eliminate electrostatic charge buildup during examination.

7.5.5 WIDE ANGLE X-RAY DIFFRACTION ANALYSIS (WAXD)

The crystallization behavior of NR and the composites was analyzed using WAXS with a synchrotron radiation source. The WAXS was performed using Beamline 1.3 W at the Siam Photon Laboratory, Synchrotron Light Research Institute (SLRI), Nakhon-Ratchasima, Thailand. The wavelength was 0.138 nm and the sample-to-detector distance was 115.34 mm. 4-Bromobenzoic acid was used as a standard material to calibrate the scattering angle. The scattering pattern of the samples was captured by a charge-coupled device (CCD) detector (SX165, Rayonix, Evanston, IL) with a diameter of 165 mm. The beam intensity before striking and after passing through the samples was monitored by an ionization chamber installed in front of the sample holder and a photodiode mounted in front of a beam stop, respectively. The dumbbell-shaped specimens were mounted to the grips of a stretching machine. WAXS measurements were taken while samples were stretched with a 50 mm/min cross-head speed.

A two-dimensional (2D) air image was subtracted from the 2D WAXS images, and the resulting images were converted to one-dimensional (1D) WAXS profiles by averaging each 2D image in the azimuthal direction using the SAXSIT program developed by SLRI. This 1D profile was integrated to calculate the area under the profile line, and the degree of crystallinity was calculated using Eq. 12.2:

$$\text{Degree of crystallinity}\,(\%) = \left(\frac{A_c}{A_c + A_a}\right) \times 100 \tag{7.2}$$

where A_c and A_a are the area under the crystalline peak of interest and amorphous halo, respectively.

The orientation parameter (OP) was also determined from the Hermann equation, as seen in Eqs. 12.3 and 12.4:

$$\text{Orientation parameter} = \frac{3(\cos^2\varphi) - 1}{2} \tag{7.3}$$

$$(\cos^2\varphi) = \frac{\displaystyle\int_0^\pi I_c(\varphi)\cos^2\varphi\sin\varphi\,d\varphi}{\displaystyle\int_0^\pi I_c(\varphi)\sin\varphi\,d\varphi} \tag{7.4}$$

where φ is the azimuthal angle relative to the stretching direction and $I_c(\varphi)$ is the diffraction intensity of the crystal component at φ. $I_c(\varphi)$ was obtained by subtracting the minimum scattering intensity in the azimuthal scattering profile from the scattering intensity of the amorphous component from the original WAXS intensity (Osaka *et al.*, 2013).

7.6 EFFECTS OF HNT LOADING

7.6.1 X-Ray Diffraction Analysis

Figure 7.2 shows the XRD pattern of raw HNT, raw NR, and NR/HNT composites containing 5 and 10 phr of HNT. The 2θ values of diffraction peak and their relative d-spacing are discussed. The peak at 12.13° of HNT powder corresponded to d_{001} basal spacing, where $d = 7.29$ Å. This indicates that the HNT was mainly in dehydrated form, typically referred to as 7Å-halloysite. Broader basal reflections obtained may be attributed to the small crystal size, the inconsistent layer spacing, and the

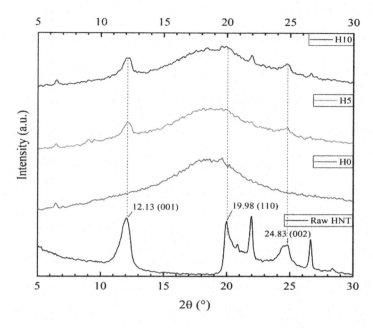

FIGURE 7.2 XRD scattering patterns of NR/HNT composites at various HNT loadings.

curvature of the layers. The dehydrated state was also confirmed by the presence of d_{002} basal reflections at 24.83°, which is equivalent to basal spacing of 3.58 Å.

On increased addition of HNT, no shifting of peak at 2θ d_{001} (7.29 Å) basal spacing was found. However, there are slight changes in the d_{110} and d_{002}, which correspond to basal spacing of 4.44 and 3.58 Å. These were shifted to lower 2θ of about 19.98° to 19.53° and 24.83° to 24.73°, respectively. These increases in HNT basal spacing indicate limited intercalation of HNT by NR and other ingredients (Berahman et al., 2016; Ismail et al., 2013). The limitation to intercalate HNT was due to the non-polar character of NR as well as the dehydrated form and small galleries of HNT (Ismail et al., 2013).

7.6.2 TENSILE PROPERTIES

Stress-strain curves of the NR/HNT composites are shown in Figure 7.3. Typical strain-induced crystallization of neat NR and of NR containing 2.5, 5, 7.5 and 10 phr of HNT is seen in the stress-strain curves. Initially, stress increases gradually as a function of applied strain, then increases sharply due to strain-induced crystallization of NR during tensile stretching. The stress and strain values appear to differ between the neat NR and the NR/HNT composites. From the stress-strain curves, it is possible to estimate the change point of the strain for each of the samples. Clearly, the strain at the onset of the stress upturn for the NR containing HNT is much lower than that of the neat NR, and the onset strain decreases with increasing HNT loading. This observation indicates that the addition of HNT affects the stress-strain

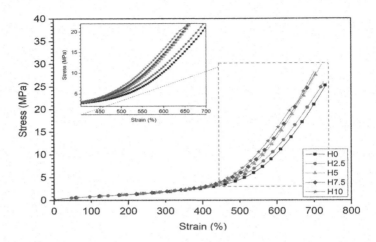

FIGURE 7.3 Stress-strain curves of NR/HNT composites.

behavior of NR and lowers the strain at the onset of the stress upturn. The relationship between the mechanical strength and strain-induced crystallization behavior is discussed in a later section.

Table 7.4 shows the tensile properties and hardness for the NR/HNT composites. The tensile strength improves up to 5 phr of HNT, but above this level the strength is reduced. HNTs have a very high elastic modulus and aspect ratio (Du *et al.*, 2010), so they are frequently combined with various rubbers to increase their mechanical strength as composites. The particle sizes of HNT are very small, resulting in strong interfacial and intertubular interactions in the NR matrix. Such interactions could induce tightly immobilized NR chains and form a solid bridge between filler and rubber (Zhong *et al.*, 2017). On stretching, the tightly immobilized part subsequently anchors and forms a proper stress transfer, leading to an enhancement of the mechanical strength. The strength enhancement could also be due to the special characteristics of HNT themselves, such as low hydroxyl content, tubular structure and unique crystal structure (Du *et al.*, 2010). These characteristics could allow the HNT to disperse well in the NR matrix and improve the stress transfer in the NR matrix (Du *et al.*, 2010; Ismail *et al.*, 2008). It was already reported in the literature (Ismail *et al.*,

TABLE 7.4
Tensile Properties of NR/HNT Composites

Sample	M100 (MPa)	M300 (MPa)	Tensile Strength (MPa)	Elongation at Break (%)
H0	0.77 ± 0.01	2.20 ± 0.02	25.3 ± 0.3	662 ± 24
H2.5	0.83 ± 0.02	2.13 ± 0.02	27.8 ± 0.6	689 ± 26
H5	0.83 ± 0.02	2.29 ± 0.04	29.9 ± 0.4	706 ± 20
H7.5	0.87 ± 0.02	2.25 ± 0.07	29.3 ± 0.7	680 ± 29
H10	0.91 ± 0.02	2.42 ± 0.08	29.3 ± 0.5	668 ± 28

2011; Rooj *et al.*, 2010) that the enhancement of tensile strength of rubber/HNT composites was contributed by good dispersion of HNT within the rubber matrix, which caused a strong interfacial and intertubular interaction between HNT and rubber.

A similar trend is also seen for the elongation at break of the NR/HNT composites. The reduction in tensile strength and elongation at break with loadings beyond 5 phr of HNT is simply due to filler agglomeration (Sadequl *et al.*, 1999). When more HNTs are integrated into the NR matrix, the HNT particles tend to interact with each other. These so-called filler-filler interactions can be seen in the SEM micrographs (Ismail *et al.*, 2011; Rooj *et al.*, 2010). The addition of HNT also results in a stress increase at 100% (M100) and 300% (M300) strains. As more HNT get into the rubber, the elasticity of the rubber is reduced, resulting in more rigid, stiffer and harder composites (Osaka *et al.*, 2013). This observation is supported by the changes in M_H and M_H–M_L reported in the preceding section.

7.6.3 Morphological Property

Figure 7.4 shows the dispersion of HNT in the NR matrix at 10,000× magnifications. At low HNT loading (H2.5), the HNTs are dispersed homogeneously in the NR

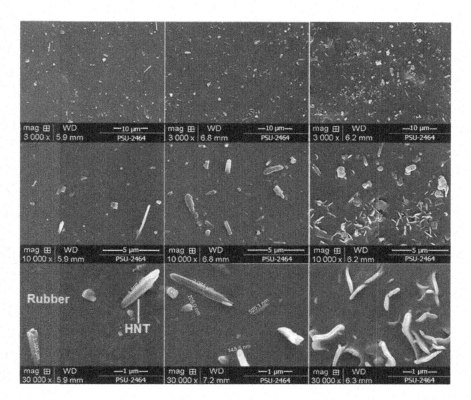

FIGURE 7.4 SEM photographs of NR/HNT composites (3000×, 10,000×, and 30,000× magnifications from top to bottom).

matrix. The homogeneity of the composites is significantly improved, especially with loading up to 5 phr (H5). The homogeneous dispersion of HNT is clearly responsible for the improved tensile strength. However, when HNTs are incorporated beyond 5 phr (H10), they tend to aggregate by the strong filler-filler interactions as well as by detachment, so less energy is required for failure of these NR/HNT composites.

7.6.4 Wide Angle X-Ray Scattering

It is well known that the outstanding mechanical strength of NR originates from strain-induced crystallization. Many researchers have reported that the incorporation of clay into NR can induce crystallization due to molecular chain alignment and orientation. Therefore, it is important to examine the effects of various contents of HNT, e.g., 0–10 phr, on the strain-induced crystallization in NR/HNT composites. To capture the development of strain-induced crystallization, WAXS analysis of the neat NR and NR/HNT composites under strain was performed, and the results are shown in Figures 7.5–7.8.

Figure 7.5 shows 1D WAXS profiles and 2D WAXS images and of neat NR and NR/HNT composites at 400% strain. Figure 7.5(a) shows the crystal diffraction peaks, attributed to the 200 and 120 plane reflections from the NR, at 2θ values 12.0–12.5 and 18.0 (Kuang *et al.*, 2016). These observations correspond to the 2D WAXS images of the neat NR and NR containing 5 and 10 phr of HNT (see Figure 7.5(b)–(d)), the 200 and 120 reflection spots are seen due to highly oriented crystallites in the NR where more crystallized spots are visible when increasing the amount of HNT. When considering the azimuthal profiles (see Figure 7.6), it is

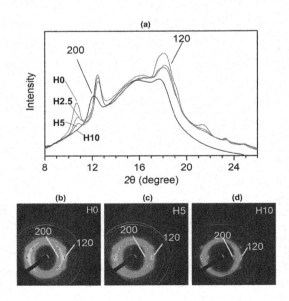

FIGURE 7.5 2θ scan 1D linear profiles of the NR/HNT composites at 400% strain (a) and coupled 2D WAXS images of H0 (b), H5 (c) and H10 (d).

Halloysite-Filled NR Composite: Morphology and Crystallization 145

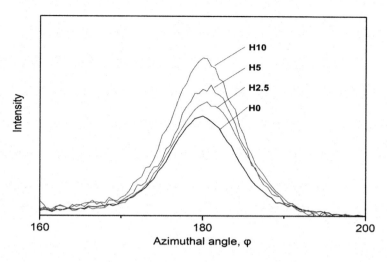

FIGURE 7.6 Azimuthal scan 1D profiles of the NR/HNT composites at 400% strain.

clear that the intensities from 160° to 200° azimuthal angles increase with increasing HNT loadings from 2.5–10 phr. This confirms that the NR chain alignment is assisted by the inclusion of HNT.

Figure 7.7 shows the azimuthal scan profiles of H5 at 300, 400 and 500% strain and it is illustrated together with the respective 2D and 3D WAXS images. The azimuthal angles are scanned from 160° to 200° or within 2θ range of 11° to 14°, corresponding to the 200 plane reflection of NR. The reflection intensity of the azimuthal profiles clearly increases with applied strain, showing that the orientation of the NR chains is changing and the magnitude of crystallization is increasing.

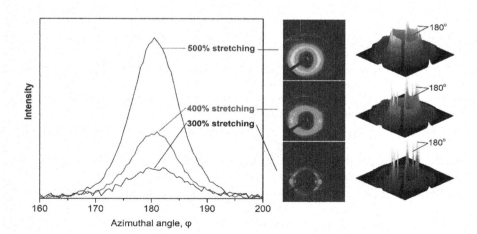

FIGURE 7.7 WAXS profiles as a function of azimuthal angle and their respective 2D and 3D WAXS images of NR/HNT composite at the loading of 5 phr (H5).

146   Mineral-Filled Polymer Composites

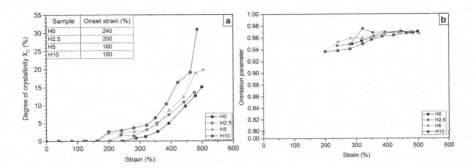

FIGURE 7.8 Degree of crystallinity determined from 200 and 120 reflection plane (a) and OP determined from 200 reflection plane (b) as a function of strain deformation for the NR/HNT composites.

The degree of crystallinity (X_C) can also be estimated from the integrated peak area of intensities for the 200 and 120 reflections (Hernández et al., 2011; Masa et al., 2015, 2016). Figure 7.8(a) shows the change in degree of crystallinity with respect to the strain deformation. The calculated onset strain is also shown in this figure in the embedded table. X_C increases with increasing applied strain, and the onset of crystallinity is observed at lower strains for increasing HNT, i.e., 240% for the neat NR, and approximately 200, 160 and 160% for the NR containing 2.5, 5 and 10 phr of HNT, respectively. HNT can induce the crystallization of NR. This effect can be attributed to the better interfacial interaction of the HNT to the rubber. This interaction can promote a tightly immobilized NR chain, which then acts as an anchor to pull the surrounding NR chains while stretching. As a result, the NR molecular chain orientation and alignment are further enhanced.

In addition to degree of crystallinity, the WAXS patterns can also be used to calculate the OP using the Hermann equation (see Eqs. 12.3 and 12.4). Figure 7.8(b) shows the OP of the neat NR and NR containing HNT as a function of applied strain. The OP increases with increasing strain. In general, the OP represents the extent of the orientation and alignment of polymer chains. Completely parallel alignment is characterized by an OP equal to 1, whereas isotropic and perpendicular alignment are represented by OPs of 0 and −0.5, respectively (White and Spruiell, 1983). Based on our findings, the Ops increase toward parallel alignment and toward the value of approximately 1, suggesting that strain produces better alignment of the NR chains. The change in the OP for the NR containing HNT is higher than that of the neat NR, except for the NR containing 10 phr of HNT (H10). As seen in the SEM images, HNTs tend to aggregate at higher loadings of HNT (H10). The inhomogeneity of HNTs throughout the matrix may restrict the alignment of the NR chains.

Based on these results, a schematic illustration representing strain-induced crystallization in NR/HNT composites is proposed in Figure 7.9. In this model, HNTs are dispersed in the cross-linked NR/HNT composite, and the NR matrix strongly interacts with the HNT in the areas where they are in contact. On stretching, the tubular-shaped HNT is oriented and aligned along the stretching direction. Crystallization of the NR matrix is then induced due to the stress concentration on

Halloysite-Filled NR Composite: Morphology and Crystallization 147

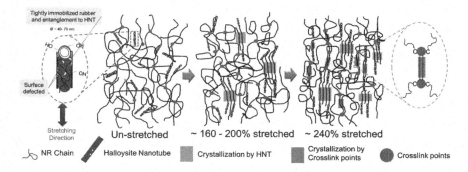

FIGURE 7.9 Schematic model representing the relationship between mechanical strength and corresponding strain-induced crystallization in the NR in the presence of HNT.

the HNT surfaces, and the crystallinity increases in association with the orientation of the HNT. Consequently, the NR chains are rearranged and crystallized at strains of approximately 160%–200%. Finally, the crystallinity of the NR matrix steeply increases due to the collaborative crystallization of NR with dispersed HNT at strains above 240%. Thus, more energy is required to break the sample, leading to a significant increase in the tensile strength.

7.7 EFFECT OF MODIFIED PALM STEARIN ON THE STRAIN-INDUCED CRYSTALLIZATION OF NR/HNT COMPOSITES

7.7.1 FUNCTIONALITIES OF MPS

The typical infrared spectra of unmodified and modified palm stearin are shown in Figure 7.10. The wave numbers and their respective assignments are summarized in Table 7.5. Similar bands of C–H stretch detected at wave numbers of 2922 and 2852 cm^{-1}, and CH$_2$ rocking band appeared at 719 and 721 cm^{-1} associated with long

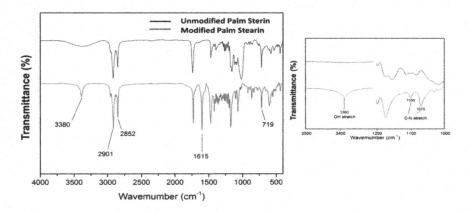

FIGURE 7.10 FTIR spectra of unmodified and modified palm stearin.

TABLE 7.5

The Observed Peaks and Respective Assignments of Unmodified and Modified Palm Stearin

Wave Numbers cm^{-1}	Suggested Assignments
3380	O–H stretch
3006	Unsaturated (C=C)
2852	Saturated (CH$_3$)
1615	C=O stretch
1375	Umbrella mode
1110, 1070	C–N stretch
719	CH$_2$ rocking

MPS chains in the fatty acids are observed in both unmodified and modified palm stearin. Further evidence of a methyl group (CH$_3$) attached to a carbon atom was also shown as the umbrella mode at 1352 cm^{-1} (Bhargava *et al.*, 2003). The distinct bands observed in the modified over unmodified palm stearin are also shown in Figure 7.2. These include the strong band of O–H stretch at 3410 cm^{-1}, the C=O stretch at 1629 and 1556 cm^{-1} and the amide C–N stretch at 1064 cm^{-1} respectively. The spectrum obtained clearly corresponds to the functional groups present in MPS as seen in the reaction scheme shown in Figure 7.1.

7.7.2 CURE CHARACTERISTICS

The curing results of the NR/HNT composites with and without MPS are listed in Table 7.6. It was found that the minimum torque (M_L) decreased with the addition of MPS. M_L represents the elastic modulus of uncured stock and also offers valuable detail about the processability of rubber compound (Nabil *et al.*, 2014). A lower value of M_L indicates better compound's processability. Here, it is clear that MPS improved the processability of the compounds. MPS is waxy in nature, it can act as an internal plasticizer resulting in lowering the viscosity and improving the processability of compound. The maximum torque (M_H) reduced after adding MPS but then

TABLE 7.6

Curing Results of the NR/HNT Composites with and without MPS

Compound	M_L (dN·m)	M_H (dN·m)	M_H–M_L (dN·m)	t_{S1} (min)	tc_{90} (min)	CRI (min^{-1})
MPS 0	0.85	7.98	7.13	3.12	6.23	32.15
MPS 0.5	0.71	7.55	6.84	1.89	4.83	34.01
MPS 0.7	0.78	7.84	7.06	1.90	4.33	41.15
MPS 1	0.76	7.94	7.18	1.92	4.29	42.19
MPS 2	0.75	8.14	7.39	1.20	3.00	55.56

increased again with further increases in the MPS portion, showing that the MPS played an important role in improving the compatibility of the NR/HNT composites. A similar finding was observed for the torque differences (M_H-M_L). As the torque difference is known to be representative of the degree of cross-linking and/or interaction within the composite system (Rattanasom et al., 2007), this could indicate that the compatibility of the NR and HNT was significantly enhanced when the MPS was added to the composite.

The amide content in the MPS also shortened the scorch and cure times of the composites. As mentioned before, MPS was synthesized from palm stearin and diethanolamine, which made MPS an alkaline substance. This has increased the pH of rubber compounds and, in most instances, enhanced the cure rate. Any chemical substance that gives the rubber compound more alkalinity will to enhance the cure rate because the acidic materials tend to retard the reactivity of accelerators (Coran, 2003; Surya et al., 2013), It was therefore expected that the amine content of the MPS can accelerate the cure rate of the composites.

7.7.3 INTERACTION OF MPS AND HALLOYSITE NANOTUBES

Figure 7.11 presents the FTIR spectra in the wave number range of 4000–400 cm^{-1} for the NR/HNT composites without MPS and with MPS at 0.5 and 2 phr. For the composite without MPS, an adsorption band around 3690 cm^{-1} was found that can be assigned to the vibrations of hydroxyl groups, specifically, the stretching vibrations of the inner surface hydroxyl groups. Other interesting peaks were detected at 684 and 534 cm^{-1}; they were attributed to the deformation of the inner hydroxyl groups of Al-OH libations.

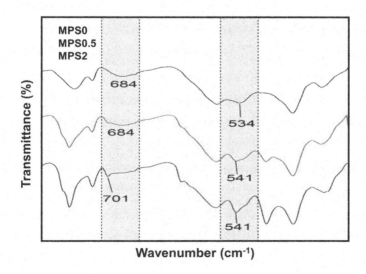

FIGURE 7.11 Attenuated total reflection (ATR)-FTIR spectra of NR/HNT composites with and without MPS.

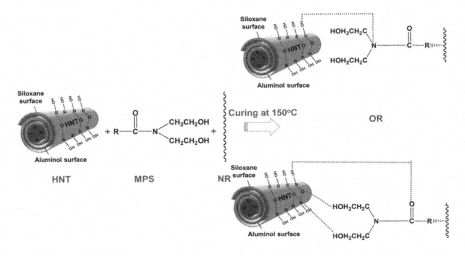

FIGURE 7.12 Schematic model representing the interaction of MPS and HNT through hydrogen bonding.

On inclusion of MPS, there was a slight shift in the Al-OH vibrations. The peaks representing the Al-OH vibrations at wave numbers of 684 and 534 cm^{-1} were shifted to 701 and 541 cm^{-1}, respectively, after the addition of 0.5 and 2 phr of MPS. The increase in the MPS loading increased the peak intensities of the Al-OH vibrations, confirming that the presence of more MPS in the NR/HNT composites creates a better rubber-filler interaction. Such interaction is able to occur through hydrogen bonding between the amide group available in the MPS and the aluminol and silanol components of the HNT where the alkyl chain (-R-) available from the MPS is dipole when interacting with the rubber chain. It has also been previously reported by Pasbakhsh et al. (2009) that the shift in Al-OH is related to the formation of hydrogen bonding between the outer and inner surfaces of the HNT and the compatibilizer. The mechanistic model of this interaction is shown in Figure 7.12.

7.7.4 XRD STUDY OF THE COMPOSITES IN THE PRESENCE OF MPS

The XRD patterns of the composites with and without MPS are shown in Figure 7.13. The characteristic (001) reflection for the HNT appears at 2θ = 12.5° corresponds to basal spacing, d = 0.79 nm, determined using Bragg's law. This indicates that the HNT was mainly in dehydrated form, typically referred to as 7Å-halloysite (Berahman et al., 2016; Rooj et al., 2010). Furthermore, the same figure shows that the d-basal spacing is shifted to the lower reflection angles over the MPS loadings (12.2°–11.9°). The interlayer space distances are 0.83–0.87 nm for MPS 0.5–2 phr, respectively. This indicates that the MPS is beneficial to expand the interlayer space of HNTs. Broader basal reflections obtained may be attributed to the small crystal size, inconsistent layer spacing and the bending of the HNT layers. However, the increasing value of d-basal spacing is considered low when compared with other types of clay due to the difference in shape and characteristics of the clay itself. A

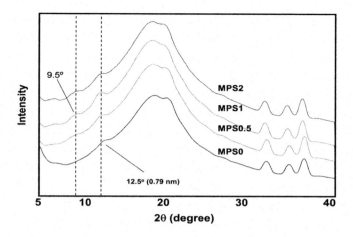

FIGURE 7.13 X-RD patterns of NR/HNT composites with and without MPS.

similar observation was reported by Lagaly *et al.* (1976) who used the fatty acids to expand the layers of clay. This is quite similar to their work, as the MPS has fatty acids in its composition.

The increment of basal spacing for the composites containing MPS occurred during the melt-compounding of the composites under the high shearing force of an internal mixer. To confirm this, a control sample was prepared differently in which the steps of preparation were modified from the original work of Das *et al.* (2011) by grinding the pure MPS and HNT in a mortar. Next, the mixture was dried at 100°C prior to characterizing the crystal structure using X-RD. Based on the results shown in Figure 7.14, only the characteristic reflections of HNT appeared in the XRD patterns. This confirms that an increase in the basal spacing occurred after mixing with an internal mixer. The high shearing of the internal mixer together with the

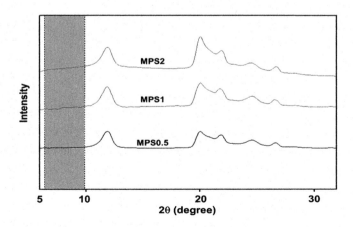

FIGURE 7.14 X-RD pattern of pure MPS and HNT mixture.

ability of the MPS to increase interlayers of HNT might be one of the reasons for the remarkable improvement in the properties of the NR/HNT composites in the presence of MPS.

7.7.5 REINFORCEMENT AND STRAIN-INDUCED CRYSTALLIZATION OF THE COMPOSITES

Reinforcement of NR/HNT in the presence of MPS was monitored through the mechanical properties as listed in Table 7.7. The tensile strength increased on the inclusion of MPS to an optimum at 0.7 phr loading, thereafter the value decreased slightly. The increment in tensile strength was simply due to the MPS itself, which had a direct effect on the interaction between the NR and HNT. The reduction in tensile strength after 0.7 phr of MPS may be attributed to the excessive interaction taking place. As a result, the stress concentration point was observed at the interacting point, creating flaws in the rubber samples during the tensile testing. This phenomenon caused a similar effect to the elongation at break of the NR/HNT composites. The strong interaction of the NR and HNT can be confirmed from the results of the stresses at 100% (M100) and 300% (M300) strains. It can be seen that M100 and M300 increased gradually with MPS loading. As more MPS was added to the rubber more interactions took place, resulting in stiffer and harder composites (Pasbakhsh et al., 2009). This finding is more obvious when considering the stress at 300% elongation (M300). This is related to the stress-strain, which will be discussed later based on the relationship between stress-strain behavior and degree of crystallinity.

A better interaction between NR and HNT is formed by the interaction of the amide groups available in the MPS and the siloxane groups on the outer layer of the HNT, and these reactions created an increase in the reinforcing efficiency of the NR/HNT composites. The reinforcing efficiency or RI (M300/M100) of the composites increased on the addition of MPS, which not only acts as a compatibilizer but also plays an important role in enhancing the dispersibility of HNT throughout the rubber matrix. As noted above, MPS is wax-like in nature, which helps to improve the dispersibility of the HNT. The evidence of this effect is adduced later in the chapter.

TABLE 7.7

Mechanical Properties of the NR/HNT Composites with and without MPS

Compound	Tensile Strength (MPa)	Elongation at Break (%)	Modulus (MPa)		M300/M100
			100%	300%	
MPS 0	26.11 ± (0.55)	728.2 ± (8.52)	0.83	1.96	2.37
MPS 0.5	27.17 ± (0.31)	686.8 ± (9.11)	0.72	1.84	2.55
MPS 0.7	28.18 ± (0.15)	675.8 ± (7.79)	0.73	1.88	2.56
MPS 1	27.56 ± (0.21)	645.1 ± (10+.12)	0.89	2.28	2.56
MPS 2	25.57 ± (0.32)	630.9 ± (5.54)	0.85	2.33	2.74

As clearly mentioned in the introduction, the main focus in this study was to correlate the reinforcing effect and strain-induced crystallization of the composites. The crystallization characteristics of the composites were also studied through synchrotron WAXS and an extension apparatus was used to examine crystallization under strain. This was done to simulate the strain-induced crystallization of the composites, which enables the monitoring of crystallization in real time, giving detailed and accurate scattering patterns with short exposure times.

MPS has influenced the mechanical properties from two main factors: one is due to an increase in the compatibility between NR and HNT by forming certain interactions and other is due to an increase in the interlayers of HNT caused by the waxy nature of the MPS. The first main factor definitely happens because of the improved compatibility between NR and HNT. The interaction, which takes place in the presence of MPS, can help to pull the surrounding molecular chains and speeds up the crystallization process. To support the observed findings, it is important to examine the effects of various contents of MPS, in this case, 0–2 phr, on the strain-induced crystallization in the NR/HNT composites. WAXS analysis of the NR/HNT composites with and without MPS was performed, and the results obtained from WAXS profiles are depicted in Figures 7.15–7.17.

Strain-induced crystallization of NR/HNT composites was discussed through the degree of crystallinity (X_c) over the strains. The X_c can also be estimated from the integrated peak area of the intensities at 200 and 120 diffractions (Hernández et al., 2011; Kuang et al., 2016). The degree of crystallinity against the strain deformation is illustrated in Figure 7.15. The onset strain in which the crystallization occurs is also shown in this figure (see the dash line). The X_c increases when increasing the applied strain where the crystallinity starts to occur at the lower strain, i.e., 250% for the composite without MPS, and about 190, 190 and 150% for the NR/HNT containing 0.5, 1 and 2 phr of MPS, respectively. Here, it is obvious that MPS shows an important role in inducing the crystallization of the NR/HNT

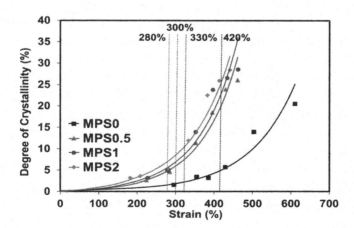

FIGURE 7.15 Degree of crystallinity determined from 200 and 120 reflection planes of NR/HNT composites with and without MPS.

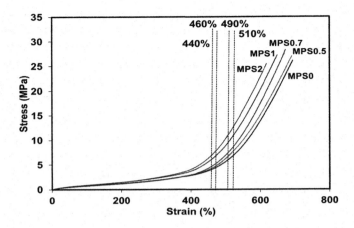

FIGURE 7.16 Stress-strain curves of NR/HNT composites with and without MPS.

composites. This phenomenon is attributable to the better interfacial interaction of NR and HNT gained by the addition of MPS. Such interactions can promote an intense interaction point, which then acts as a hook to pull the surrounding molecular chains during stretching. Subsequently, the molecular chain orientation and alignment are further enhanced.

The result of X_c over the strain clearly corresponds to the stress-strain curves of the NR/HNT composites with and without MPS, as shown in Figure 7.16. The typical strain-induced crystallization of NR/HNT composites with and without MPS can also be observed from the stress-strain curves. Initially, stress increases slightly when the strain is applied, then increases steeply due to the strain-induced crystallization of the NR during tensile stretching. The stress and strain values appear to differ when the NR is with or without MPS. From the stress-strain curves, it is possible to predict the crystallization of the composites from the turning point of the stress and strain. It is obvious that the stress started to increase toward the MPS content. This is responsible to the formation of interaction in the system, which was discussed earlier in Figure 7.12.

To widen the focus, WAXS profiles and 2D WAXS images of the NR/HNT composites with and without MPS at 400% strain are shown in Figure 7.17. Here, the peaks appeared at the 2θ degree of 12.5° and 18.0° corresponding to 200 and 120 reflection spots (Hernández et al., 2011; Kuang et al., 2016), indicating the crystallization of the NR/HNT composites. The diffraction intensity slightly increased with increases in the MPS content, indicating that the crystallization of the NR/HNT composite was induced by the addition of MPS. This crystallization is more visible when captured in the 2D images from the WAXS profiles. The crystalline spots, assigned to the 200 and 120 plane reflections were more intense after the inclusion of MPS. This clearly indicates that the MPS plays a very crucial role in promoting the strain-induced crystallization of NR/HNT composites. To measure the small amount of strain-induced crystallinity due to the weak intensity of the WAXD pattern in the deformed sample, only the azimuthal scan profiles were analyzed. Specifically, the

Halloysite-Filled NR Composite: Morphology and Crystallization 155

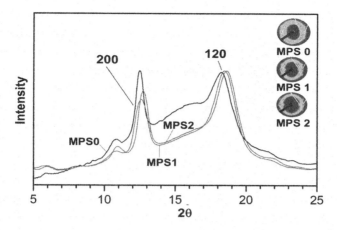

FIGURE 7.17 WAXS profiles and 2D WAXS images of NR/HNT composites with and without MPS at 400% strain.

diffraction intensity near the equator from 160° to 200° was integrated and termed as the total intensity. This is especially pertains to the composite containing 1 phr of MPS (Figure 7.18). Such azimuthal scan profiles shown were at 300, 400 and 500% strains. It can be clearly seen that the reflection intensity of the azimuthal profiles for the respective composite increases with applied strain. This finding clearly shows that the orientation of the NR chains is changed, leading to the crystallization of the NR.

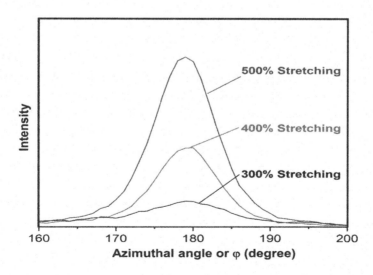

FIGURE 7.18 WAXS profiles as a function of azimuthal angle and the respective 2D WAXS images of NR/HNT with MPS at 1.0 phr.

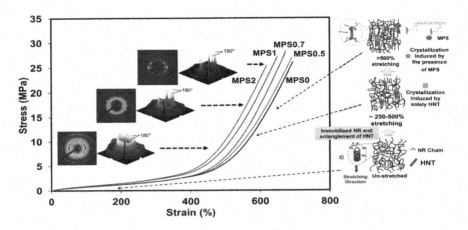

FIGURE 7.19 Schematic model representing the relationship between mechanical strength and corresponding strain-induced crystallization in the NR/HNT composites with MPS as a compatibilizer.

From these results, correlation between the strain-induced crystallization and corresponding interaction between MPS and the composites is represented in a schematic model (Figure 7.19). In this scheme, two stages of crystallization are represented. The first stage happens at a lower strain of approximately 160%–200%. In this stage, the NR matrix may be in contact with the HNT due to the interfacial interaction created by the unique characteristics of the HNT. On stretching, HNT is orientated and aligned along the stretching direction. Crystallization of the NR matrix is then induced due to the stress concentration point on the HNT surfaces, and the crystallinity increases in association with the orientation of the HNT. As a consequence, the NR chains are rearranged and crystallized. Second, at the strains over 240%, the crystallinity of the NR matrix increases steeply due to the collaborative crystallization of NR and HNT in association with the contribution of the MPS. The hydrogen bonding formed by the presence of the MPS plays a major role in pulling the surrounding molecular chains. Thus, a significant increase in crystallization is observed at higher strains and this is in agreement with results observed previously in the stress-strain behaviors and WAXS profiles.

7.8 CONCLUSIONS

The following conclusions can be drawn:

- The optimum tensile strength and elongation at break were exhibited at 5-phr HNT loading, due to the acceleration of strain-induced crystallization in the NR.
- A mechanistic model for the strain-induced crystallization and orientation evolution of the network in the NR/HNT composite was proposed, as it was supported by the tensile fractured surfaces and WAXS profiles.

Halloysite-Filled NR Composite: Morphology and Crystallization

- The overall properties of NR/HNT composites were further enhanced by the addition of MPS-based palm stearin.
- Incorporating MPS caused a shifting of the peak to lower $2\theta°$ of $9.5°$. This indicates that the MPS is helps to expand the interlayer space of HNT. As a result, the dispersibility of the HNT is improved throughout the NR matrix.

REFERENCES

Berahman, Reyhaneh, Maryam Raiati, Majid Mehrabi Mazidi, and Seyed Mohamad Reza Paran. 2016. "Preparation and characterization of vulcanized silicone rubber/halloysite nanotube nanocomposites: Effect of matrix hardness and HNT content." *Materials & Design* 104: 333–345.

Bhargava, Rohit, Shi-Qing Wang, and Jack L Koenig. 2003. "FTIR microspectroscopy of polymeric systems." In *Liquid Chromatography/FTIR Microspectroscopy/Microwave Assisted Synthesis*, 137–191. Springer: Heidelberg, Germany.

Carretero-González, Javier, Haris Retsos, Raquel Verdejo, Shigeyuki Toki, Benjamin S Hsiao, Emmanuel P Giannelis, and Miguel A Lopez-Manchado. 2008. "Effect of nanoclay on natural rubber microstructure." *Macromolecules* 41 (18): 6763–6772.

Coran, AY. 2003. "Chemistry of the vulcanization and protection of elastomers: a review of the achievements." *Journal of Applied Polymer Science* 87 (1): 24–30.

Das, Amit, Klaus Werner Stöckelhuber, René Jurk, Dieter Jehnichen, and Gert Heinrich. 2011. "A general approach to rubber–montmorillonite nanocomposites: Intercalation of stearic acid." *Applied Clay Science* 51 (1): 117–125.

Du, Mingliang, Baochun Guo, and Demin Jia. 2010. "Newly emerging applications of halloysite nanotubes: a review." *Polymer International* 59 (5): 574–582.

Hernández, Marianella, Miguel A López-Manchado, Alejandro Sanz, Aurora Nogales, and Tiberio A Ezquerra. 2011. "Effects of strain-induced crystallization on the segmental dynamics of vulcanized natural rubber." *Macromolecules* 44 (16): 6574–6580.

Ismail, H, Pooria Pasbakhsh, MN Ahmad Fauzi, and A Abu Bakar. 2008. "Morphological, thermal and tensile properties of halloysite nanotubes filled ethylene propylene diene monomer (EPDM) nanocomposites." *Polymer Testing* 27 (7): 841–850.

Ismail, H, SZ Salleh, and Z Ahmad. 2013. "Properties of halloysite nanotubes-filled natural rubber prepared using different mixing methods." *Materials & Design* 50: 790–797.

Ismail, Hanafi, Siti Zuliana Salleh, and Zulkifli Ahmad. 2011. "Curing characteristics, mechanical, thermal, and morphological properties of halloysite nanotubes (HNTs)-filled natural rubber nanocomposites." *Polymer-Plastics Technology and Engineering* 50 (7): 681–688.

Kohjiya, Shinzo, Preeyanuch Junkong, and Yuko Ikeda. 2017. "Crystallization of natural rubber: Its unique feature." *KGK-Kautschuk Gummi Kunststoffe* 70 (10): 38–48.

Kuang, Wenyi, Zhijun Yang, Zhenghai Tang, and Baochun Guo. 2016. "Wrapping of polyrhodanine onto tubular clay and its prominent effects on the reinforcement of the clay for rubber." *Composites Part A: Applied Science and Manufacturing* 84: 344–353.

Lagaly, G, M Fernandez Gonzalez, and Armin Weiss. 1976. "Problems in layer-charge determination of montmorillonites." *Clay Minerals* 11 (3): 173–187.

Masa, Abdulhakim, Sougo Iimori, Ryota Saito, Hiromu Saito, Tadamoto Sakai, Azizon Kaesaman, and Natinee Lopattananon. 2015. "Strain-induced crystallization behavior of phenolic resin crosslinked natural rubber/clay nanocomposites." *Journal of Applied Polymer Science* 132 (39): 42580.

Masa, Abdulhakim, Ryota Saito, Hiromu Saito, Tadamoto Sakai, Azizon Kaesaman, and Natinee Lopattananon. 2016. "Phenolic resin-crosslinked natural rubber/clay nanocomposites:

Influence of clay loading and interfacial adhesion on strain-induced crystallization behavior." *Journal of Applied Polymer Science* 133 (12): 43214.

Nabil, H., H. Ismail, and C. T. Ratnam. 2014. "Simultaneous enhancement of mechanical and dynamic mechanical properties of natural rubber/recycled ethylene-propylene-diene rubber blends by electron beam irradiation." *International Journal of Polymer Analysis and Characterization* 19 (3): 272–285.

Osaka, Noboru, Masahiro Kato, and Hiromu Saito. 2013. "Mechanical properties and network structure of phenol resin crosslinked hydrogenated acrylonitrile-butadiene rubber." *Journal of Applied Polymer Science* 129 (6): 3396–3403.

Pasbakhsh, Pooria, H Ismail, MN Ahmad Fauzi, and A Abu Bakar. 2009. "Influence of maleic anhydride grafted ethylene propylene diene monomer (MAH-g-EPDM) on the properties of EPDM nanocomposites reinforced by halloysite nanotubes." *Polymer Testing* 28 (5): 548–559.

Rattanasom, N, T Saowapark, and C Deeprasertkul. 2007. "Reinforcement of natural rubber with silica/carbon black hybrid filler." *Polymer Testing* 26 (3): 369–377.

Ray, Suprakas Sinha, and Masami Okamoto. 2003. "Polymer/layered silicate nanocomposites: a review from preparation to processing." *Progress in Polymer Science* 28 (11): 1539–1641.

Rooj, Sandip, Amit Das, Varun Thakur, RN Mahaling, Anil K Bhowmick, and Gert Heinrich. 2010. "Preparation and properties of natural nanocomposites based on natural rubber and naturally occurring halloysite nanotubes." *Materials & Design* 31 (4): 2151–2156.

Sadequl, AM, BT Poh, and US Ishiaku. 1999. "Effect of filler loading on the mechanical properties of epoxidized natural rubber (ENR 25) compared with natural rubber (SMR L)." *International Journal of Polymeric Materials* 43 (3–4): 261–278.

Surya, Indra, H Ismail, and AR Azura. 2013. "Alkanolamide as an accelerator, filler-dispersant and a plasticizer in silica-filled natural rubber compounds." *Polymer Testing* 32 (8): 1313–1321.

Toki, Shigeyuki, Igors Sics, Shaofeng Ran, Lizui Liu, Benjamin S Hsiao, Syozo Murakami, Kazunobu Senoo, and Shinzo Kohjiya. 2002. "New insights into structural development in natural rubber during uniaxial deformation by in situ synchrotron X-ray diffraction." *Macromolecules* 35 (17): 6578–6584.

White, James L, and Joseph E Spruiell. 1983. "The specification of orientation and its development in polymer processing." *Polymer Engineering & Science* 23 (5): 247–256.

Zhong, Bangchao, Zhixin Jia, Yuanfang Luo, Demin Jia, and Fang Liu. 2017. "Understanding the effect of filler shape induced immobilized rubber on the interfacial and mechanical strength of rubber composites." *Polymer Testing* 58: 31–39.

8 Alumina Filled Rubber Composites

Application, Mechanical Properties, Morphological Characteristics and Processability

Noraiham Mohamad, Jeefferie Abd Razak, and Hairul Effendy Ab Maulod
Universiti Teknikal Malaysia Melaka
Durian Tunggal, Melaka, Malaysia

Andanastuti Muchtar and Mariyam Jameelah Ghazali
Universiti Kebangsaan Malaysia
Bangi, Malaysia

Dahlan Hj. Mohd
Malaysian Nuclear Agency
Bangi, Malaysia

Che Husna Azhari
Entruss Ventures Sdn Bhd
Bangi, Malaysia

CONTENTS

8.1	Introduction	160
8.2	What Is Alumina?	161
8.3	Alumina as Fillers in Polymer Matrix Composites	164
8.4	Rubber Matrices in Alumina-Filled Rubber Composites	166
	8.4.1 Natural Rubber	166
	8.4.2 Silicone Rubber (SiR)	168
	8.4.3 Epoxidized Natural Rubber (ENR) Matrix	168
	8.4.4 Ethylene Propylene Diene Monomer (EPDM) Rubber	169

DOI: 10.1201/9781003220947-8

8.5	Application of Alumina-Reinforced Rubber Composites	170
	8.5.1 Alumina-Reinforced Rubber for Electronic Application	170
	8.5.2 Application as Insulator in Power Transmission and Distribution Lines	172
8.6	Mechanical Properties of Alumina-Filled Rubber Composites	173
	8.6.1 Effect of Alumina Loadings on Tensile Properties of Rubber Composites	178
	8.6.2 Effect of Alumina Particle Sizes (Micro vs Nano) to the Tensile Properties of Rubber Composites	179
	8.6.3 Effect of Alumina Surface Treatment to the Tensile Properties of Rubber Composites	179
	8.6.4 Effect of Curing Agent on the Tensile Properties of Rubber Composites	180
	8.6.5 Effect of Matrix Modification on the Tensile Properties of Rubber Composites	181
	8.6.6 Effect of Hybrid Alumina Particle Sizes on Tensile Properties of Rubber Composites	181
	8.6.7 Hardness of Alumina-Filled Rubber Composites	182
8.7	Morphological Characteristics of Alumina-Filled Rubber Composites	183
	8.7.1 Scanning Electron Microscopy (SEM)	184
	8.7.2 Transmission Electron Microscopy (TEM)	188
8.8	Processability of Alumina-Filled Rubber Composites	190
8.9	Conclusions	191
	Acknowledgment	191
	References	191

8.1 INTRODUCTION

Polymer particulate composites can be defined as the combination of a polymer matrix (virgin polymer or blend) with particulate form filler(s) or reinforcement materials that are either metallic or non-metallic. They have aroused widespread interest by academics and industries due to their ability to enhance the physical, mechanical and functional properties of polymeric matrices. To date, polymer particulate composites are widely used in a variety of applications.

In line with the evolution of materials toward advanced materials and nanomaterials, many new polymer particulate composites filled with microparticles and nanoparticles have been developed to achieve sets of desired properties for various applications. With careful selection of reinforcement materials, matrices and manufacturing processes, materials scientists and engineers can tailor material properties to meet specific needs. For example, composites with directed strengths that are similar or surpass the strength of metal and ceramic materials can be produced. Together, selected functional properties, such as resistance to heat, chemicals and weathering, can be made by selecting appropriate matrix materials. The biggest advantage of composite materials is their strength to weight ratio. By choosing the right combination of reinforcement materials and matrices, manufacturers can produce properties that suit the needs of a particular structure and for a specific purpose.

Alumina Filled Rubber Composites

In a composite system there are two main components: (1) matrix material and (2) filler or reinforcing material. Polymer matrices are categorized into two main groups called thermosets and thermoplastics. Thermoplastics are normally low-melting solids at room temperature, capable of being reformed and reshaped once subjected to heat. Meanwhile, thermosets are usually liquid in their original form. During production, this thermoset goes through a curing process using a catalyst, heat or a combination of both. Once cured, the solid thermoset cannot be converted back to its original liquid form. Unlike thermoplastics, a cured thermoset will not melt and flow, hence, it cannot be reshaped once formed; rather, it will lose its hardness once softened under heat (Park and Seo 2011). The third underdog but important engineering material is known as an elastomer or rubber. It takes on a structure almost similar to thermoset materials, which requires curing to achieve elastic properties via the formation of three-dimensional (3D) structures called cross-links. They have relatively low strength but are extremely elastic; some can be stretched for up to 1000% elongation before rupture (Kalle et al. 2007). Not like thermosets that require tedious processing, rubber can be processed using the established process for thermoplastic materials with specific alterations for curing steps.

Particulate-shaped fillers are another type of second-phase materials used in composites. They are used as reinforcement in addition to fiber reinforcement. The main function of the use of fillers in polymer matrix materials is for mechanical reinforcement and most likely called "reinforcing fillers" in many references (Park and Seo 2011). Also, they are used for the enhancement of other functional properties such as optical effects, thermal conductivity, thermal expansion control, electrical properties, magnetic properties, heat resistance and others. Particulate-shaped fillers are also used to obtain better processing properties in addition to density control, water resistance, hardness, staining ability and cost reduction (Park and Seo 2011). Each type of filler has different properties depending on the particle size measurement, shape and surface chemistry. Today, nano-sized fillers are very popular with researchers because of their ability to enhance composite properties without sacrificing more of their functional properties. However, the widespread use of nanoparticles in the industry is still limited due to various issues such as high cost, material handling, occupational safety, and health laws, standards and others.

In this chapter, the focus is on a type of rubber composite, which reinforced or filled with alumina particles forms alumina-filled rubber composites. Several rubber matrices including natural rubber (NR) and synthetic rubber are addressed for specific applications. Their reported mechanical properties and the correlation between mechanical properties and morphological characteristics and its processability are also included.

8.2 WHAT IS ALUMINA?

Alumina is a very important ceramic material in the main support industry and is a key ingredient in integrated circuits (ICs) and ultra-large-scale integration (LSI) semiconductor substratum, heat head substratum for facsimile machines, high-voltage sodium lamps (known as "Lucalox"), hard plates in rigid body shields, certain parts of automobiles and spark plugs. Also, it is used as an artificial gem, ceramic tool eye, in cermet systems (i.e., Al_2O_3-Cr) and as an abrasive (Ichinose 1987). All of these applications utilize the properties of alumina, such as for insulation, high thermal conductivity, high strength and high corrosion and wear resistance. The presence of alumina can improve the dielectric performance and thermal conduction (Li et al. 2007) and the mechanical properties (Zhang et al. 2005) of composite insulation.

Alumina can be classified as advanced ceramic or fine ceramic. Almost all ceramics are compounds of electropositive and electronegative elements. Most ceramic bonds are ionic, but in some cases covalent and metal bonds also exist. Each combination of elements has many configurations and produces a variety of functions. Common features of ceramics are high thermal resistance, electrical or semiconductor insulation with various dielectric and magnetic properties, strong resistance to deformation, brittle fragility and low toughness. Although there are weaknesses in terms of very real properties, various researches are (Siegel et al. 2001; Sim et al. 2005; El-Sabbagh et al. 2006; Li et al. 2007; Chandra et al. 2008; McGrath et al. 2008; Mohamad et al. 2011; Roy et al. 2018; Chen et al. 2019; Latief et al. 2019) always conducted to develop and expand the benefits of good ceramic properties as reinforcment or filler materials in various polymer-based compounds or composites.

Alumina is the oxide of aluminum metal (Al). It is the second most abundant material after silica compared with the natural minerals that exist in the environment. Most alumina exists in feldspar, mica and other aluminosilicates and is rarely found as pure alumina. Bauxite is alumina hydrated and consists of a mixture of $Al_2O_3 \cdot H_2O$ and $Al_2O_3 \cdot 3H_2O$. Ongoing research has confirmed that hydrated alumina also exists in the form of diaspore (α-$Al_2O_3 \cdot 3H_2O$), boehmite (–$Al_2O_3 \cdot H_2O$), hydrargillite (–$Al_2O_3 \cdot 3H_2O$), and bayerite (–$Al_2O_3 \cdot 3H_2O$). However, bauxite is the common name for aluminum hydroxide ore. Only a little corundum (anhydrous alumina) is found in the environment (Figure 8.1). Thus, alumina is mostly man-made from the modification of various chemical salts through chemical treatment of either wet or dry methods. Fused alumina (stable crystalline state) is produced through the mixing of raw materials containing α-Al_2O_3 crystals, which resemble natural corundum (Ichinose 1987).

Apart from α-Al_2O_3, there are various polymorphs of alumina, namely η, γ, θ, δ alumina and others. At temperatures above 1000°C, it is converted to an α configuration without reversible reaction. Similarly, when a configuration appears in

FIGURE 8.1 Crystal structure of alumina mineral corundum. (From Mills 2008.)

Alumina Filled Rubber Composites

$Na_2O \cdot 11Al_2O_3$, it is known as a sodium ion conductor. In corundum, oxygen ions (anions) are arranged in dense hexagons and all Al ions meet two-thirds of the octave site (Ichinose 1987). In alumina, every two cations of Al^{3+} need to be balanced by three O^{2-} anions, hence, the chemical formula is Al_2O_3. The M and X coordination numbers of the corundum are 6:4 M_2X_3. The ionic and covalent bonds that exist in alumina molecules cause it to have a very high melting point of 2050°C, high hardness and excellent electrical insulation. Also, alumina is capable of taking various forms and functions. The properties of conventional alumina are listed in Table 8.1 (Ichinose 1987; Sim et al. 2005; Pinto et al. 2015).

The use of alumina as a filler in polymer composites for commercial applications is increasingly attracting the attention of some to improve the combination of properties obtained by using nano-sized fillers. However, the original nature of hydrophilic natural alumina makes it difficult to form an interaction between alumina and the polymer matrix. With further scientific developments, this effect has been minimized with various methods of surface chemical modification with the use of

TABLE 8.1
Properties of General Alumina

Properties	Value
Water absorption (%)	0–0.00
Relative density	3.4–3.7
Coefficient of thermal expansion 25°C–700°C ($\times 10^{-4}$)	7.5–7.9
Tensile strength (kg/cm^2)	1400–1750
Bulk modulus (GPa)	247
Shear modulus (GPa)	158
Compression strength (kg/cm^2)	10,000–28,000
Flexural strength (kg/cm^2)	2800–4200
Abrasive strength (kg cm/cm^2)	5.6–6.2
Thermal conductivity (W/mK)	30
Insulation capacity (V/mm)	10,000
Maximum operating temperature (°C)	1700
Volume-based resistivity	
100°C	2.0×10^{13}
300°C	5.0×1010–6.0×10^{11}
500°C	1.0×108–1.0×10^9
700°C	3.0×106–4.0×10^7
T_c Value (°C)	800–930
Dielectric constant	
1 mC/s	8.3–9.3
10,000 mC/s	8.0–9.1
Dielectric loss ($\times 10^{-4}$)	
1 mC/s	3–7
10,000 mC/s	14–15
Dielectric stiffness (2.5 mm, kV/mm)	10

various coupling and stabilizing agents. For example, the hydroxyl group of $-Al_2O_3$ was found to react with the isocyanate group on the particle surface through an additional reaction on the double bond between atoms C and N in the isocyanate group (Li et al. 2007). This reaction adds a hydrophobic tail to the surface of the alumina particle, which allows a reaction with a polymer matrix. Moreover, the surface properties of alkaline (base) alumina cause alumina to be dispersed in acidic dispersers for the production of good dispersion in composites (Kakui et al. 2005).

Due to the alkaline surface properties of alumina, mixing it into the polymer matrices is a good step toward the aging properties of many rubber vulcanized systems. An analogy of the benefits of calcium stearate mixing can reduce the effects of oxidation hardening in volcanic formulation using the rubber matrix.

8.3 ALUMINA AS FILLERS IN POLYMER MATRIX COMPOSITES

Although conventional alumina has gained a place as a commercial material and is used as a filler to improve thermal and mechanical properties due to its high performance, the literature has only accumulated since 2000 (Zhang et al. 2005). The efforts to investigate the ability of alumina as fillers in polymer matrices and several factors are listed in Table 8.2.

From Table 8.2, it could be deduced that most of the research is targeted to improve the mechanical properties of thermoplastics and thermosets. In early 2000, there are still limited studies reporting on the mechanical properties of rubber-based composites with alumina as reinforcement. Most of the studies focus on the use of alumina as inorganic electrical insulating filler in silicon rubber (SiR) to improve the thermal conductivity and coefficient of thermal expansion (CTE) for rubber materials in electronic packaging and elastomeric thermal pads (Viswanath et al. 2000; Sim et al. 2005). The mechanical properties of surface-treated alumina-filled NR composites are reported by El-Sabbagh et al. (2006). Meanwhile, the first attempt at the incorporation of alumina nanoparticles into epoxidized natural rubber (ENR) was by Mohamad et al. (2008). This effort has also attracted the interest of other researchers studying alumina performance in the matrix with the presence of ENR as a stabilizing material (Konar et al. 2010). The effects of the use of alumina with two different sizes, namely microscale and nanoscale, and the addition of ENR as a stabilizing agent on the cure characteristics, mechanical properties and aging properties of composites have been studied. The addition of alumina was found to further enhance the composite properties compared with the original matrix, and these properties were further enhanced with the use of alumina nanoparticles. NR-nanoparticle alumina composites show strong interaction with the presence of ENR; this is evidenced by the increase in cross-density in the composite. Also, alumina exhibits high oxidation resistance behavior compared with conventional matrix materials or composites produced.

In recent research, the use of nano-sized fillers in polymer composites has received more attention than micro-fillers. Most researchers believe that fillers need to have a high surface area to enable excellent matrix-filler interaction. Among the requirements of fillers for rubber other than the appropriate surface structure and chemistry is that a filler must have a high specific surface area and particle size must

TABLE 8.2
Works on Alumina-Filled Polymer Composites

References	Polymer	Type of Filler Particles	Factor	Targeted Properties
Siegel et al. (2001)	PMMA	Nano-size alumina (particulate)	Filler loadings	Mechanical properties
Ash et al. (2004)	PMMA	Nano-size alumina (particulate)	Filler loadings	Mechanical and thermal properties
Bhimaraj et al. (2005)	PET	Nano-size alumina (particulate)	Filler loadings	Tribological properties
Zhang et al. (2005)	LLDPE and epoxy	Micro-size alumina (particulate)	Type of matrix (polar and non-polar) and filler loadings	Dielectric properties
Kakui et al. (2005)	PEI	Nano-size alumina (particulate)	Dispersant molecular weight	Dispersibility in ethanol suspension
Zhao et al. (2006)	Nylon-6	Micro- and nano-size alumina (particulate)	Filler particle size and filler loadings	Tribological properties
Jung et al. (2006)	PP	PS grafted-alumina nanoparticles (particulate)	Filler loadings and the dose of gamma rays	Mechanical properties and dispersibility of nano-size fillers
Li et al. (2007)	Diphenylmethane-4-4'-diisocyanate (MDI)	Nano-size alumina (particulate)	MDI surface treatment	Dispersibility of nano-size alumina
Zhao et al. (2008)	Epoxy	Nano-size alumina (particulate)	Filler loadings and silane surface treatment	Tensile and morphological properties
McGrath et al. (2008)	Epoxy	Micro-size alumina (particulate)	Filler particles dimension, filler loadings and cross-linking	Mechanical properties
Shukla et al. (2008)	Epoxy	Micro-size alumina (platelets)	Filler loadings and silane treatment	Mechanical properties
Chandra et al. (2008)	Polycarbonate	Micro-size alumina (particulate)	Filler loadings and chemical modifications (silane and styrene-maleic anhydride)	Dispersibility of fillers and optical properties
Zhao and Li (2008)	Epoxy	Nano-size alumina	Filler loadings and water absorption	Mechanical and dielectric properties
Omrani et al. (2009)	Epoxy	Nano-size alumina	Filler loadings	Thermal, viscoelastic and mechanical properties
Zhou et al. (2009)	Epoxy	Nano-size alumina	Filler loadings	Acoustic properties
Latief et al. (2019)	Polyester	Nano-size alumina	Filler loadings	Physical and mechanical properties

Abbreviations: LLDPE, linear low density polyethylene; PEI, polyethyleneimine; PET, polyethylene terephthalate; PMMA, polymethyl methacrylate; PP, polypropylene; PS, polystyrene.

be less than 1 μm. Today, the interest in utilizing alumina particles in the rubber matrix mostly focuses on electronic packaging and electrical insulations. There are several types of matrix that have received the most attention in the preparation of alumina-filled rubber matrix composites.

8.4 RUBBER MATRICES IN ALUMINA-FILLED RUBBER COMPOSITES

The main function of the matrix material is to bind the filler/reinforcement material together, protecting it from environmental and mechanical damage. It serves to transfer the applied stress and disperse it between the reinforcing fibers. For fillers to endure the imposed loading, the matrix is a material with a lower modulus and is capable of resisting higher elongation than reinforcement. The matrix determines the operating temperature of the composite service as well as the processing parameters for the manufacture of parts. Rubber or elastomer is a type of thermoset polymer material with elastic properties. There are two categories of rubber: (1) NR obtained from natural sources and (2) synthetic rubber derived from petrochemicals. Several rubber matrices have been investigated by researchers for the development of alumina-filled rubber composites for various purposes. Rubber has unique properties compared with other types of polymer materials including:

1. *Physical and mechanical properties:* Rubber is elastic and flexible, has high elongation at break (EB) and is impermeable to air/water.
2. *Abrasive properties:* Rubber has a flexible coefficient of friction, it is lower on a wet surface and higher on a dry surface, which makes it suitable for the application in lubricant bearings used in a wet environment and belting for power transmission.
3. *Viscoelastic behavior:* It shows the Mullin effect where the stress properties against strain under large deformation depend on maximum load. Rubber also shows the effects of Payne associated with decreased energy storage capacity with increased strain. It is more pronounced at small stretch amplitudes and is attributed to the weakening physical bonds caused by its deformation. This property can be measured by a stress relaxation or creep test. These phenomena are frequently observed in carbon black-filled rubber composites.
4. *Thermal properties*: Rubber has low heat conduction and is prone to experience thermal fatigue due to heat buildup under dynamic mechanical conditions.
5. *Electrical properties:* It has good electrical resistance. This makes rubber suitable for use in electrical protective clothing and as in insulation packaging.

8.4.1 NATURAL RUBBER

NR is a natural biosynthesis polymer processed from the latex of the *Hevea brasiliensis* tree. This species originates from Brazil but thrives in continents with an

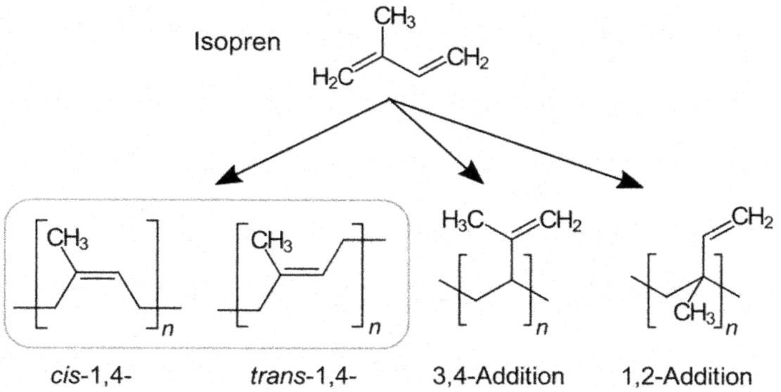

Alumina Filled Rubber Composites

FIGURE 8.2 Structure of NR and polyisoprene. (From Roland.chem 2016.)

equatorial climate such as Asia, Africa and South America. The largest producing countries of rubber in Asia today are Indonesia, Thailand and Malaysia who contribute about 75% of all-natural rubber world production (Song 2017). However, only 40% of the 30 million tonnes of the production of the rubber per year is NR; the rest are synthetic rubber derived from petrochemical sources (Song 2017). The chemical structure of NR is *cis*-1,4-polyisoprene and it contains small amounts of fatty acids and protein residues as well as resins that promote sulfur vulcanization. Synthetic rubber consists of polyisoprene backbones derived from the polyacetylene backbone through the saturation of every other double bond. The chemical structure of NR and other derivations of polyisoprene are shown in Figure 8.2. NR is a non-polar hydrocarbon and contains chemically reactive double-unsaturated bonds. Non-polar configuration tends to accelerate the curing rate compared with other synthetic rubbers. The high double bond content of NR causes low thermal instability and limited heat resistance, hence it is vulnerable to heat. It is also prone to environmental elements such as oxygen attack by ozone, light, radiation and moisture. It is completely unsuitable for most applications that require long-term resistance to operating temperatures above 100°C and operating environments that are exposed to oil and hydrocarbon solvents.

The glass transition temperature for NR is about –70°C. NR curing is usually performed at a relatively low temperature of less than 170°C with strict control throughout the curing cycle. NR with sulfur curing forms a polysulfide link (C-Sx-X; X > 2) that has transformed the soft state of NR into a technically useful form (Abd Razak 2016). These cross-links provide relatively long cross-links, as a barrier to permanent flow. NR vulcanizates with high polysulfide cross-linking content are more concentrated compared with mono- or disulfide cross-links. NR has high tensile strength (TS), good dynamic properties and good processing characteristics.

Crystallization increases NR strength and provides high resistance to fracture propagation during deformation. The cross-linking structure and density of the cross-linking influence the physical and mechanical properties of the NR. It is used in the application of high-resilient bearings, vibration isolators, dampers, impact pads and various other high dynamic stress and bending uses.

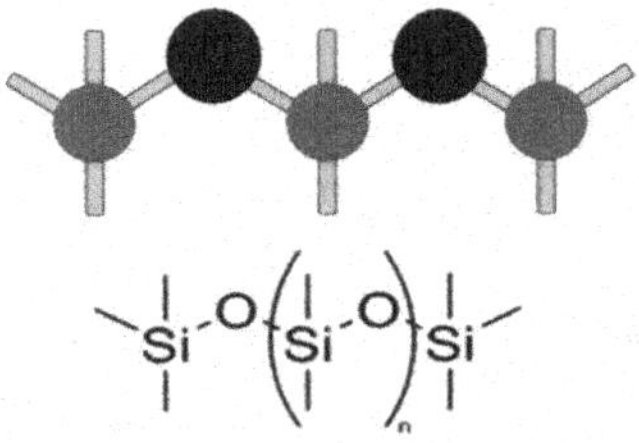

FIGURE 8.3 Chemical structure of silicone rubber. (From Jesse 2006.)

8.4.2 SILICONE RUBBER (SIR)

SiR is a synthetic elastomer consisting of hydrocarbon chains with the presence of silicon and oxygen atoms (Figure 8.3). SiR requires specific curing conditions to convert gel or liquid forms into a useful solid polymer. It can be either vulcanized or catalyzed to cure. SiR has a density of 1.07 gcm^{-3} and TS of approximately 1.57–30 MPa based on its types. Solid SiR is thermally stable at the temperature range from –120°C up to 300°C with coefficient thermal expansion of 300×10^{-6} K^{-1} and thermal conductivity of 0.18–0.2 $Wm^{-1}K^{-1}$. Unlike NR and other organic rubbers, SiR has limited susceptibility toward ozone, heat, ultraviolet (UV) light or other raging factors due to the presence of silicon atoms.

SiR has relatively excellent high-temperature properties such as TS and toughness, fire resistance and thermal conductivity, tear strength and compression strength, creep strength and cyclic flexing (Song 2017). Furthermore, it has a dielectric constant in the range of 2.6–6.3 (Sim et al. 2005). The applications of SiR include electrical, electronic and automotive components, medical apparatus and implants, lubricants, sealants, cookware, apparel and toys (Song 2017).

8.4.3 EPOXIDIZED NATURAL RUBBER (ENR) MATRIX

ENR is a derivative of NR resulting from chemical modifications. The oxidizing reaction of NR is stereoregular, hence, the ENR is *cis*-1,4- polyisoprene with the epoxide group randomly located along the polymer spine (Figure 8.4). It has been stated that oxidation of NR from 1–90 mol% is feasible, but only three ENR grades are considered commercial grades, i.e., ENR 10, ENR 25 and ENR 50, which are

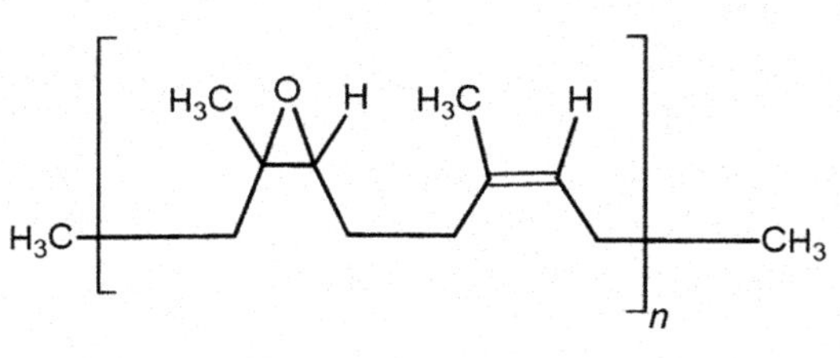

FIGURE 8.4 Chemical structure of ENR. (From Baker and Gelling 1987.)

Alumina Filled Rubber Composites

integers 10, 25, and 50 that represent the percentage of moles of epoxide incorporated into the NR chain (Mohamad 2011). In functional groups of ENR, C=C can be bonded, respectively, with metal ions, Mn^+, and metal particles, MnO. COC groups can also be bonded to metal atoms through O atoms, but the binding of oxygen to metals is weak. The higher the percentage of oxidation in the NR chain, the higher is the polarity and the transition temperature of the ENR glass. This also means that it is increasingly difficult for ENRs to be dissolved in non-polar solvents. The chemical and physical properties of ENR change with the degree of oxidation (mol%) introduced into the NR chain. Some of these properties are more similar to the properties of synthetic rubber than the properties of NR. ENR has high miscibility with more polar components in its polymeric chains and compatibility to interact with inorganic fillers. Consequently it offers remarkable properties, for example, great oil resistance, limited air permeability, higher wet grip and moving obstruction. The oil resistance of ENR vulcanizates with 50% epoxidation level (ENR 50) approaches the qualities of medium-acrylonitrile-content nitrile rubber and outperforms chloroprene rubber. The protection to air permeability of ENR 50 has been reported to be equivalent to medium-acrylonitrile-content nitrile rubber and butyl rubber. As a result, ENR can be used to replace most of the NR-based products with improvement in thermal and ozone resistance.

8.4.4 ETHYLENE PROPYLENE DIENE MONOMER (EPDM) RUBBER

Ethylene propylene diene monomer (EPDM) is a synthetic rubber obtained from the polymerization of ethylene and propylene, with a slight presence of non-conjugated diene content of 3%–9%. It is a very saturated polymer and non-polar due to the low content of –C=C– (Figure 8.5). The temperature of the glass transition, T_g, for EPDM rubber is about –60°C. The ratio of ethylene to propylene for commercial-grade EPDM is in the range of 50/50 to 75/25 (Abd Razak 2016). EPDM is generally an amorphous polymer and can be designed to be semi-crystalline to increase the green strength. However, with increasing ethylene content, the crystallization of rubber becomes more than 55%–65%. These crystals usually melt in the temperature range between 30°C and 90°C. Therefore, EPDM has processability below 90°C for the best product with good strength and shape retention. However, EPDM exhibits good resistance to high temperatures and does not undergo a reversal process during curing.

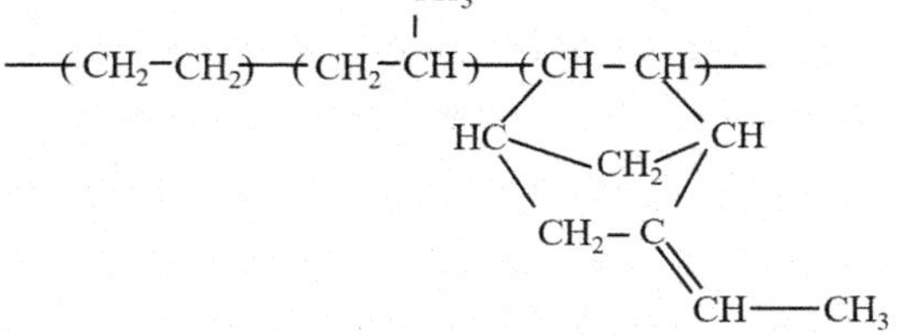

FIGURE 8.5 Chemical structure of EPDM. (From Wang et al. 2018.)

EPDM can be cured by vulcanization by sulfur and peroxide. EPDM does not have any polar group or chemical group with high electron density. The absence of these groups in the EPDM spinal chain causes poor molecular chain interactions. This situation complicates the bond and interactions between EPDM and other materials. However, at a high degree of saturation and effective chain modification, EPDM is more compatible with other rubber materials such as NR. Plenty of works have explored this potential by forming NR/EPDM blends to improve their resistance to environmental factors such as moisture, weather, heat, and ozone. It combines both of their good properties for a specific application (Abd Razak 2016).

EPDM is a non-halogen rubber with a saturated and environmentally friendly spinal chain, making it suitable for external application. This rubber has resistance to chemicals, but not to other oils or hydrocarbons. It has low absorption and adhesion value due to its compact chain structure, which is very beneficial in exhibiting the toughness properties of a plastic material and the flexibility of an elastomer phase. EPDM also has good resistance to aging, heat, oxidation and flexibility at low temperatures and concentrations. EPDM also has a good balance of chemical, electrical, thermal and mechanical properties, so it is widely used as a polymeric material for industrial use. Among the automotive vehicle products made using EPDM rubber base materials are gaskets, sealing systems, weather strips, heat insulation pads, sound dampers, anti-vibration parts, radiators, heating hoses, brake hoses, wires and cable insulation.

8.5 APPLICATION OF ALUMINA-REINFORCED RUBBER COMPOSITES

8.5.1 Alumina-Reinforced Rubber for Electronic Application

Polymers are widely used in the electronic application for the development of electronic packaging materials and thermal interface materials (TIMs) because of their low dielectric constant, light weight and excellent adhesive properties. Also, polymer-based materials are easy to process at a relatively low cost. These materials occupy 90% of the packaging of ICs and TIMs, in particular. The general property requirements for high-performance packaging materials are shown in Figure 8.6 (Chen et al. 2019).

Materials suitable for this function must have sufficient thermal conductivity but a low CTE. Also, for covering all rough mating surface areas, the material must be easily molded using only low contact pressure. Rubber filled with thermally conductive fillers seems like an effective method for solving thermal management problems. However, the integration and miniaturization of IC systems generates a high amount of heat in tiny spaces, shortening the life of encapsulation materials. Because the reliability and life span of electronic devices are highly influenced by operating temperatures, the wider use of virgin polymeric materials for electronic packaging is largely unsatisfactory. This is due to the low thermal insulating properties of the polymers where the thermal conductivity is only approximately 0.2 W/mK. In addition, large differences in the CTE between organic polymeric substrates and silicon

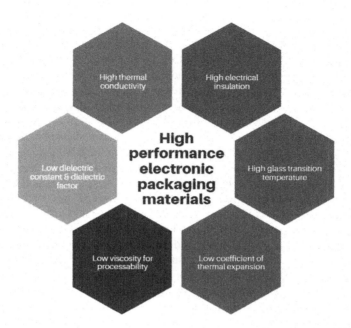

FIGURE 8.6 General property requirements for high-performance packaging materials.

chips result in higher pressures during the thermal cycle, especially at their interfaces, causing serious warping and soldering fatigue problems.

Two different types of thermally conductive fillers can be integrated into rubber to increase the thermal conductivity of rubber-based materials: (1) conventional micro-size ceramic particles and (2) advanced nanomaterials (Chen et al. 2019). First, the most common approach in fixing the heat removal problems is to use conventional ceramic micro-size fillers. For example, aluminum nitride (AlN), silica (SiO_2), alumina (Al_2O_3) and silicon carbide (SiC) have high thermal conductivity but are electrically insulating. This method does not, however, substantially increase the thermal conductivity of the rubber-based materials before the thermal percolation threshold is reached with very high filler loadings. On the other hand, the viscosity has an exponential increase with the increase of the filler loading, which degrades the flow properties suitable for the underfilling. Therefore, having good fluidity (i.e., low viscosity) is also important for rubber as encapsulants. It needs to be balanced out to fulfill the strict requirements for low thermal expansion and thermal dissipation.

Second, the alternative route is utilizing advanced nanomaterials such as carbon nanotubes (CNTs), graphene, nanotubes of boron nitride (BN), and nanosheets. These materials have remarkably high thermal conductivity and ultrahigh surface-to-volume ratio for high-performance rubber composites. Due to the extremely large surface area for interaction, it has a high tendency to form a well-connected heat-conducting network in the rubber matrices (Chen et al. 2019). However, because of the presence of an extremely high surface area, the nanomaterials have higher tendencies to form aggregates and agglomerates in the rubber matrices. This will create an acoustic mismatch between both materials, hence, strong interfacial thermal resistance imposing between both matrix and filler materials. As a result, the improvement in the thermal conductivity of the rubber composites is trivial. Also, carbon nanomaterials' high electrical conductivity often limits their applications in electronic packaging. The aligned nano-filler architecture can be effectively used in the orientation direction to increase the thermal conductivity of polymers, but the thermal conductivity is much lower in the perpendicular direction. Furthermore, for large-scale manufacturing, filler orientation is hardly adaptable and it is hard to meet the strict requirements of the current complex flip-chip underfill packaging process.

Virgin rubber has its inherent drawbacks; they limit its further application in electronics. It needs to achieve both excellent dielectric properties and low thermal conductivity for this purpose. To overcome these disadvantages, rubber modification is highly important. Numerous efforts have been carried out in designing and synthesizing polymeric materials of this kind, providing a wide variety of rubber composites that are processable and heat dissipating. Distribution of surface-treated inorganic thermally conductive fillers, such as Al_2O_3, AlN, BN, SiC etc., or its nanoparticles into polymers has been reported to increase the thermal conductivity of the composites to the polymer matrix by about 10 times. Zha et al. (2012) explored the effect of hybrid fillers in their work. They combined microsized silicone nitride (Si_3N_4) and nanosized Al_2O_3 particles in SiR composites. They found that adding a suitable ratio of these fillers into SiR gives higher thermal conductivity and lower relative dielectric permittivity than single-sized filler reinforced SiR.

8.5.2 Application as Insulator in Power Transmission and Distribution Lines

Today, there are increasing demands for composite insulators for power transmission and distribution lines. Polymer matrix composites are widely used as the main components in the composite non-ceramic insulators both for (1) composite rods that normally are glass-reinforced polymer (GRP) composites and (2) polymeric housing with multiple weather sheds. The rods can be made from various thermoset polymer matrices such as epoxy, polyester and vinyl ester resins. The later component is used to cover the surface of the composite rods for protection against environmental factors, such as corona discharges, moisture and chemical attacks. The most common housing materials today are SiRs, ethylene-propylene rubber and ethylene-vinyl acetate elastomers. SiR is widely utilized due to its good electrical insulation at relatively high temperatures, excellent hydrophobicity, high resistance to different forms of irradiation and chemical inertness. However, heat buildup easily occurs for insulators operating under high voltage, accelerating rubber aging. Despite being thermally stable, SiR needs further improvement in its thermal conductivity to mitigate the accumulation of heat. This is normally carried out by adding thermally conductive fillers, similar to the case of electronic packaging materials. Alumina has been one of the most common commercial choices for this purpose because of its electrical insulation properties, relatively high thermal conductivity and low cost.

However, reports mentioned the dispersion issues of using conventional microsized alumina in the rubber matrix and causing the composites to perform rather

Alumina Filled Rubber Composites

poorly. The reasons for these issue lie in the poor compatibility between hydrophobic surfaces of hydrocarbon SiR with hydrophilic alumina. This resulted in limited interactions between alumina particles and rubber. Numerous efforts have been made to improve these properties such as via surface treatment using chemicals and grafted polymers to activate surface particles, using submicron and nano-alumina particles, fillers hybridizations, matrix alteration etc. Silane coupling agents are widely used to enhance the efficiency of filler-filled rubber composites. It facilitates interface adhesion between alumina and organic rubber matrix by acting as the molecular bridges. As stated by He et al. (2018), bis(triethoxysilylpropyl)tetrasulfide-modified clay increased the TS of styrene-butadiene rubber (SBR) matrix from 8.8 to 14.5 MPa and increased stress at 100% strain (M100) from 3.1 to 8.3 MPa. Meanwhile, the thermal conductivity of silane-treated BN-filled SBR composite improved from 0.43 to 0.57 W/mK at only 10.5 vol% filler content. In the case of SiR-based composites, hexamethyldisilazane-fumed silica, methacryloxypropyltrimethoxyl silane and a pre-synthesized macromolecular silane coupling agent are explored for their ability to enhance the compatibility between inorganic fillers with SiR for better reinforcement.

Due to the extensive research on developing alumina-filled rubber composites for electronic packaging and electrical insulators, the following topics address mainly the mechanical properties of rubber composites for these applications.

8.6 MECHANICAL PROPERTIES OF ALUMINA-FILLED RUBBER COMPOSITES

To maintain tensile loading and flexural loading during operation, strength and flexibility is an essential property for an electrical cable and substrate material. However, the flexibility of the component needs to be compensated with an appreciable amount of rigidity or elasticity. Bad rigidity typically results in excessive warping and delamination. The characteristics and properties of both matrix and filler, as well as their proportion and the interfacial adhesion between them, highly affect the mechanical properties of the composites. The factors contributing to the physical, mechanical and functional properties of rubber composites (Boonstra 1979) include the following:

1. Interaction between rubber molecules (chemical structure of the rubber molecules, segmental motion, steric hindrance and presence of cross-linking).
2. Filler particle-rubber matrix interaction (hydrodynamic effect, bound rubber and the effect of swelling).
3. Filler-filler particle interaction (dynamic elasticity and hysteresis, Payne effect and Mullins effect).

The values of the TS, tensile modulus at 100 (M100) and 300 (M300) or elastic modulus, EB and hardness of several alumina-filled rubber composite systems are listed in Tables 8.3 and 8.4. The comparisons of mechanical properties are made for both NR and synthetic rubber-based composites. The general characteristics of

TABLE 8.3
Comparison of Mechanical Properties of Alumina-Filled Natural Rubber-Based Composites

References	Rubber	Type of Particles/ Loading	Tensile Strength (MPa)	Tensile Modulus (MPa)		Elongation at Break (%)	Hardness (Shore A)
El-Sabbagh et al. (2006)	NR	Micron-alumina treated with ammonium molybdate pigment (0, 20, 30 and 40 phr)	9.20 (0) 17.50–22.60 (20) 17.60–22.80 (30) 17.90–23.20 (40)	Elastic modulus: 1.23 (0) 2.61–3.26 (20) 2.70–3.42 (30) 2.80–3.61 (40)		754 (0) 587–734 (20) 593–702 (30) 650–670 (40)	41 (0) 42.6–49 (20) 44–50 (30) 43.6–55 (40)
Mohamad et al. (2008); Mohamad (2011)	ENR	Nano-alumina (0, 5, 10, 20, 30, 40, 50 and 60 phr)	17.02–20.93 (0) 17.44 (5) 17.29–17.35 (10) 17.12–17.16 (20) 16.40–16.45 (30) 16.31–16.36 (40) 15.65–15.71 (50) 14.72–14.80 (60)	M100: 0.61–0.63 (0) 0.63 (5) 0.74 (10) 0.75 (20) 0.97 (30) 0.99 (40) 1.15 (50) 1.34 (60)	M300: 2.64–2.68 (0) 2.68 (5) 2.94 (10) 3.70 (20) 4.16 (30) 4.26 (40) 4.96 (50) 5.44 (60)	594–625 (0) 614 (5) 557 (10) 540 (20) 540 (30) 525 (40) 521 (50) 495 (60)	11.7 (0) 11.79 (5) 12.5 (10) 13.63 (20) 14.43 (30) 15.73 (40) 17.13 (50) 18.93 (60)
Konar et al. (2010)	NR	Raw micron-alumina (20, 40 and 60 phr)	5.60 (0) 5.78 (20) 4.80 (40) 4.43 (60)	M300: 1.22 (0) 1.68 (20) 1.40 (40) 1.00 (60)		800 (0) 478 (20) 450 (40) 402 (60)	50 (0) 50 (20) 52 (40) 54 (60)
Konar et al. (2010)	NR	Active micron-alumina (20 and 40 phr)	5.60 (0) 7.69 (20) 7.40 (40)	M300: 1.22 (0) 2.04 (20) 1.84 (40)		800 (0) 500 (20) 490 (40)	50 (0) 51 (20) 53 (40)

Konar et al. (2010)	NR	Nano-alumina (20 phr)	5.60 (0) 16.22 (20)	M300: 1.22 (0) 3.01 (20)		800 (0) 633 (20)	50 (0) 58 (20)
Tangboriboon et al. (2011)	NR	Micro-alumina (~35%)	1.23–4.93	M100: 0.41–0.95	M300: 1.03	79–652	
Roy et al. (2018)	Maleated NR	Nano-alumina (1, 2 and 3 phr)	14.58 (0) 22.94 (1) 25.27 (2) 23.49 (3)	M100: 0.83 (0) 0.99 (1) 1.04 (2) 0.95 (3)		1000 (0) 1331 (1) 1394 (2) 1322 (3)	57 (0) 58 (1) 60 (2) 61 (3)
Roy et al. (2018)	NR	Nano-alumina (2 phr)	14.58 (0) 17.73 (2)	M100: 0.83 (0) 0.75 (2)		1000 (0) 1358 (2)	57 (0) 54 (2)

TABLE 8.4
Comparison of Mechanical Properties of Alumina-Filled Synthetic Rubber-Based Composites

References	Rubber	Type of Particles/ Loading	Tensile Strength (MPa)	Tensile Modulus (MPa)	Elongation at Break (%)
Zhou et al. (2008)	SiR	Hybrid sizes micron-alumina (55 %)	~1.25–3.5		~60–90
Wang et al. (2010)	EPDM	Nano-alumina (0, 5, 10, 15 and 20 vol%)	2.0 (0) 2.2 (5) 4.0 (10) 9.5 (15) 10.0 (20)	M100: 0.75 (0) 1.0 (5) 1.25 (10) 1.75 (15) 2.19 (20)	
Wang et al. (2010)	EPDM	Silane-treated nano-alumina (0, 5, 10, 15 and 20 vol%)	~2.0 (0) ~3.0 (5) ~5.5 (10) ~11.5 (15) ~13.0 (20)	M100: ~0.75 (0) ~1.10 (5) ~1.30 (10) ~2.00 (15) ~2.45 (20)	
Wang et al. (2010)	EPDM	Stearic acid-treated nano-alumina (0, 5, 10, 15 and 20 vol%)	~2.0 (0) ~2.0 (5) ~2.2 (10) ~4.0 (15) ~4.0 (20)	M100: ~0.75 (0) ~0.90 (5) ~1.00 (10) ~1.15 (15) ~1.25 (20)	
Namitha et al. (2013)	SiR	Micron-alumina (10 and 20 phr)	~5 (0) ~5.2 (10) ~5.2 (20)	M100: ~1.00 (0) ~1.00 (10) ~2.00 (20)	~500 (0) ~500 (10) ~400 (20)
Namitha et al. (2013)	SiR	Nano-alumina (10 and 20 phr)	~5 (0) ~6.5 (10) ~1.5 (20)	M100: ~1.00 (0) ~1.90 (10) No value due to premature failure (20)	~500 (0) ~500 (10) ~70 (20)
He et al. (2018)	SiR	Nano-alumina (0, 5, 10 and 15 vol%)	~0.5 (0) ~1.6 (5) ~4.8 (10) ~8.5 (15)	M100: ~0.35 (0) ~0.50 (5) ~0.72 (10) ~0.98 (15)	~150 (0) ~220 (5) ~410 (10) ~450 (15)
He et al. (2018)	SiR	VTMS treated nano-alumina (0, 5, 10 and 15 vol%)	~0.5 (0) ~1.8 (5) ~6.2 (10) ~10.0 (15)	M100: ~0.35 (0) ~0.60 (5) ~1.00 (10) ~1.60 (15)	~150 (0) ~275 (5) ~500 (10) ~610 (15)

Abbreviations: VTMS, vinyl trimethoxysilane.

Alumina Filled Rubber Composites

filler particles that influence the properties of composites (Boonstra 1979) include the following:

1. The particle size of fillers dictates the surface area per volume/weight as well as the total filler-matrix interface per volume of composites.
2. Specific surface activity per square of surface area normally improves with surface treatment.
3. Shape and structure of particles includes packing factor and porosity (pore sizes), which normally improve with particle sizes hybridization.

The incorporation of organic or inorganic solid filler particles as reinforcing materials is largely capable of controlling the mechanical properties of rubber matrix. In principle, the reinforcing effect can be induced in a rubber matrix by either or more of the following mechanisms (Tangboriboon et al. 2011):

1. The stress transfer from the matrix to the irregular shaped or non-isometric filler particles.
2. The chain stiffening from the partial replacement of softer matrix by stiffer filler/fillers.
3. The hindering of chain segmental movements or chain immobilization due to the interaction between the polymer chains and the filler surfaces.

In the case of highly flexible polymeric matrix chains, the stress transfer mechanism from the matrix to reinforcing filler is a size-independent contribution; it is hard to have fully isometric particles. This mechanism is highly influenced by the filler's aspect ratio, the strength of the interface between filler and matrix and the orientation of fillers to the external load. The second mechanism is the contributions of fractions between fillers to matrix materials (filler:matrix ratio) in the compound or composites. Third, the overall composite reinforcement is an attribute of the segmental immobilization mechanism. The contribution is a factor of filler particle size in the aspect of surface-to-volume ratios, where major differences are observed between incorporation of either micron, submicron or nano-size filler particles into the polymer matrix.

The ability of a material to reinforce a rubber matrix in either microcomposites or nanocomposites can be measured using a reinforcing index (RI), which can be calculated using Eq. 1 (El-Sabbagh et al. 2006):

$$RI = \left(\frac{N}{N_\circ} \right) \left[\frac{\% \text{ filler content}}{100} \right] \tag{8.1}$$

where N and $N_\circ$ are the nominal values of the properties obtained through measurements made from mechanical tests on composite samples with and without fillers. When different fillers are mixed into the rubber matrix, the materials show different tendencies to form aggregate networks because the differences in chemical properties, surface properties and dispersing abilities of a filler (determined by the filler, particle size, structure and surface activity) provide different levels of interaction between the filler material and the polymer matrix. The level of this interaction is also determined by the properties of the rubber and the formulation used whether it involves any chemical modification or not. The strength of the interaction between the mixed materials can indicate the processability and numbers of cured mechanical properties such as TS, modulus at a specific percentage of elongation, EB, yield strength and tear resistance. RI could be used as a single parameter to summarize the reinforcing level imparted by specific filler materials to the specific rubber compounds.

8.6.1 Effect of Alumina Loadings on Tensile Properties of Rubber Composites

The effect of alumina particles loadings is mostly studied together with other effects such as surface treatment (El-Sabbagh et al. 2006; Wang et al. 2010; He et al. 2018), particle sizes (Mohamad et al. 2008; Konar et al. 2010; Mohamad 2011; Namitha et al., 2013) and particle hybridization (Zhou et al. 2008). In most cases, the TS reached the maximum at optimum loadings of alumina particles and decreased when overloaded for both micro- and nanocomposites. Meanwhile, the modulus increases with filler loadings most of the time. Rather complex effects are observed in the flexibility of the composites in which both decrement and increment patterns manifested by the composites are represented by the EB values.

The effects of alumina loadings for the range of low to high loadings on the tensile properties of rubber composites are reported by Mohamad et al. (2008) and Mohamad (2011). The nano-size alumina particles were investigated between 5 and 60 phr. The motivation is due to the superior performance of rubber nanocomposites and postulation of better compatibility that might be observed between polar ENR with the alumina particles rather than to those of non-polar rubber. In their study, the developed materials are called epoxidized natural rubber filled with alumina nanoparticle (ENRAN) composites. The TS of ENRAN was found to increase when the ENR matrix was loaded with only 5 phr of alumina nanoparticles and subsequently decreased gradually with increasing particle loadings. However, the increase in TS value observed in ENRAN filled with 5 phr alumina is reported to be less significant due to the high bar error value (Mohamad 2011). This is due to the uneven distribution of alumina particles and scattered particles with uneven shapes. The material modulus of M100 and M300 increased with the increase in fillers in the ENR matrix. The observed increase in modulus supports the fact that alumina particles have good physical and chemical interaction with ENR. However, the reduction of the matrix to filler ratio decreases the EB value because the plastic deformation capability is dominated by the rubber phase. The recorded TSs are lower when compared with the control sample due to the direct effect of the increase in the density of agglomerates formed in the material rather than the reflection of the interaction that exists between the matrix-fillers. The indication of interaction between the filler-matrix can be further investigated via higher magnification characterization tools such as field emission scanning electron microscopy (FESEM) and transmission electron microscopy (TEM) micrographs on the cross-sectional surfaces of rubber

Alumina Filled Rubber Composites

composites. The embedment of particles inside a matrix can be an indication of good interaction between the materials. In their study, the ENR composites are predicted to show better performance if loaded with alumina particles at a low filler loading of less than 10 phr.

8.6.2 EFFECT OF ALUMINA PARTICLE SIZES (MICRO VS NANO) TO THE TENSILE PROPERTIES OF RUBBER COMPOSITES

Despite the reporting increment in mechanical properties due to the utilization of nano-size filler particles, these small particles have a high tendency to agglomerate due to the interaction forces between the particles. Therefore, to compare the contributions of alumina size particles to improve the mechanical properties, Konar et al. (2010) investigated the effect of using various alumina particles, such as active or calcined alumina (200 nm) and nano-alumina (28 nm). They have used non-polar NR as the matrix material. The properties are compared with the large-particle-size alumina of 1000 nm. The motivation for the study is the versatility of alumina as an advanced structural and heat-resistant material. Both active alumina and nano-alumina improved the TS, tensile modulus, and hardness of the composites compared with the control sample. Meanwhile, for the composite filled with large particle alumina, it only improves the strength at low filler loading of only 20 phr. The highest increment in the TS was observed in the NR composite filled with nano-alumina at 20 phr. In all cases, the flexibility showed by the EB values reduces with the increment of alumina loadings in the composites as reported in earlier work by El-Sabbagh et al. (2006).

Namitha et al. (2013) compared the effects between micro-sized alumina particles with nano-sized alumina to the properties of SiR composites for the potential to be used in microelectronic packaging. In their work, the TS of SiR composites was found to increase with the addition of the alumina filler for both micro-size or nano-size particles, where the latter showed a higher reinforcing effect. The inclusion of smaller fillers at nano-size resulted in stronger composites. However, the flexibility of the SiR composites decreases with the increment of alumina loadings. The worst flexibility was observed in the SiR nanocomposites at alumina loading of 20 phr where the EB is recorded to be lower than 100%. This is due to the excessive loading of nano-alumina particles, which are then prone to form agglomerates acting as weak points in the composites. Later, it reduces the mechanical properties of the composites.

8.6.3 EFFECT OF ALUMINA SURFACE TREATMENT TO THE TENSILE PROPERTIES OF RUBBER COMPOSITES

The activity of the alumina particle surfaces is important for their interaction with hydrocarbon rubbers. The presence of functional groups on the filler particles might improve or reduce the mechanical properties of the composites. Among the earliest established work on alumina-filled rubber composites was that of El-Sabbagh et al. (2006). They used NR as matrix material and micron-alumina treated with ammonium molybdate pigment as the filler to produce a more stable alumina phase (α-alumina). However, their motivation in developing this material is to produce color-possible NR composites filled with white filler due to the superior performance observed from black-filled NR composites in tire application. They found that alumina doped with ammonium molybdate had reinforced the NR matrix and improved both its physical and mechanical properties. The modified fillers increased the TS, tensile modulus and hardness and maintained the flexibility of the composites to high elongation of approximately 600%. Some of the modified alumina showed better performance when improving composite properties than the ones filled with either clay, carbon black or unmodified Al_2O_3. Their results are confirmed with the calculated RI for each system.

Wang et al. (2010) investigated the effect of surface treatment on alumina particles on the performance of EPDM composites. They compared three types of alumina nanoparticles: (1) untreated alumina, (2) silane-treated alumina and (3) stearic acid (SA)- treated alumina. Their motivation is to produce rubber material that can perform well under a dynamic condition with higher service life expectancy by introducing nano-alumina as a thermally conductive filler. In their work, the nano-alumina treated with a silane coupling agent, bis-(3-triethoxy silyl propyl)-tetrasulfide (Si69), showed the highest impact on the improvement of the tensile properties for nano-alumina-filled EPDM composites. Meanwhile, the worse dispersion of SA-treated alumina particles resulted in the decrement of the mechanical properties. The SA-treated alumina showed inferior properties even compared with the untreated alumina in EPDM matrix composites.

8.6.4 Effect of Curing Agent on the Tensile Properties of Rubber Composites

Because there are plenty of studies conducted by the previous researchers on the effect of filler contributions on types, sizes and surface modification, Tangboriboon et al. (2011) published their work on the effects of curing agents. The motivation of the research is due to the potential of polyisoprene material as the candidate for materials used in various electronic devices such as field-effect transistors (FETs), solar cells and light-emitting diodes (LEDs). Their study is conducted to measure the contribution of dicumyl peroxide (DCP) content as the curative agent to the mechanical properties of alumina-filled NR composites at a constant amount of NR (100 g), and alumina particles loading (60 g). The DCP is targeted to produce thermally stable covalent bonding C–C in the composites, which exhibits higher resistance to heat and creep when used together with a suitable activator and accelerator system. The DCP amount in the NR composites is varied from 1, 3 and 5 g. The increment of DCP amount was observed to reduce both the TS and the flexibility of the composites, which is represented by the EB value. Meanwhile, the rigidity shown by the tensile modulus increases with the increasing amount of cross-linking agent (DCP). However, overall the tensile properties observed are rather low when compared with the other alumina-filled NR composite systems.

Alumina Filled Rubber Composites

8.6.5 EFFECT OF MATRIX MODIFICATION ON THE TENSILE PROPERTIES OF RUBBER COMPOSITES

Roy et al. (2018) focused on tailoring the properties of nano-alumina-filled NR composites by modifying the matrix materials. In their work, the mechanical properties were compared between nanocomposites produced using either pure NR or maleated NR (MNR) at different alumina loadings. The MNR is produced via modification of the NR with maleic anhydride before the preparation of the composites. Overall, the mechanical properties for both NR and MNR nanocomposites are observed to improve with the increment of nano-alumina loading in the composites. At only 2 phr of nano-alumina, MNR nanocomposites showed a 73.35% increment in their TS when compared with the control MNR vulcanizate. This is due to the outstanding nano-alumina dispersion in polar MNR matrix. A slight decrement in TS of MNR composites is observed at nano-alumina loading above 2 phr resulting from the formation of agglomerates. A strong reinforcing effect is created by nano-alumina at a 2 phr loading due to its improved compatibility with more polar MNR particles. An excellent enhancement by 26.18% is observed in the tensile modulus at 100% elongation (M100) indicating good interfacial interaction between matrix and alumina particles. The incredible improvement in the flexibility of these filled rubber composites reported to be higher than 1000% is astonishing. It seems to indicate that changes to fully increase the tensile properties including strength, rigidity and flexibility can be achieved at a very low level of nano-alumina loading paired with a compatible matrix material and a suitable curing system. Furthermore, the variation of hardness was quite analogous with that of the modulus value of MNR nanocomposites.

8.6.6 EFFECT OF HYBRID ALUMINA PARTICLE SIZES ON TENSILE PROPERTIES OF RUBBER COMPOSITES

The effects of alumina particle size hybridization to SiR composites were studied by Zhou et al. (2008). They introduced hybrid alumina fillers of different sizes to enhance the packing factor of filler distribution in the SiR matrix structures to increase the thermal conductivity of the composites. The smaller particles are hypothesized to fill up the spaces between larger particles leading to more conductive pathways or networks between filler particles for phonon transportation. They used the term "binary mixture" to represent two different alumina particle sizes loaded in the matrix material to form the composites. Three different binary mixtures were investigated in their work. In their study, the amount of alumina is constant at 55 vol% and the volume of small alumina particles (Vs) is varied from 0, 10, 20, 30, 40 to 50%. Three different binary mixtures of alumina particles consisting of large particles (DL) and small particles (DS) are studied at 30 μm/0.5 μm = 60, 10 μm/0.5 μm = 20 and 5 μm/0.5 μm = 10. The DS is maintained at 0.5 μm. The TS and EB as a function of Vs for the alumina-filled SiR composites are shown in Figure 8.7. The TS of the composites followed a normal distribution pattern showing the maximum values at Vs = 0.2 in both DL/DS = 20 and 10 binary mixtures of fillers. Meanwhile, the composites with a filler binary mixture of DL/DS = 60 exhibiting maximum strength at Vs = 0.3. The observation is simply an attribute of different optimum compactions achieved

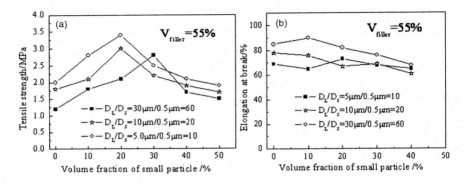

FIGURE 8.7 (a) Tensile strength and (b) elongation at break of composite rubber as a function of Vs. (From Zhou et al. 2008.)

at different hybrid particle size combinations. Flexibility and deformability of the alumina-filled SiR composites is indicated by the percentage of EB.

At high size ratio factor (DL/DS at 20 and 60) the composites manifest negative linear relationships because the elongation decreases with the increase of Vs values; meanwhile, it is monotonic for DL/DS at 10. The increment of Vs value at this ratio has a trivial effect on the percentage of EB. The highest deformability is obtained when only 10 vol% DS is added to the composite with DL/DS = 60. For other composites the highest EB values are obtained when there is a single DL presence in the SiR matrices.

In Zhou et al. (2008), they found that larger filler particles of 30 μm played a better role in increasing the percentage of elongation than the smaller particles at 10 and 5 μm. However, the increment of this value corresponds to the SiR without fillers and it cannot be deduced because no data of control samples is incorporated. They have concluded that the mechanism of reinforcement between alumina fillers and the SiR matrix is due to the effect of binding conditions of the polymer matrix to the aggregate of the filler particles. Single polymeric chains in the matrices are considered to be absorbed on two different aggregate surfaces, leading to the formation of a physical cross-linking. According to them, the larger particle size of the filler particles results in a smaller site for physical cross-linking, which in turn increases the mobility of polymer chains in composites. Meanwhile, the formation of more physical cross-links on the surface of small particle filler particles increases the chain stiffness. Therefore, increasing Vs in the binary filler mixture reduces the elongation capacity of the rubber under stress load.

8.6.7 Hardness of Alumina-Filled Rubber Composites

Most of the studies on the alumina-filled NR-based composites report on the effect of hardness values (Tables 8.3 and 8.4). In all cases, the hardness value of alumina-filled rubber composites increases with the increasing level of alumina loading in the rubber matrix. Hardness is a property dominated by alumina hard particles compared with the rubber matrix. Thus, the observed increase in hardness value is in line with the increase in the alumina ratio to the rubber matrix as the alumina load

Alumina Filled Rubber Composites

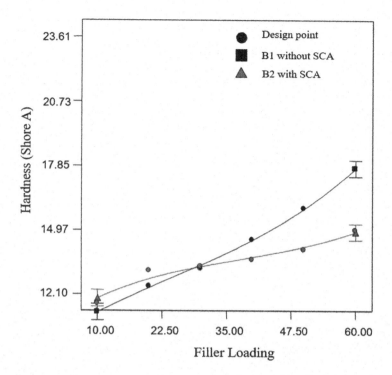

FIGURE 8.8 Interaction graph between filler loading level and silane coupling agent (SCA) presence against the value of hardness. (From Mohamad 2011.)

in the matrix increases. However, the hardness value recorded by composites filled with alumina at less than 1 wt% is very low and almost equals the hardness value of rubber vulcanizate in most cases. Hardness is one of the important properties of rubber products. Commercially, hardness values are used to estimate the improvement of tensile properties. The hardness of alumina-filled rubber composites is also a product of filler distribution. Inhomogeneous alumina filler distributions in the rubber matrix will result in inaccurate measures of hardness values and high standard deviation in readings. Also, the hardness of alumina-filled rubber composites was influenced by the surface treatment performed on the fillers before compounding. Figure 8.8 shows the variation of hardness when alumina is pretreated with a silane coupling agent (Mohamad 2011).

8.7 MORPHOLOGICAL CHARACTERISTICS OF ALUMINA-FILLED RUBBER COMPOSITES

The level of alumina dispersion is also a function of its size particles whether or not micro-alumina or nano-alumina incorporates into the rubber matrix; hence, the amount of alumina that could form uniform dispersion varies.

8.7.1 Scanning Electron Microscopy (SEM)

The mechanical properties of particulate fillers in rubber composites are the cumulative effect of particle distributions and dispersion in rubber matrices. The tendency of aggregation and agglomeration of nanomaterials' particles above a certain maximum level is commonly observed in rubber compounds. These phenomena are mostly reported to be the causes of mostly reduction in the mechanical properties of rubber-based materials and polymer matrix composites as a whole. As found in the case of alumina-filled rubber composites, the value of EB mostly decreases due to the addition of alumina particles regardless of their size. However, this worsens in the case of using nano-fillers. In most cases, the value of EB showed minimal improvement with the incorporation of nano-alumina into the rubber matrix. However, the opposite trend was also reported by different researchers. In some conditions in which fine alumina nanoparticles were uniformly dispersed, catastrophic failure of rubber materials are seen to restrict the crack growth (Roy et al. 2018). This is in line with the observed increment in the EB of MNR specimens with the addition of nano-size alumina (Table 8.3). Figure 8.9 displays SEM images of micro-size alumina-filled

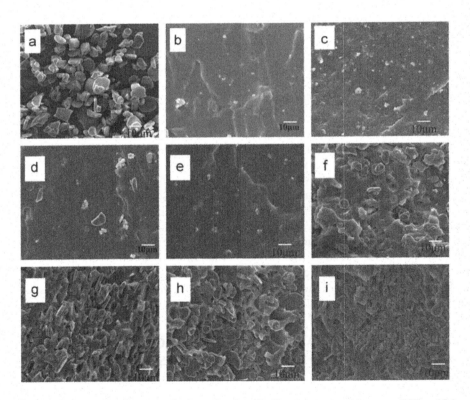

FIGURE 8.9 (a) SEM images of micro-alumina. (b–i) cross-sectional images of SR-mAL1, SR-mAL2, SR-mAL3, SR-mAL4, SR-mAL5, SR-mAL6, SR-mAL7 and SR-mAL8. (From Namitha et al. 2013.)

Alumina Filled Rubber Composites 185

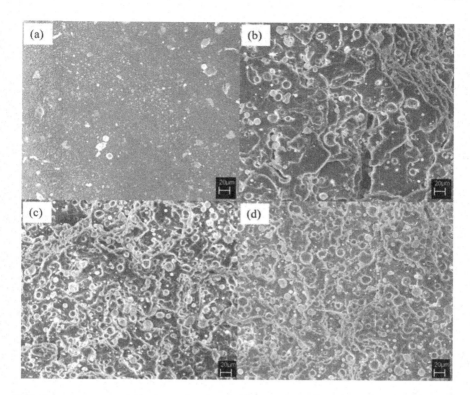

FIGURE 8.10 SEM images of nano-alumina-filled ENR at different filler loadings of (a) 5, (b) 10, (c) 20 and (d) 30 (about 5.0–20 volume fractions). (From Mohamad 2011.)

SiR composites (SR-mAL) at various filler loadings from 1 to 8 wt%. It is obvious from the figure that the micro-alumina particles are uniformly distributed throughout the matrix. It shows irregular shapes with an average size of less than 10 mm. The matrix wraps the ceramic particles at lower filler loading, but the interparticle distance decreases as the filler loading increases despite the increment of filler particle agglomerations. Porosity is also observed to increase with an increase in filler loadings.

Figures 8.10 and 8.11 show the SEM fractured surface images of nano-alumina-reinforced ENR composites at different magnifications. It is possible to conclude from the figures that alumina aggregate particles are distributed almost evenly in the matrix. However, nano-alumina particles exhibit worse agglomerations at higher filler loadings of more than 5 phr (Figure 8.11). A smaller matrix yielding mechanism is observed on the fracture morphological surfaces at these loadings where nano-alumina is higher than 30 phr.

Moreover, as can be observed in Figure 8.12, the content of alumina particles in the ENR matrix also affects the shape and size of the dispersed alumina particles because, for composites with lower filler ratio to ENR matrix, alumina particles lose surface energy immediately when added to the matrix during compounding.

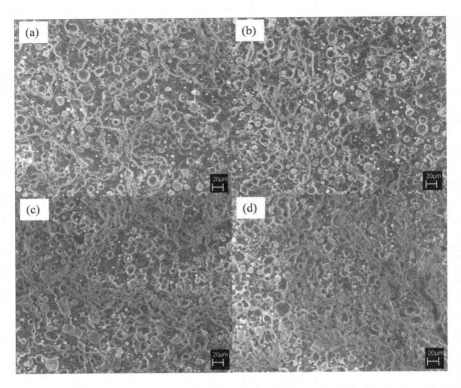

FIGURE 8.11 SEM images of nano-alumina-filled ENR at different filler loadings of (a) 40, (b) 50, (c) 60 and (d) 100 (about 5.0–20 volume fractions). (From Mohamad 2011.)

These alumina particles do not have much time to form spherical bodies. Thus, dispersed alumina aggregates of various sizes (ultimate size ≤15 μm) and shapes can be observed in composites. On the other hand, as the particle ratio to the ENR matrix increases, it is more likely they are attracted to each other than to the matrix. This phenomenon produces dispersed agglomerate particles that are more spherical and more uniform in size (ultimate size ≤20 μm) to reduce surface energy.

The rigidity of the size and shape of the filler dispersed in the low-loading ENRAN results in a higher asymmetry in the typical distribution of alumina particles. This is evidenced by the higher skewness value, β (skewness), obtained at 10-phr alumina loading, which is as high as 0.73 compared with 0.53 for ENR filled with 60-phr nano-size alumina (Table 8.5). The sloping value represents the degree of asymmetry of a statistical distribution at the average value. Although the size of the dispersed alumina agglomerate particles is relatively large, the almost spherical shape has reduced its effectiveness as a stress concentrator in alumina-filled ENR composites. Therefore, agglomerate size does not entirely negatively affect the tensile properties. It can increase the tensile modulus and maintain the EB value at a relatively high of about 500% at an alumina load of 60 phr.

Alumina Filled Rubber Composites

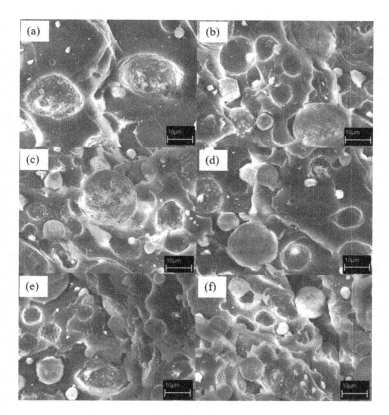

FIGURE 8.12 FESEM images showing changes in shape and size of scattered nano-alumina-filled ENR at (a) 10, (b) 20, (c) 30, (d) 40, (e) 50 and (f) 60 phr at magnification of 2500×. (From Mohamad 2011.)

TABLE 8.5
Skewness Values for the Microstructure of Each ENRAN Composites

Nano-Alumina Loading (phr)	Skewness (β)
10	0.73
20	0.64
30	0.60
40	0.58
50	0.55
60	0.53

Source: Mohamad (2011).

8.7.2 Transmission Electron Microscopy (TEM)

It is crucial to examine the morphological characteristics of a rubber nanocomposite at magnification higher than 10 000× when dealing with nano-size alumina whether via FESEM or TEM. Figure 8.13 shows the TEM images for filled ENR nanocomposites at alumina loadings of 10 and 60 phr under 5000× and 50,000× magnification, respectively. The TEM image obtained is in good understanding with SEM micrographs for both of these materials.

At 10-phr nano-size alumina (Figure 8.13(a)), composites exhibit larger dispersed filler sizes and a wider space between them compared with the composite filled at 60 phr (Figure 8.13(b)). If we compare SEM micrographs (Figures 8.11 and 8.12) and TEM images (Figure 8.13) it can be concluded that the dispersion scale of alumina particles in the ENR matrix includes micro-, meso- and nanoscale dispersed fillers. The fillers are dispersed in a microscale, which in comparison is the filler agglomerate that exists due to the electrostatic forces that physically attract alumina particles from each other by forming a filler network. It is accelerated by the presence of hydroxyl groups on the surface of alumina particles. The meso-scattering filler is an aggregate formed in alumina-filled ENR nanocomposites as a result of high shear during processing using an internal mixer.

The formation of agglomerates is often associated with the interaction of fillers that are also capable of trapping or enclosing rubber particles. Rubber trapped in this

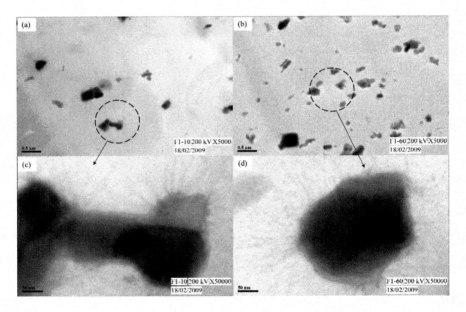

FIGURE 8.13 TEM image for an ENR filled with nano-size alumina at (a) 10 phr loading at 5000× magnification and (c) at 50,000× magnification, and at (b) 60 phr loading at 5000× magnification and (d) at 50,000× magnification. The circles represent the possible area of magnifications, and the arrows pointed to the magnification images. (From Mohamad 2011.)

filler network is either partially "dead" or loses its identity as an elastomer and tends to act as a foreign object in its stress-strain behavior. This leads to the Payne effect shown by most silica and carbon-black-reinforced rubber elastomers (Wang 1999; Manna et al. 2002) where the presence of agglomerates reduces the modulus of the resulting composite material. However, the use of polar matrix ENR combined with alumina reduces the Payne effect because the epoxide group on ENR is more easily absorbed on the alumina surface by reducing the interaction of fillers (Wang et al. 2000). Therefore, the presence of more fillers is still able to increase the modulus value of alumina-filled ENR nanocomposites.

However, what is interesting about the TEM images of alumina-filled ENR nanocomposites is that there is a "brush"-like structure that extends out into the ENR matrix on some scattered alumina (Figure 8.13(c) and (d)). The structure of this brush is proof of the notion that there is a physical interaction between the ENR matrix and alumina. The physical interaction between ENR and alumina produces a very unique interface structure, and this structure is mostly observed in alumina aggregates measuring more than 100 nm up to 0.5 μm as observed in Figure 8.14. This structure is also believed to occur in scattered alumina particles that are smaller in size but due to the high matrix contrast and fillers of various sizes, it is very difficult to obtain image clarity for particles that are too small. However, there are still scattered alumina particles that do not show the brush structure as claimed. The structure of this brush is believed to be the effect of the absorption of ENR rubber molecules on the surface of alumina (Mohamad 2011). The chemisorption interaction between ENR chains (transparent) with alumina (opaque) produces a visible brush structure that extends out of the alumina surface into the ENR. According to Bhat et al. (2006), polymeric chains are forced to stretch normally to the oxide surface as the grafting density of chains on the surface increases due to the increase of osmotic pressure among the chains. It forms an equilibrium conformation called polymer brush in which polymer chains are stretched away from the grafting surface.

FIGURE 8.14 Schematic representation of surface-anchored polymers in brush conformation on the alumina surface.

8.8 PROCESSABILITY OF ALUMINA-FILLED RUBBER COMPOSITES

From the investigation by Namitha et al. (2013), the blending turned out to be more troublesome at higher nano-alumina loadings due to the high surface area to volume ratio of the nano-fillers. The primary disadvantage of nano-fillers is that the nanoparticles tend to form aggregates and agglomerates in the rubber matrix. The hydrophilicity of the nano-alumina, as well as surface area to volume ratio, worsens this condition once it interacts with hydrophobicity and viscous rubber matrix. The highest filler loading of about 0.45Vf is accomplished for microcomposites (SR-mAL) composites, while only 0.05Vf, is workable for nanocomposites (SR-nAL). The level of dispersion and distribution of alumina particles in the rubber matrix highly influence the physical, mechanical and functional properties of the materials.

Figure 8.15 shows the rheometer test result of torque against time curve for the rheological properties of alumina-filled ENR compounds. According to Mohamad (2011), the torque behavior also represents the processability as well as the curing properties for each compound produced. It describes the kinetics of vulcanization or the formation of cross-links in rubber material. The flow meter measures the torque required for the rotor swing as a function of time as the compound is heated up to a selected temperature. In most works, the temperature is set in between 140 to 175°C based on the type of rubber matrices.

From the Figure 8.15, alumina-filled ENR composites show a typical flow curve for a rubber material. There is a sudden increase in torque as soon as the reading is taken. The curve describes the initial torque of a material that is still in a solid state. After that, with heating, the viscosity of the material decreases, and the torque value also decreases until it reaches a minimum value. Currently, the torque is known as

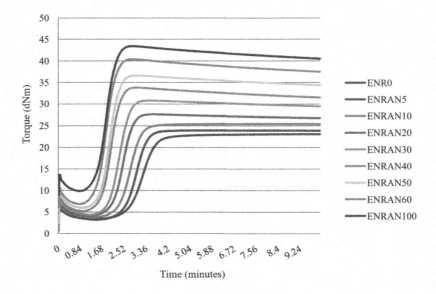

FIGURE 8.15 Torque versus time for alumina-filled ENR nanocomposites at different alumina loadings of 0, 5, 10, 20, 30, 40, 50, 60 and 100 phr. (From Mohamad 2011.)

Alumina Filled Rubber Composites

the minimum torque (ML), and it is usually used to represent the melting viscosity of a material. Slowly the rubber compound begins to form and transform into an elastic solid and the torque value begins to increase. Although the state of molecular chain scissoring may occur, increasing torque usually indicates cross-linking is dominant.

Alumina loading of 0–30 phr (ENR0 and ENRAN5 to ENRAN30) has very stable curves and is shaped like "plateau." This indicates that curing has ended and a stable molecular chain network is formed. Meanwhile, the continuous increase in alumina particles indicates that reversion conditions are beginning to occur. It is a condition in which cutting and/or breaking of molecular chains begins to become dominant due to exposure to prolonged heating processes. The torque value increases to the maximum value and subsequently decreases. However, the reversal conditions that occur are not so significant even though the ENR matrix has been loaded by 100-phr alumina particles. Thus, it can be concluded from the flowmeter flow curve that the ENR and alumina matrices have a positive interaction with the formation of a stable cross-connection.

8.9 CONCLUSIONS

Development of alumina-filled rubber composites is based on the desire to impart alumina properties of high strength, high thermal stability, low thermal conductivity, good electrical insulation, high chemical stability and corrosion resistance to the rubber materials. These purpose of these efforts is to produce excellent composite materials for structural, microelectronic and electrical insulation applications. Various factors could be tailored to produce alumina-filled rubber composites for sustaining structural functions such as particle sizes, surface treatment, compaction factor, filler hybridization and matrix modifications. Outstanding mechanical performance of alumina-filled rubber composites in both natural and synthetic matrices equipped with low cost and coloring potential placed these materials as products and processes viable for use in bulk for the manufacturing industry.

ACKNOWLEDGMENT

The authors would like to acknowledge Fakulti Kejuruteraan Pembuatan, Universiti Teknikal Malaysia Melaka, and Universiti Kebangsaan Malaysia for their expert advice, facilities and resources before and upon completion of this chapter. The authors thank the Ministry of Higher Education Malaysia for granting the Fundamental Research Grant Scheme (FRGS/1/2012/TK04/UTEM/02/2/F00132 and UKM-RS-02-FRGS0003-2007) that partly contributed to the success of this work.

REFERENCES

Abd Razak, Jeefferie. 2016. Preparation and Characterization of Natural Rubber – Ethylene Propylene Diene Filled Graphene Nanoplatelets Nanocomposite Blends. PhD Thesis, Universiti Kebangsaan, Malaysia.

Ash, B. J., Siegel, R. W., and Schadler, L. S. 2004. Glass-Transition Temperature Behavior of Alumina/PMMA Nanocomposites. *Journal of Polymer Science Part B: Polymer Physics* 42(23): 4371–4383. doi:10.1002/polb.20297

Baker, C. S. L., and Gelling, I. R. 1987. Epoxidized Natural Rubber. *Developments in Rubber Technology* 4: 87–117. doi:10.1007/978-94-009-3435-1_3

Bhat, R. R., Tomlinson, M. R., Wu, T., and Genzer, J. 2006. Surface-Grafted Polymer Gradients: Formation, Characterization, and Applications. *Advances in Polymer Science* 198: 51–124. doi:10.1007/12_060

Bhimaraj, P., Burris, D. L., Action, J., Sawyer, W. G., Toney, C. G., Siegel, R. W., and Schadler, L. S. 2005. Effect of Matrix Morphology on the Wear and Friction Behavior of Alumina Nanoparticle/Poly(ethylene) Terephthalate Composites. *Wear* 258: 1437–1443. https://doi.org/10.1016/j.wear.2004.09.077

Boonstra, B. B. 1979. Role of Particulate Fillers in Elastomer Reinforcement: A Review. *Polymer* 20(6): 691–704. doi:10.1016/0032-3861(79)90243-x

Chandra, A., Turng, L. S., Gopalan, P., Rowell, R. M., and Gong, S. 2008. Study of Utilizing Thin Polymer Surface Coating on the Nanoparticles for Melt Compounding of Polycarbonate/Alumina Nanocomposites and Their Optical Properties. *Composites Science and Technology* 68: 768–776. https://doi.org/10.1016/j.compscitech.2007.08.027

Chen, C., Xue, Y., Li, X., Wen, Y., Liu, J., Xue, Z., Shi, D., Zhou, X., Xie, X., and Mai, Y.-W. 2019. High-performance Epoxy/Binary Spherical Alumina Composite as Underfill Material for Electronic Packaging. *Composites Part A: Applied Science and Manufacturing*, 118: 67–74. https://doi.org/10.1016/j.compositesa.2018.12.019

El-Sabbagh, S. H., Ahmed, N. M., and Selim, M. M. 2006. Preparation and Characterisation of High Performance Rubber Vulcanizates Loaded with Modified Aluminium Oxide. *Pigment & Resin Technology* 35(3): 119–131. doi:10.1108/03699420610665148

He, S., Hu, J., Zhang, C., Wang, J., Chen, L., Bian, X., Lin, J., and Du, X. 2018. Performance Improvement in Nano-Alumina Filled Silicone Rubber Composites by using Vinyl Tri-Methoxysilane. *Polymer Testing* 67: 295–301. doi:10.1016/j.polymertesting.2018.03.023

Ichinose, Noboru. 1987. *Introduction to Fine Ceramics (Application in Engineering).* Chichester, UK: John Wiley & Sons Ltd.

Jesse. 2006. Chemical structure of Polydimethylsiloxane (PDMS). Wikimedia Commons. *Silicone Rubber.* https://upload.wikimedia.org/wikipedia/commons/6/6a/Pdms.png

Jung, C. H., Choi, J. H., Lim, Y. M., Jeun, J. P., Kang, P. H., and Nho, Y. C. 2006. Preparation and Characterization of Polypropylene Nanocomposites Containing Polystyrene-Grafted Alumina Nanoparticles. *Journal of Industry Engineering Chemistry* 12(6): 900–904.

Kakui, T., Miyauchi, T., and Kamiya, H. 2005. Analysis of the Action Mechanism of Polymer Dispersant on Dense Ethanol Alumina Suspension Using Colloidal Probe AFM. *Journal of the European Ceramic Society* 25: 655–661. https://doi.org/10.1016/j.jeurceramsoc.2004.03.014

Kalle Hanhi, Minna Poikelispää, and Hanna-Mari Tirilä. 2007. *Elastomeric Materials.* Hervanta, Finland: Tampere University of Technology.

Konar, B. B., Roy, S. K., and Pariya, T. K. 2010. Study on the Effect of Nano and Active Particles of Alumina on Natural Rubber–Alumina Composites in the Presence of Epoxidized Natural Rubber as Compatibilizer. *Journal of Macromolecular Science, Part A* 47(5): 416–422. doi:10.1080/10601321003659531

Latief, F. H., Chafidz, A., Junaedi, H., Alfozan, A., and Khan, R. 2019. Effect of Alumina Contents on the Physicomechanical Properties of Alumina (Al2O3) Reinforced Polyester Composites. *Advances in Polymer Technology* 2019: 5173537. doi:10.1155/2019/5173537

Li, H., Yan, Y., Bin, L., Chen, W., and Chen, S. 2007. Studies of Surface Functional Modification of Nanosized α-Alumina. *Powder Technology* 178: 203–207. https://doi.org/10.1016/j.powtec.2007.04.020

Manna, A. K., De, P. P., and Tripathy, D. K. 2002. Dynamic Mechanical Properties and Hysteresis Loss of Epoxidized Natural Rubber Chemically Bonded to the Silica Surface. *Journal of Applied Polymer Science* 84: 2171–2177. https://doi.org/10.1002/app.10382

Alumina Filled Rubber Composites 193

McGrath, L. M., Parnas, R. S., King, S. H., Schroeder, J. L., Fischer, D. A., and Lenhart, J. L. 2008. Investigation of the Thermal, Mechanical, and Fracture Properties of Alumina-Epoxy Composites. *Polymer* 49: 999–1014. https://doi.org/10.1016/j.polymer. 2007.12.014

Mills, B. 2008. "Ball-and-Stick Model of Part of the Crystal Structure of Corundum, α-Al2O3." Wikimedia Commons. *Aluminium Oxide.* https://upload.wikimedia.org/ wikipedia/commons/c/cc/Corundum-3D-balls.png

Mohamad, N., Muchtar, A., Ghazali, M. J., Dahlan, H. M., and Azhari, C. H. 2008. The Effect of Filler on Epoxidised Natural Rubber-Alumina Nanoparticles Composites. *European Journal of Scientific Research* 24(4): 538–547.

Mohamad, Noraiham. 2011. *Development of Epoxidised Natural Rubber-Alumina Composites (ENRAN) for the Absorption of Ballistic Impact Energy in Body Armour.* PhD Thesis, Universiti Kebangsaan, Malaysia.

Namitha, L. K., Chameswary, J., Ananthakumar, S., and Sebastian, M. T. 2013. Effect of Micro- and Nano-Fillers on the Properties of Silicone Rubber-Alumina Flexible Microwave Substrate. *Ceramics International* 39(6): 7077–7087. doi:10.1016/j.ceramint. 2013.02.047

Omrani, A., Simon, L. C., and Rostami, A. A. 2009. The Effects of Alumina Nanoparticle on the Properties of an Epoxy Resin System. *Materials Chemistry and Physics* 114: 145–150. https://doi.org/10.1016/j.matchemphys.2008.08.090

Park, S-J., and Seo, M-K. 2011. Chapter 6 – Element and Processing. In *Interface Science and Technology*, edited by Min-Kang Seo Soo-Jin Park (pp. 431–499). Amsterdam: Elsevier.

Pinto, D., Bernardo, L., Amaro, A., and Lopes, S. 2015. Mechanical Properties of Epoxy Nanocomposites using Alumina as Reinforcement – A Review. *Journal of Nano Research* 30: 9–38. doi:10.4028/www.scientific.net/jnanor.30.9

Roland.chem. 2016. Deutsch: Isomere der Polyisoprene. Wikimedia Commons. *Polyisoprene.* https://upload.wikimedia.org/wikipedia/commons/0/05/Polyisopren-Strukturen.svg

Roy, K., Jatejarungwong, C., and Potiyaraj, P. 2018. Development of Highly Reinforced Maleated Natural Rubber Nanocomposites based on Sol-Gel-derived Nano Alumina. *Journal of Applied Polymer Science* 135: 46248(1–9). https://doi.org/10.1002/app.46248

Shukla, D. K., Kasisomayajula, S. V., and Parameswaran, V. 2008. Epoxy Composites Using Functionalized Alumina Platelets as Reinforcements. *Composites Science and Technology* 68: 3055–3063. https://doi.org/10.1016/j.compscitech.2008.06.025

Siegel, R. W., Chang, S. K., Ash, B. J., Stone, J., Ajayan, P. M., Doremus, R. W., and Schadler L. S. 2001. Mechanical Behavior of Polymer and Ceramic Matrix Nanocomposites. *Scripta Materialia* 44: 2061–2064. doi:10.1016/S1359-6462(01)00892-2

Sim, L. C., Ramanan, S. R., Ismail, H., Seetharamu, K. N., and Goh, T. J. 2005. Thermal Characterization of Al_2O_3 and ZnO Reinforced Silicone Rubber as Thermal Pads for Heat Dissipation Purposes. *Thermochimica Acta* 430(1–2): 155–165. doi:10.1016/ j.tca.2004.12.024

Song, K. 2017. Micro- and Nano-fillers Used in the Rubber Industry. In *Progress in Rubber Nanocomposites*, edited by Sabu Thomas and Hanna J. Maria (pp. 41–80). Amsterdam: Woodhead Publishing. doi:10.1016/b978-0-08-100409-8.00002-4

Tangboriboon, N., Chaisakrenon, S., Banchong, A., Kunanuruksapong, R., and Sirivat, A. 2011. Mechanical and Electrical Properties of Alumina/Natural Rubber Composites. *Journal of Elastomers & Plastics* 44(1): 21–41. doi:10.1177/0095244311416579

Viswanath, R., Wakharkar, V., Watwe, A., and Lebonheur, V. 2000. Thermal Performance Challenges from Silicone to Systems. *Intel Technology Journal Q3*, 1–16. http://citese-erx.ist.psu.edu/viewdoc/summary?doi=10.1.1.14.8322

Wang, M.-J. 1999. The Role of Filler Networking in Dynamic Properties of Filled Rubber. *Rubber Chemistry and Technology* 72(2): 430–448. doi:10.5254/1.3538812

Wang, M.-J., Lu, S. X., and Mahmud, K. 2000. Carbon-Silica Dual-Phase Filler, a New-Generation Reinforcing Agent for Rubber. Part VI. Time-Temperature Superposition of Dynamic Properties of Carbon-Silica-Dual-Phase-Filler-Filled Vulcanizates. *Journal of Polymer Science Part B: Polymer Physics* 38(9): 1240–1249. doi:10.1002/(sici)1099-0488(20000501)38:9<1240::aid-polb15>3.0.co;2-q

Wang, W., Tanaka, Y., Takada, T., Iwata, S., Uehara, H., and Li, S. 2018. Influence of Oxidation on the Dynamics in Amorphous Ethylene-Propylene-Diene-Monomer Copolymer: A Molecular Dynamics Simulation. *Polymer Degradation and Stability* 147: 187–196. doi:10.1016/j.polymdegradstab.2017.12.001

Wang, Z.-H., Lu, Y.-L., Liu, J., Dang, Z.-M., Zhang, L.-Q., and Wang, W. 2010. Preparation of Nanoalumina/EPDM Composites with Good Performance in Thermal Conductivity and Mechanical Properties. *Polymers for Advanced Technologies* 22(12): 2302–2310. doi:10.1002/pat.1761

Zha, J.-W., Zhu, Y.-H., Li, W.-K., Bai, J., and Dang, Z.-M. 2012. Low Dielectric Permittivity and High Thermal Conductivity Silicone Rubber Composites with Micro-Nano-Sized Particles. *Applied Physics Letters* 101(6): 062905. https://doi.org/10.1063/1.4745509

Zhang, C., Mason, R., and Stevens, G.C. 2005. Dielectric Properties of Alumina Polymer Nanocomposites. *CEIDP '05. 2005 Annual Report Conference on Electrical Insulation and Dielectric Phenomena*, Nashville, TN, pp. 721–724. doi:10.1109/ceidp.2005.1560784

Zhao, H., and Li, R.K.Y. 2008. Effect of Water Absorption on the Mechanical and Dielectric Properties of Nano-Alumina Filled Epoxy Nanocomposites. *Composites: Part A* 39(4): 602–611. doi:10.1016/j.compositesa.2007.07.006

Zhao, L. X., Zheng, L. Y., and Zhao, S.G. 2006. Tribological Performance of Nano-Al2O3 Reinforced Polyamide 6 Composites. *Materials Letters* 60: 2590–2593. https://doi.org/10.1016/j.matlet.2006.01.042

Zhou, Q., Cha, J. H., Huang, Y., Zhang, R., Cao, W., and Shung, K. K. 2009. Alumina/Epoxy Nanocomposite Matching Layers for High-Frequency Ultrasound Transducer Application. *IEEE Transactions in Ultrasonics Ferroelectrics and Frequency Control* 56(1): 213–219. doi:10.1109/tuffc.2009.1021

Zhao, S., Schadler, L. S., Duncan, R., Hillborg, H., and Auletta, T. 2008. Mechanisms Leading to Improved Mechanical Performance in Nanoscale Alumina Filled Epoxy. *Composites Science and Technology* 68(14): 2965–2975. https://doi.org/10.1016/j.compscitech.2008.01.009

Zhou, W., Yu, D., Wang, C., An, Q., and Qi, S. 2008. Effect of Filler Size Distribution on the Mechanical and Physical Properties of Alumina-Filled Silicone Rubber. *Polymer Engineering & Science* 48(7): 1381–1388. doi:10.1002/pen.21113

9 Magnetite Filler Reinforcement for Magnetorheological Elastomer Damping Performance

Raa Khimi
Universiti Sains Malaysia
Nibong Tebal, Malaysia

CONTENTS

9.1 Introduction 195
9.2 Distribution of Magnetite Mineral.. 196
9.3 Chemical Properties 197
9.4 Magnetic Properties... 197
    9.4.1 Diamagnetism... 198
    9.4.2 Paramagnetism 198
    9.4.3 Ferromagnetism 199
    9.4.4 Antiferromagnetism..200
    9.4.5 Ferrimagnetism...201
9.5 Damping Mechanisms of MRE..202
    9.5.1 Viscoelastic Damping...202
    9.5.2 Interfacial Damping..204
    9.5.3 Magnetostrictive Damping 206
9.6 Conclusion 208
Acknowledgment 208
References...208

9.1 INTRODUCTION

Material with high damping capability is desired for vibration suppression in structures. Damping relates to the energy dissipated in a material during vibration and assists in stabilizing a structure when it vibrates. In the last decade there has been development in high damping materials for structures and engineering applications.

DOI: 10.1201/9781003220947-9

A major goal has been to develop material that combines excellent mechanical properties and good damping for structural purposes.

Although rubber has proved useful in structural vibration control, its low stiffness, low strength, low toughness and relatively low glass transition and melting temperatures limit its usefulness in practical applications. More recently, magnetic mineral particles have been included in rubber to create elastomeric magnetic composites, resulting in improvement of damping performance and structural properties. Magnetic mineral particles provide an additional energy absorbing mechanism involving magnetic domain wall movement, which is explained later in this chapter. Generally, combinations of rubber with magnetic mineral particles are termed magnetoelastic or magnetorheological elastomers (MREs) or elastomer-ferromagnetic composites (Stepanov, Abramchuk et al. 2007). The magnetic mineral particles used are usually magnetite (Shuib and Pickering 2016) and ferrite (Soloman, Kurian et al. 2004; Kruželák, Dosoudil et al. 2017) and the reported polymer matrices include silicone elastomer, polyvinyl alcohol, gelatin and natural rubber (Wang, Hu et al. 2006).

MREs can be classified into two groups: isotropic and anisotropic. Isotropic MREs have a uniform magnetic particle distribution in the matrix. Anisotropic MREs have a special chainlike structure of magnetic particles in a matrix resulting from curing the matrix under a strong magnetic field. When a magnetic field is applied, the magnetic particles arrange into chains parallel to the magnetic field lines. Once the matrix is cured, the particle arrangement is set in place (Kaleta, Królewicz et al. 2011). Curing the MREs under an applied magnetic field produces materials with a much higher Young's modulus and better damping compared with those cured in the absence of a magnetic field. Furthermore, during service, a magnetic field can be used to affect Young's modulus and hence provide benefits in vibration control (Chokkalingam, Rajasabai Senthur et al. 2010).

MREs hold promise in a large variety of engineering applications such as automotive and machinery bearing and mounting as well as earthquake isolators. Early commercialization of the material by the Ford Motor Company, detailed in 1997, was a patented tunable automotive bushing based on MREs (Watson 1997), which can be applied to reduce suspension deflection and improve passenger comfort.

9.2 DISTRIBUTION OF MAGNETITE MINERAL

Magnetite is the name given to dark and high-density rock minerals and one of the main iron ores with the chemical formula Fe_3O_4. This iron ore is an oxide of iron and attracted to a magnet and can be further magnetized to produce a permanent magnet. Magnetite is mined as iron ore and has a Mohs' hardness of 5–6. The chemical IUPAC name is iron (II,III) oxide and the common chemical name is ferrous-ferric oxide.

Magnetite is sometimes found in large quantities in beach sand. The magnetite deposit, eroded from rocks, has been moved by ocean currents along the coastline and the action of wind and waves has concentrated them on the seafloor, beaches and in dunes (Cribb 1998). This deposit can be found in various places across the globe,

TABLE 9.1
Chemical Analyses of Titanomagnetite

Mineral	Concentration (%)
Magnetite	83.10
Titanium oxide	8
Aluminum oxide	4
Manganese oxide	3
Vanadium oxide	0.50
Silica	0.30
Calcium oxide	0.30
Others	0.80

such as Lung Kwu Tan, Hong Kong; California and the west coast of the North Island of New Zealand. Large deposits of magnetite are also found in the Atacama region of Chile; the Valentines region of Uruguay; Kiruna, Sweden; the Pilbara, Midwest and Northern Goldfields regions in Western Australia; the Eyre Peninsula in South Australia; the Tallawang Region of New South Wales; and in the Adirondack region of New York in the United States. Deposits are also found in Norway, Mexico, Italy, South Africa, India, Indonesia, Hong Kong and in Oregon, Germany, New Jersey, Pennsylvania, Switzerland, North Carolina, West Virginia, Virginia, New Mexico, Utah and Colorado in the United States (Chang and Kirschvink 1989; Leaman 1997; Klein 2005).

9.3 CHEMICAL PROPERTIES

The chemical composition of magnetite is $Fe^{2+}Fe_2^{3+}O_4^{2-}$. The crystal structure is inverse spinel, with O^{2-} ions forming a face-centered cubic lattice and iron cations occupying interstitial sites. Half of the Fe^{3+} cations occupies tetrahedral sites, whereas the other half, along with Fe^{2+} cations, occupies octahedral sites.

Rich layers of magnetite deposit are dominated by opaque minerals, mostly magnetite with minor constituents of titanium oxide, aluminum oxide, manganese oxide, vanadium oxide, silica, calcium oxide and others. Table 9.1 shows the general chemical analysis for magnetite mineral.

9.4 MAGNETIC PROPERTIES

Magnetism is the phenomenon by which materials exert attractive or repulsive forces on other materials in response to an applied magnetic field (Callister and Rethwisch 2010). The source of magnetism is magnetic dipoles, which are found to exist in magnetic material and can be thought of as small bar magnets composed of north and south poles. A magnetic field exerts a torque that tends to orient the dipoles with the field. Orientation of magnetic dipoles contributes to the magnetic behavior of materials. The strength of a magnetic dipole, called the magnetic moment, may be thought of as a measure of a dipole's ability to align itself with an applied magnetic field.

Generally, the macroscopic behavior of magnetic materials can be classified using a few magnetic parameters. The most significant parameter is susceptibility. Susceptibility is a dimensionless proportionality between magnetic moment (m) and magnetic field strength (H) that indicates the degree of magnetization of a material in response to an applied magnetic field (Jakubovics 1994), and it varies with temperature. With increasing temperature, the increased thermal motion of atoms tends to randomize the directions of dipoles that may be aligned and gradually diminishes the susceptibility which abruptly drops to zero at what is called the Curie temperature (T_c) (Jakubovics 1994; Jiles 1998). Magnetic behavior can be classified principally into diamagnetism, paramagnetism, ferromagnetism, antiferromagnetism and ferrimagnetism.

9.4.1 Diamagnetism

Diamagnetism is a very weak form of magnetism that is only present while a magnetic field is being applied; diamagnetic materials possess no magnetic dipoles in the atoms or molecules in the absence of an applied field. In an applied magnetic field, magnetic moments are induced and dipoles align in opposition to the field direction. A weak negative magnetization is produced, which causes repulsion instead of attraction. The susceptibility for diamagnetic materials is of the order of -10^{-5} (Callister and Rethwisch 2010). The susceptibility is constant at constant temperature for relatively low values of magnetic field. Figure 9.1 illustrates the magnetic dipoles for a diamagnetic material with and without an applied field. Many materials exhibit diamagnetism, the most common materials being graphite, quartz and silica.

9.4.2 Paramagnetism

In paramagnetic materials, each atom or molecule has a net magnetic moment in the absence of a magnetic field, but the orientations of dipoles are random leading to no

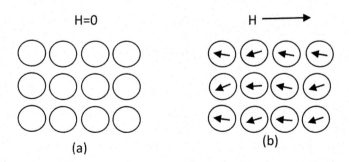

FIGURE 9.1 The magnetic dipoles for a diamagnetic material with (a) and without a magnetic field (b). In the absence of an external field, no magnetic moments exist; in the presence of a field, magnetic moments are induced and dipoles are aligned opposite to the field direction.

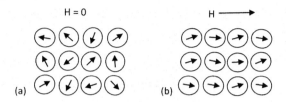

FIGURE 9.2 Magnetic dipole orientations with (a) and without an applied magnetic field (b) for a paramagnetic material.

net magnetization. In an applied magnetic field, these dipoles start to align parallel to the field, resulting in weak positive magnetization. However, a large magnetic field is required to align all of the dipoles because the dipoles behave individually with no interaction between adjacent dipoles. Susceptibility for paramagnetic materials ranges from about 10^{-5} to 10^{-2} and because thermal agitation randomizes the direction of the magnetic dipoles, an increase in temperature decreases the paramagnetic effect (Callister and Rethwisch 2010). In addition, the magnetization is lost as soon as the magnetic field is removed. Figure 9.2 illustrates the magnetic dipoles for a paramagnetic material with and without an applied field. Examples of paramagnetic materials are aluminum, calcium, titanium and alloys of copper. Both diamagnetic and paramagnetic materials are considered as non-magnetic because they exhibit magnetization only in presence of an external field (Telford, Geldart et al. 1976).

9.4.3 Ferromagnetism

Ferromagnetism is explained by the concept that some magnetic materials possess atoms with permanent magnetic moments that align parallel to each other due to interatomic forces arising from the spin of electrons on their own axes. In ferromagnetic material, coupling interaction of adjacent magnetic moments creates small regions in which there is alignment of all magnetic dipoles, as illustrated in Figure 9.3. Such a region is called a domain and each one has different dipole orientations. Adjacent domains are separated by domain walls, across which the direction of dipoles gradually changes (Figure 9.4). Normally, domains are microscopic in size and in polycrystalline materials a single grain may consist of more than a single domain. As a magnetic field is applied, the domains change shape and size by the movement of domain walls. The domains that are favorably aligned to the applied field grow at the

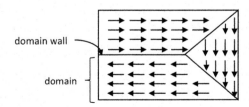

FIGURE 9.3 Schematic depiction of domains in a ferromagnetic material.

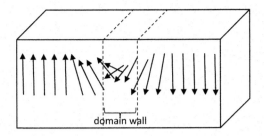

FIGURE 9.4 Schematic illustration of the gradual change in magnetic dipole orientation across a domain wall.

expense of those that are unfavorably aligned. This process continues with increasing applied field until the favorably aligned domains diminish other domains and become a large domain at which the magnetization approaches a definite limit called saturation. The new domain alignment persists once the field is removed. Figure 9.5 illustrates the mutual alignment of atomic dipoles and domains in the absence of a magnetic field, in an applied field and after the field is removed for ferromagnetic materials. The magnetization remaining after a magnetic field is removed is called remanent magnetization. Susceptibility for ferromagnetic materials is greater than 1 and typically can have values as high as 10^6. The value of susceptibility varies with temperature; when temperature rises above the T_c, ferromagnetic materials lose their magnetization and behave as paramagnetic materials in the absence of a field (Telford, Geldart et al. 1976; Paranis 1979; White 1999). Examples of ferromagnetic materials are nickel, cobalt and samarium.

9.4.4 ANTIFERROMAGNETISM

Antiferromagnetic materials can be regarded as anomalous paramagnets because they have a small positive susceptibility in an applied magnetic field, but their magnetic dipole alignment after the magnetic field is removed is entirely different to paramagnets. When the magnetic field is removed, the coupling interaction of magnetic moments tends to align the dipoles anti-parallel to each other and magnetic moments cancel out. As a consequence, antiferromagnetic materials possess no net magnetization. Manganese oxide and hematite are the most common examples.

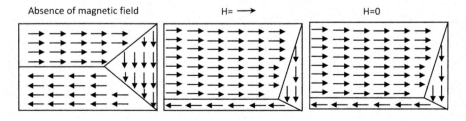

FIGURE 9.5 Schematic illustration of the mutual alignment of atomic dipoles and domains for a ferromagnetic material.

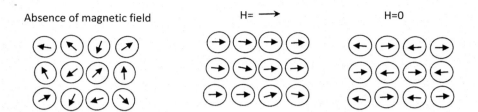

FIGURE 9.6 Schematic representations of antiparallel magnetic moments for antiferromagnetic materials.

Figure 9.6 shows schematic representation of antiparallel magnetic moments for antiferromagnetic materials (Cullity and Graham 2008a).

9.4.5 Ferrimagnetism

The magnetic characteristics of ferromagnets and ferrimagnets are similar; the distinction lies in the source of the net magnetic moments (Jakubovics 1994; Cullity and Graham 2008b; Callister and Rethwisch 2010). Like ferromagnetic materials, ferrimagnetic materials consist of magnetically saturated domains separated by domain walls, and they exhibit the phenomena of magnetic saturation and remanent magnetization. Their magnetization also disappears above T_c when then they become paramagnetic. The most important ferromagnetic substances are called ferrites. Ferrites are ionic compounds and their magnetic properties are influenced by the magnetic ions they contain. One of most commonly known ferrites is magnetite. The formula can be written as $Fe^{2+}O^{2-}(Fe^{3+})_2(O^{2-})_3$ in which the Fe ions exist in both +2 and +3 valence states in the ratio of 1:2. A net spin magnetic moment exists for Fe^{2+} as well as Fe^{3+}, but there are antiparallel spin coupling interactions between the Fe^{3+} indicating that the moments of the Fe^{3+} ions cancel out. The net magnetization is equal to the magnetic moments of the Fe^{2+} ions (Jakubovics 1994). Thus, the net magnetization for ferrimagnetic materials is not as high as for ferromagnetic materials. Figure 9.7 illustrates the alignment of ionic dipoles and domains in the absence of a magnetic field, in an applied field and after the field is removed for ferrimagnetic material. Examples of ferrimagnetic materials are magnetite and ilmenite.

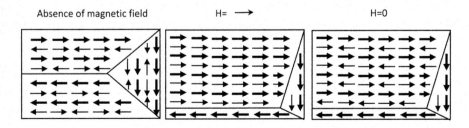

FIGURE 9.7 Schematic representations of magnetic moments for ferromagnetic materials.

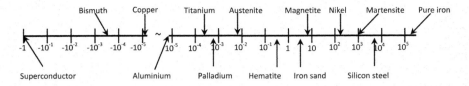

FIGURE 9.8 Susceptibility spectrum. The diagram uses a logarithmic scale to indicate the full range of magnetic susceptibility values. It extends from susceptibility = –1.0 for superconductors to susceptibility >100,000 for pure iron.

Magnetite is categorized as a ferrimagnetic material (Telford, Geldart et al. 1976; Paranis 1979). The susceptibility of magnetite is around 6–10. Figure 9.8 compares the susceptibility of a range of materials including magnetite (John 1996). It has also been reported that the susceptibility of magnetite is not affected by variation of particle size (Lawton 1979). In addition, magnetite also possesses a remanent magnetization. The value of remanence is about 6.23 Am^{-1} (Lawton 1979) and T_c ranges between 290°C and 520°C with no sharp Curie point, such that magnetization of magnetite decreases gradually over a range of temperatures rather than suddenly at a single clearly defined temperature (Wright 1964).

9.5 DAMPING MECHANISMS OF MRE

9.5.1 Viscoelastic Damping

Viscoelastic damping of MREs is mainly provided by the rubber matrix. A rubber material can be regarded as a huge three-dimensional coherent network form of long chains of carbon atoms that are joined strongly together by cross-links on vulcanization. Such material regains its pre-stressed shape on release of stress after deformation. The cross-links in rubber keep the chains from moving away from their relative position and flowing when stress is applied, such that the chains are able to recover their conformations once the stress is released. Energy absorption occurs during relaxation and recovery of the network during deformation (Burtscher, Dorfman et al. 1998; Jones 2001).

Rubber is a viscoelastic material that exhibits both viscous and elastic behavior. Figure 9.9 shows a cyclic stress-strain viscoelastic curve split up into its two primary components, viscous and elastic. The elastic stress perfectly follows Hooke's law where stress is directly proportional to strain while the viscous stress follows Newton's law, which states that viscous stress is proportional to the strain rate. At the point of maximum strain (at a 90° phase angle), the elastic stress reaches a maximum, but the viscous stress is zero; the viscous stress is out of phase with elastic stress by 90° and is always lagging behind the elastic stress. The elastic stress can be expressed as a real part of the complex modulus, whereas the viscous stress is described as an imaginary part of the complex modulus. Under cyclic deformation, the elastic components allow rubber to return quickly to its original shape and the viscous components convert kinetic energy into heat by internal friction of the disentangling long chain molecules. This conversion is known as hysteresis (Ciesielski

Magnetite Filler Reinforcement

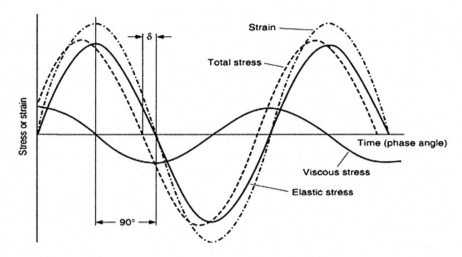

FIGURE 9.9 Cyclic stress-strain viscoelastic curve split up into viscous and elastic components.

1999; Harris and Piersol 2002).The total stress curve (a combination of the viscous stress and elastic stress) precedes the strain curve by the phase angle δ. The phase angle δ is a measure of the materials damping; the larger the angle the greater the damping.

Viscoelastic damping is influenced by temperature, frequency and cyclic strain amplitude. Temperature and frequency are considered to be the most influential (Jones 2001). The effect of temperature is illustrated in Figure 9.10, which highlights four distinct regions. In the glassy region, the chains are rigidly ordered and crystalline in nature, possessing glasslike behavior; the storage modulus is at a maximum value while loss modulus is at minimum. As temperature increases into the transition region, the storage modulus decreases while the loss factor and loss modulus

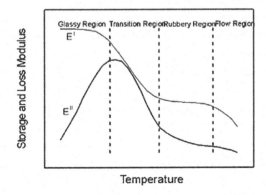

FIGURE 9.10 Variation of viscoelastic properties with temperature.

increase to a peak value and start to drop off. In this region, the long molecular chains are in a semi-rigid and semi-flow state, and they are able to rub against adjacent chains. These frictional effects result in damping mechanisms of viscoelastic material. In the rubbery region, the storage modulus, loss modulus and loss factor remain essentially constant. At this region, storage modulus and loss factor only vary slightly with changes in temperature. As temperature increases into the flow region, storage modulus starts to decrease and the loss factor increases (Speer 1996; Macioce 2010).

A frequency change may have the same effect on material damping as a temperature change. At low frequency, an applied stress deforms the long chains by rotation and bending. This is a slow process for which low frequency allows time for the chains to readjust back to the equilibrium state. Deformations do not dissipate much energy and follow in phase with slow change of stress and strain. As the frequency increases, chains undergo coiling and uncoiling motion and break cross-links. In this region, high damping occurs by internal friction between molecular chains during deformation. At high frequencies, molecular chains are not permitted to relax and energy dissipates as heat; stress and strain are out of phase (Arcanjo 1985).

9.5.2 Interfacial Damping

MREs are composite materials consisting of magnetically polarizable particles as filler in a soft rubber matrix. Fillers can be considered to have three main roles, such as reinforcement/improvement of mechanical performance, space filling/reduction of material costs (for which the material is commonly referred to as extender fillers) and improvement in responsive properties such as damping, which is the main focus for MREs (Chokkalingam, Rajasabai Senthur et al. 2010). In MREs, energy dissipation mechanisms are contributed by the matrix and the particles, as well as the interface between matrix and the particles. The matrix absorbs energy through viscoelastic damping, and the magnetic particles provide energy absorption through magnetostrictive damping, which relates to domain wall movement, as well as through interparticle attraction. The interface plays an important role in interfacial friction, which suppresses vibration (Hathaway, Clark et al. 1995).

Incorporation of magnetic particles into the rubber matrix leads to interfacial bonding, which can occur through physical absorption and chemical bonding. Interfacial bonding constrains the mobility of the rubber molecules; the constraint is greater the closer to the particle surface; therefore, close to the particles, the Young's modulus of the rubber increases gradually as the distance from the particle decreases. Consequently, the interfacial bonding of rubber molecules on the particle surface effectively forms an interphase, as illustrated in Figure 9.11. The new interphase provides high energy absorption through interfacial friction damping (Sun, Gibson et al. 2009).

In anisotropic MREs, when the particles are aligned in the direction of the magnetic field, they form a joint interphase between neighboring particles (Figure 9.12) (Wang 1998). This interaction further attenuates the mobility of the rubber molecules and increases the Young's modulus. Considerable change in both elastic and viscous behavior occurs at a joint interphase. The breakdown and reformation of

Magnetite Filler Reinforcement

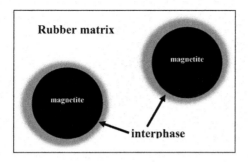

FIGURE 9.11 Interphase between rubber matrix and filler particle surface.

the joint interphase is the dominant mechanism that originates energy dissipation in anisotropic MREs.

Elastic behavior relates to the strength of the interphase, which is reduced during dynamic strain, whereas viscous behavior is related to the breakdown and reformation of interphase during the deformation. Therefore, tan δ (E''/E'), which effectively describes the ratio of the work converted to heat, compared with that recovered during deformation, is an important parameter to assess energy dissipation in materials. It is influenced by the portion of filler networking capable of being broken down and reconstituted and that remaining unchanged during dynamic strain (Wang 1998).

Under low strain amplitudes, the shear stress between particles and the matrix is lower and cannot break the interphase so that the tan δ would be lower. As the strain amplitude increases, high shear stress occurs at the interphase, which results in interfacial bonding breakdown. Then the rubber that formed an interphase becomes free to take part in the energy dissipation process, resulting in a higher tan δ. Furthermore, under this condition, reformation of new interfacial bonding after deformation would also impart additional energy dissipation to the MREs. Formation of joint interphases in anisotropic MREs as described above increases shear stress between high modulus rubber at the joint and hence originates higher energy absorption compared with isotropic MREs (Wang 1998; Sun, Gibson et al. 2009).

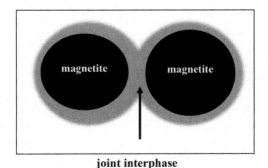

FIGURE 9.12 A joint interphase between two adjacent particles in anisotropic MREs.

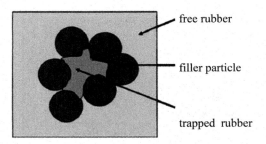

FIGURE 9.13 Restrained rubber and free rubber in agglomerate.

The main factors that influence the interfacial properties include particle size, particle loading, dispersion and formation of agglomerates. For smaller particles there is a larger overall surface area for the same particle volume fraction; therefore, the total interfacial surface area available for internal friction at the interphase increases and energy dissipation increases. However, the tendency of smaller particles to form agglomerates is higher as the particle loading increases and poor dispersion occurs. When the particles agglomerate, some rubber segments will be trapped within the particles, as shown in Figure 9.13 (Yanceng, Xinglong et al. 2011). The rubber, which is located outside the agglomerate, is defined as free rubber, whereas the rubber inside the agglomerate is defined as trapped rubber. The trapped rubber reduces the effective interfacial friction area between the free rubber and the particles and behaves as a hard filler, leading to a decrease in MRE hysteresis. The agglomeration is strongly amplitude and temperature dependent. At high amplitude, the agglomerates are broadly destroyed and release the trapped rubber to take part in energy absorption. On the other hand, increasing the temperature would increase the mobility of the trapped rubber molecules and weaken the interparticle interaction in the agglomerates. Consequently, breakdown of agglomerates would be expected.

9.5.3 Magnetostrictive Damping

Magnetostriction is a phenomenon that describes the interaction between magnetism and elasticity in ferromagnetic materials such that a change in a material's physical dimensions occurs in response to a change of magnetic field. MREs exhibit significant magnetostriction, which makes them attractive for damping (Bednarek 2006; Olabi and Grunwald 2008). The magnetostrictive effect results in damping in MREs through energy dissipation associated with magnetic domain movement under mechanical loading, a process that transforms elastic energy into magnetic energy, which then dissipates by magnetic hysteresis (Hathaway, Clark et al. 1995). Generally, the matrix phase transfers the vibrational energy to the magnetic particles, which allows the particles to take part in damping.

Ferromagnetic particles are divided into regions of uniform magnetic polarization, known as domains. On application of an applied magnetic field during curing, the particles align and form continuous columnar structures in the magnetic field

Magnetite Filler Reinforcement

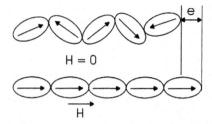

FIGURE 9.14 Magnetic domain wall orientation under external magnetic field.

direction. The magnetic domains, nominally in random orientation, are oriented, resulting in anisotropic MREs (Greg and Geoffrey 2004).

The optimum damping is seen in anisotropic MREs where the domains rotate and align in response to an external magnetic field during curing. Rotation and alignment allow the material to change domain orientation, producing maximum internal strain in the structure. Figure 9.14 shows the mechanism of the domain orientation. The internal strain in the structure causes stretching of the material in the direction of the magnetic field, resulting in a change in length of the material. Applying a stronger field increases the numbers of domains that align in the direction of the magnetic field, generating more definite orientation. The saturation point is achieved when all magnetic domains become aligned with the magnetic field (Ginder, Clark et al. 2002; Guan, Dong et al. 2008).

The crucial process for energy absorption is the domain interaction with the mechanical stress. The magnetic domains are strongly coupled with the mechanical stress whereby stress changes the magnetic domain structure within the material, resulting in the damping of the applied load (Choudhury and Singh 2005). The results of domain interaction with tensile, compressive and shear stresses is shown in Figure 9.15. Considering a tensile and compressive cyclic load, under initial tensile stress, the matrix phase transfers the load to the damping phase and at a critical stress value, the domains realign parallel to the loading direction. Subsequent compressive loading

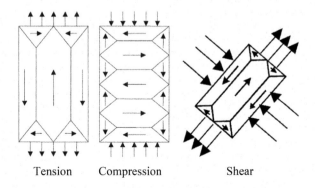

FIGURE 9.15 Results of domain interaction with tensile, compressive and shear stresses.

realigns the domains perpendicular to the loading direction, when a minimum critical value of an applied stress is exceeded. The elastic strain vanishes on removing the stress but the magnetostrictive strain does not return to the original state. This is evidence of a loss of energy that results in damping of the stress. Shear loading generates a biaxial state in which two stresses act perpendicular to each other but in opposite directions, producing a stress that is applied at an orientation of 45° from either stress. Tensile stress tends to align domains parallel to the tensile load while the compressive stress also orientates domains parallel to the compressive load. Shear stress domain orientation can be represented by coalescences of tension and compression stresses and is expected to have similar energy absorption mechanisms (Mcknight and Carman 1999; Geoffrey and Gregory 2000; Choudhury and Singh 2005).

The energy absorption by magnetostriction is strongly dependent on vibration amplitude and independent of vibrational frequency (Hathaway, Clark et al. 1995). The reason for this is related to the finite number of stable magnetic domain configurations within the magnetostrictive particles inside the matrix phase of MREs. An application of stress along a plane of aligned domain walls lowers the energy barrier, causing movement of the magnetic domains within the material. At a critical stress level, the domains switch from one stable orientation to another. Each domain reorientation absorbs a quantifiable amount of energy under an applied cyclical load. After the domains have orientated, they behave elastically until an opposite critical stress is applied, causing them to reorient back to a new state, absorbing more energy. Furthermore, the mechanical energy required for domain motion increases when an external magnetic field is added during services. Thus, to increase the number of domain reorientations for higher energy absorption, the level of magnetic energy must be increased (Greg and Geoffrey 2004; Piersol and Paez 2010).

9.6 CONCLUSION

Magnetic mineral filler in MREs appears to have a very promising future for a wide range of vibration damping applications and will have a positive impact on market growth. Magnetic mineral filler, on the other hand, may soon be competitive with conventional filler used in MREs, such as carbonyl iron and pure iron. The use of magnetic mineral filler in MREs is in conjunction with Sustainable Development Goal (SDG) 12 to ensure sustainable consumption and efficient use of natural resources and SDG 9 to build resilient infrastructure, promote inclusive and sustainable industrialization and foster innovation.

ACKNOWLEDGMENT

The authors would like to thank Professor Kim Louise Pickering of the University of Waikato and Universiti Sains Malaysia for her support.

REFERENCES

Arcanjo, L. (1985). "The use of damping material in industrial machines." Doctoral thesis, University of Southampton, UK.

Bednarek, S. (2006). "The giant linear magnetostriction in elastic ferromagnetic composites within a porous matrix." *Journal of Magnetism and Magnetic Materials* **301**(1): 200–207.

Burtscher, S., A. Dorfman, K. Bergmeister (1998). "Mechanical aspects of high damping rubber." *Second International PhD Symposium in Civil Engineering.* Budapest, Hungary, 1–7.

Callister W. D. and D. G. Rethwisch (2010). *Materials Science and Engineering: An Introduction.* New York, John Wiley and Sons.

Chang, S.-B. R. and J. L. Kirschvink (1989). "Magnetofossils, the magnetization of sediments, and the evolution of magnetite biomineralization." *Annual Review of Earth and Planetary Sciences* **17**(1): 169–195.

Chokkalingam, R., P. Rajasabai Senthur, et al. (2010). "Magnetomechanical behavior of Fe/PU magnetorheological elastomers." *Journal of Composite Materials* **45**(15): 1545–1552.

Choudhury, P. K. and O. N. Singh (2005). "Electromagnetic materials." *Encyclopedia of RF and Microwave Engineering.* New York, John Wiley & Sons, Inc., 1227–1228.

Ciesielski, A. (1999). *An Introduction to Rubber Technology.* Shawbury, UK, Rapra Technology Limited.

Cribb, W. (1998). "Dana's minerals and how to study them, fourth edition." *Eos, Transactions American Geophysical Union* **79**(31): 374–374.

Cullity, B. D. and C. D. Graham (2008a). "Antiferromagnetism." *Introduction to Magnetic Materials.* John Wiley & Sons, Inc.: 151–173.

Cullity, B. D. and C. D. Graham (2008b). "Ferrimagnetism." *Introduction to Magnetic Materials.* New York, John Wiley & Sons, Inc., 175–195.

Geoffrey, P. M. and P. C. Gregory (2000). "Energy absorption in axial and shear loading of particulate magnetostrictive composites." *Smart Structures and Materials 2000: Active Materials: Behavior and Mechanics.* Newport Beach, CA, SPIE.

Ginder, J. M., Clark, S. M., Schlotter, W. F., Nichols, M. E. (2002). "Magnetostrictive phenomena in magnetorheological elastomers." *International Journal of Modern Physics B* **16**(17–18): 2412–2418.

Greg, P. C. and P. M. Geoffrey (2004). "Damping in composite materials through domain wall motion." U.S. Patent. US 2004/0138366: 1–6.

Guan, X., X. Dong, et al. (2008). "Magnetostrictive effect of magnetorheological elastomer." *Journal of Magnetism and Magnetic Materials* **320**(3–4): 158–163.

Harris, C. M. and A. G. Piersol (2002). *Harris' Shock and Vibration Handbook.* New York, McGraw-Hill.

Hathaway, K., A. Clark, et al. (1995). "Magnetomechanical damping in giant magnetostriction alloys." *Metallurgical and Materials Transactions A* **26**(11): 2797–2801.

Jakubovics, J. P. (1994). *Magnetism and Magnetic Materials.* London, Maney Publishing.

Jiles, D. (1998). *Introduction to Magnetism and Magnetic Materials.* Boca Raton, Florida, CRC Press.

John, F. S. (1996). "The role of magnetic susceptibility in magnetic resonance imaging: MRI magnetic compatibility of the first and second kinds." *Medical Physics* **23**(6): 815–850.

Jones, D. I. G. (2001). *Handbook of Viscoelastic Vibration Damping.* New York, John Wiley & Sons.

Kaleta J., M. Królewicz, et al. (2011). "Magnetomechanical properties of anisotropic and isotropic magnetorheological composites with thermoplastic elastomer matrices." *Smart Material and Structures* **20**(085006): 12.

Klein, C. (2005). "Some Precambrian banded iron-formations (BIFs) from around the world: Their age, geologic setting, mineralogy, metamorphism, geochemistry, and origins." *American Mineralogist* **90**(10): 1473–1499.

Kruželák, J., R. Dosoudil, et al. (2017). "Rubber composites cured with sulphur and peroxide and incorporated with strontium ferrite." *Bulletin of Materials Science* **40**(1): 223–231.

Lawton, D. C. (1979). "Geophysical Exploration of Quaternary Ironsand deposits at Taharoa, Waikato north head and Raglan, West Coast North Island, New Zealand." Doctoral dissertation, University of Auckland, Auckland, New Zealand.

Leaman, D. (1997). "Magnetic rocks-their effect on compass use and navigation in Tasmania." Papers and Proceedings of the Royal Society of Tasmania, Hobart, Tasmania.

Macioce, P. (2010). *Viscoelastic Damping 101 - Insight*. Livonia, Michigan, Roush Industries, Inc., 1–3.

Mcknight, G. P. and G. P. Carman (1999). "Energy absorption and damping in magnetostrictive composites." *Materials Research Symposium, Smart Materials*. Boston, MA, Cambridge University Press.

Olabi, A. G. and A. Grunwald (2008). "Design and application of magnetostrictive materials." *Materials & Design* **29**(2): 469–483.

Paranis, D. S. (1979). *Principles of Applied Geophysics*. Boca Raton, Florida, Chapman & Hall.

Piersol, A. G. and T. L. Paez (2010). *Harris' Shock and Vibration Handbook* (6th Edition). New York, McGraw-Hill, 35.31–35.29.

Shuib, R. K. and K. L. Pickering (2016). "Effect of carbon black on the dynamic properties of anisotropic magnetorheological elastomer." *Journal of Engineering Science* **12**: 1–12.

Soloman, M., P. Kurian, et al. (2004). "Evaluation of the magnetic and mechanical properties of rubber ferrite composites containing strontium ferrite." *Polymer-Plastics Technology and Engineering* **43**(4): 1013–1028.

Speer, J. A. (1996). "Integrated system damping and isolation of a three dimensional structure." MSc thesis, Naval Postgraduate School, Monterey, CA.

Stepanov, G. V., S. S. Abramchuk, et al. (2007). "Effect of a homogeneous magnetic field on the viscoelastic behavior of magnetic elastomers." *Polymer* **48**(2): 488–495.

Sun, L., R. F. Gibson, et al. (2009). "Energy absorption capability of nanocomposites: A review." *Composites Science and Technology* **69**(14): 2392–2409.

Telford, W. M., L. P. Geldart, et al. (1976). *Applied Geophysics*. Cambridge, UK, Cambridge University Press.

Wang, M. J. (1998). "Effect of polymer-filler and filler-filler interactions on dynamic properties of filled vulcanizates." *Rubber Chemistry and Technology* **71**(3): 520–589.

Wang, Y., Y. Hu, et al. (2006). "Magnetorheological elastomers based on isobutylene–isoprene rubber." *Polymer Engineering & Science* **46**(3): 264–268.

Watson, J. R. (1997). "Method and apparatus for varying the stiffness of a suspension bushing." U.S. Patent 5609353. Motor Co. 5609353: 1–3.

White, M. A. (1999). *Properties of Materials*. New York, Oxford University Press.

Wright, J. B. (1964). "Iron-titanium oxides in Some New Zealand ironsands." *New Zealand Journal of Geology and Geophysics* **7**(3): 424–444.

Yanceng, F., G. Xinglong, et al. (2011). "Interfacial friction damping properties in magnetorheological elastomers." *Smart Materials and Structures* **20**(3): 1–8.

10 Characterization and Properties of Montmorillonite-Reinforced Thermoplastic Composites

Sung Ting Sam, Pei Gie Gan, Sin Yee Lew, and Nik Noriman Zulkepli
Universiti Malaysia Perlis
Aaru, Malaysia

Hanafi Ismail
Universiti Sains Malaysia
Nibong Tebal, Malaysia

CONTENTS

10.1 Introduction 212
10.2 Montmorillonite 212
10.3 Processing Methods of Montmorillonite-Reinforced
Thermoplastic Composites 214
    10.3.1 Solution Blending 214
    10.3.2 Melt Mixing 217
    10.3.3 In Situ Polymerization 218
10.4 Properties of Montmorillonite-Reinforced Thermoplastic
Composites 219
    10.4.1 Mechanical Properties 219
    10.4.2 Thermal Properties 221
        10.4.2.1 Dynamic Mechanical Properties 221
        10.4.2.2 Thermal Stability 222
        10.4.2.3 Thermal Behavior 224
        10.4.2.4 Barrier Properties 225
        10.4.2.5 Biodegradation Properties 226
10.5 Conclusions 228
References 228

DOI: 10.1201/9781003220947-10

10.1 INTRODUCTION

Plastics have become the basic ingredients of our daily lives. It is estimated that approximately 8300 million metric tons (Mt) of plastics have been produced since 1950 (Geyer, Jambeck, and Law 2017). The growing popularity of plastic products is not solely because of its low synthesis cost, but also because of their attractive characteristics such as light weight, ease of processing and outstanding barrier properties (Guidotti et al. 2017). Plastics are generally divided into two broad categories, thermoplastics and thermosetting plastic. Both thermoplastics and thermoset plastics are composed of long chain molecules but differ in the bonding. The long chain molecules of thermoplastic are held together by a weak van der Waals force, whereas the polymer chains of thermosetting plastic are bonded by strong covalent bonding (Ratna 2009). Thermoplastics such as acrylonitrile butadiene styrene (ABS), ethylene vinyl alcohol (EVOH), polypropylene (PP), polystyrene (PS) and polyethylene (PE) with minimum cross-linking can be reconstructed into various shapes for various applications at a high temperature (Sun, Kharbas, and Turng 2015).

To meet the requirements of consumers, the properties of thermoplastic composites can be altered by the incorporation of minerals to adapt to various applications. The introduction of minerals such as montmorillonite (MMT) as a promising reinforcing filler is found to be effective in enhancing the properties of thermoplastic composites. MMT has received a great level of attention from the scientific and industrial community. It has been the topic of a wide range of research efforts aimed at various applications due to its low cost, high mechanical strength, superior thermal stability and good flame retardancy (Kumar and Kannan 2014). Hence, this chapter provides an overview of MMT's structure and properties. Concurrently, the processing methods and properties of MMT-reinforced thermoplastic composites are also discussed.

10.2 MONTMORILLONITE

MMT can be considered as the most widely used expandable clay mineral in the preparation of composites. It can be naturally found in volcanic rocks (bentonites). MMT-reinforced polymer composites are well known for their applications including coating and adhesive materials and heat-resistant automotive components, and in industries such as aerospace, electronics, packaging, optical, and medical devices (Serwicka et al. 2018). The morphology structure of MMT is shown in Figure 10.1. MMT is stacked together and forms a dispersed-layer structure.

MMT belongs to the smectite group of clay, which is a member of structural family of the 2:1 clay layers (Nur Aimi and Anuar 2016). The crystal structure of MMT is composed of layers formed by the two-silica tetrahedral bonded to an edge-shared octahedral sheet of either magnesium or aluminum ions. The aluminum ions are substituted by the magnesium ions, which resulted in a difference in valances and excessive negative charge between the interlayers of MMT. The negative charges are compensated by the positively charged ions such as Ca^{2+} and Na^+, as shown in Figure 10.2 (Bee et al. 2018). The layers could be held together in the clay crystallite by interlayer cations, electrostatic force, van der Waals force or hydrogen bonding

Montmorillonite-Reinforced Thermoplastic Composites 213

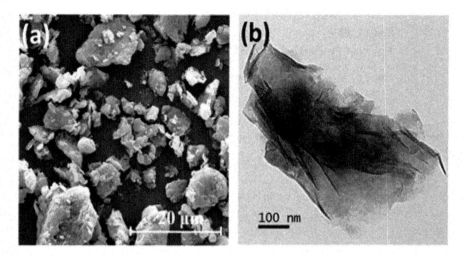

FIGURE 10.1 (a) Scanning electron microscopic (SEM), and (b) transmission electron microscopic (TEM) images of MMT. (Adapted from Peng et al. 2019.)

(Bhattacharya 2016). The layered structure of MMT allows the water and other polar molecules to intercalate depending on its uptake tendency (Bertuoli et al. 2014). Furthermore, the high cation exchange capacity of the MMT could offer the surface activity needed for surface treatment and modification.

The MMT is a plate-shaped clay particle with a diameter of 0.2–2 μm and a thickness of approximately 1 nm (Cui et al. 2019). The physical properties of MMT are summarized in Table 10.1. The difference in color is attributed to the replacement of interlayer cations by high-valance iron, manganese or titanium within the

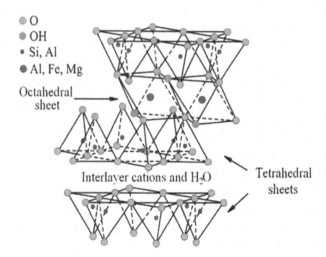

FIGURE 10.2 The structure of MMT. (Adapted from Sidorenko et al. 2018.)

TABLE 10.1

Physical Properties of MMT

Property	Description
Density	2–3 g/cm^3
Crystal system	Monoclinic
Hardness	1–2 on Mohs' scale
Fracture	Irregular, uneven
Cleavage	Perfect
Color	White, buff, yellow, green, rarely pale pink to red
Transparency	Translucent
Luster	Earthy, dull

Source: Uddin (2018).

lattice structure (Rahromostaqim and Sahimi 2020). MMT has garnered tremendous interest from researchers in the preparation of numerous composites due to its low cost, high specific surface area, great cation exchange capacity, good sorption ability, abundant source and high degree of exfoliation/intercalation (Vilarinho, Vaz, and Silva 2019). However, MMT is hydrophilic in nature, which makes it difficult to disperse homogeneously within the polymer matrices and limits its application in the organophilic polymers (Batool et al. 2018). This is attributed to the higher surface energy of MMT compared with the host matrix, which produces a stronger cohesive interaction between the layers and hinders the incorporation of polymer chains into the interlamellar domain of MMT (Bhattacharya 2016; Zulfiqar et al. 2008). Hence, the surface modification and treatment of MMT play an important role in promoting a more favorable MMT-polymer matrix interaction and permitting the MMT to expand its applications for different purpose. The scattering of MMT in a polymer matrix could be in immiscible, exfoliated or intercalated form as exhibited in Figure 10.3. The interaction between MMT and polymer matrix can influence the dispersion of the clay within the polymer matrix, which in turn affects the final properties of the composites.

10.3 PROCESSING METHODS OF MONTMORILLONITE-REINFORCED THERMOPLASTIC COMPOSITES

10.3.1 SOLUTION BLENDING

Solution blending is a processing method based on a solvent system in which the polymer or prepolymer is soluble and the clay layers swellable. In general, the solution blending process is comprised of three steps: MMT dispersion in the polymer solution, removal of solvent and casting of MMT/polymer mixture. The MMT is exfoliated into a single layer using solvents, such as chloroform, toluene or water. The dissolved polymer matrix is then added into the MMT solution. After mixing, the polymer chains embed within the interlayers of MMT. On removal of solvent, the

Montmorillonite-Reinforced Thermoplastic Composites

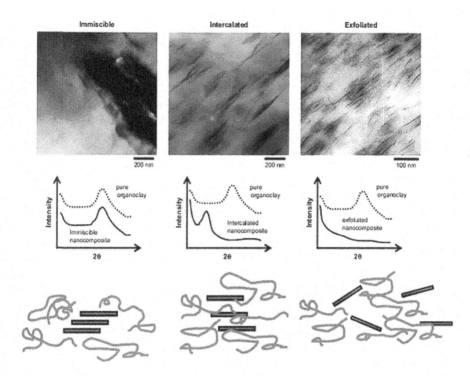

FIGURE 10.3 Different MMT dispersion state in polymer matrix with transmission electron microscopy (TEM) and X-ray diffraction (XRD) results. (Adapted from Nagy and Kókai 2018.)

sheets reassemble and result in the MMT/thermoplastic composites as depicted in Figure 10.4 (Mtibe et al. 2018). The advantage of solvent blending is that the fabrication of thermoplastic composites can be performed without any specialized facility or equipment. Also, the composites produced by solvent blending offer a more uniform and homogeneous dispersion of filler.

Numerous studies have applied the solution blending technique to attain a high degree of interaction and dispersion between the MMT and polymer matrix. The properties of polylactic acid (PLA) thermoplastic composites with the incorporation of MMT via the solvent blending method were determined (Arjmandi et al. 2014). The field emission scanning electron micrograph (FESEM) of MMT/PLA thermoplastic composites prepared by solvent blending presented an evenly dispersed and homogeneous surface. A similar finding was also reported by Allison et al. (2015) in which the SEM of MMT-reinforced polyvinyl alcohol (PVOH) thermoplastic composites showed a smooth and homogeneous surface at a low concentration of MMT. However, they observed that the 25 wt% MMT-reinforced PVOH thermoplastic composites presented an ordered brick and mortar structure as shown in Figure 10.5. The layers observed in the MMT/PVOH thermoplastic composite could be attributed to the stacks of MMT sheets that were not fully exfoliated but intercalated with the PVOH.

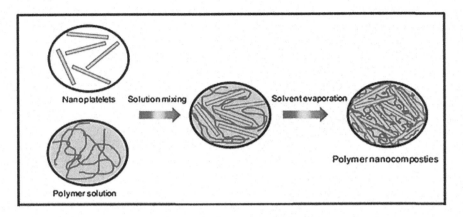

FIGURE 10.4 Schematic diagram of preparation of MMT/polymer composites by solution blending. (Adapted from Huang and Cheng 2017.)

The MMT dispersion requires energetic agitation such as magnetic stirring, reflux, shear mixing or sonication. Ultrasonication excitation has been employed as a technique to break up the MMT clusters by cavitation in the solution and/or exciting resonance vibrations of the MMT clusters (Bittmann, Haupert, and Schlarb 2009). Alshabanat et al. (2013) synthesized the MMT-based PS thermoplastic composite by using an ultrasonication-assisted solvent blending technique. The SEM and transmission emission micrographs (TEMs) showed that intercalation of PS in the interlamellar spaces of MMT with a very small quantity of exfoliation of the layers within

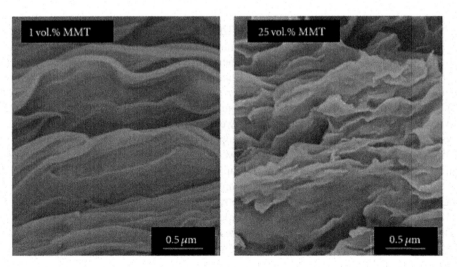

FIGURE 10.5 SEM images of MMT/PVOH thermoplastic composite. (Adapted from Allison et al. 2015.)

the polymer matrix. Improved miscibility between MMT and PS was observed in MMT/PS composites prepared by ultrasonication.

On the other hand, due to the hydrophilic characteristic of MMT, the choices of compatible matrices are limited to polar polymers only. Therefore, a great deal of research had been performed to overcome the incompatibility problem between hydrophilic MMT and hydrophobic polymer matrices. Ozdemir et al. (2016) studied the effect of different organic modifiers (represented as Cloisites 15A, 20A and 30 B) on the compatibility between MMT and PLA matrix. TEM and X-ray diffraction (XRD) results showed the presence of intercalated and exfoliated structures in the three MMTs in PLA matrix, implying the successful formations of MMT/PLA thermoplastic composites.

10.3.2 Melt Mixing

Melt mixing is a popular and effective technique in fabricating clay/polymeric thermoplastic composite, which involves the mixing of two or more polymers at melt condition with the aid of a mixer or extruder as presented in Figure 10.6. It can be considered as an environmental-benign technique as no organic solvent is needed during the blending of thermoplastic composites (Fornes and Paul 2003). Also, the melt-mixing method is more compatible with the current industrial productions as it provides a greater degree of freedom in product specifications (Qaiss, Bouhfid, and Essabir 2015).

MMT/low-density PE (LDPE) composites with various MMT content (0, 0.5, 1, 3, 5, and 10 wt%) were melt compounded by using a twin-screw extruder. The temperature profile of the extruder was set as 110, 110, 180, 190, 185, 180, 175, and 170°C from the feeder to the header of extruder. The extrusion process was carried out at a speed of 300 rpm. The composite films produced have a thickness of approximately 60 mm. FESEM revealed the homogeneous dispersion of MMT within the LDPE

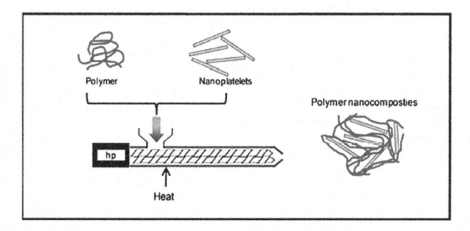

FIGURE 10.6 Schematic diagram of preparation of MMT/polymer composites by melt mixing. (Adapted from Huang and Cheng 2017.)

matrix. This result was further supported by the TEM images in which the most of the MMTs were in exfoliated state. The shear force was applied during the extrusion and promoted the MMT dispersion by disturbing the stacking order of MMT layers. At the same time, the molten polymer matrix penetrated into the MMT interlayers and led to the well-dispersed exfoliated layers (Bumbudsanpharoke et al. 2017). Similar observation was also reported by Li et al. (2015), who reported the well dispersion of MMT in PVOH polymer matrix prepared by the melt-mixing method.

Compatibility between polymer matrix and reinforcing filler plays an essential role in enhancing the properties of the thermoplastic composites. Zandsalimi et al. (2019) proposed that the organophilization of MMT could overcome the incompatibility issue between MMT and hydrophobic polyetheretherketone matrix. A series of potential cations (1-n-butyl-3-methylimidazolium [BMI]), 1-n-hexyl-3-methylimidazolium [HMI] and 1-n-octyl-3-methylimidazolium [OMI]) and anions (tetrafuoroborate [BF_4], bis (trifluoromethyl sulfonyl) imide [$(CF_3SO_2)_2N$] and hexafluorophosphate [PF_6]) were compared and the most suitable organic modifier (BMI-PF_6) was selected. Agglomeration of MMT in the unmodified MMT/polyetheretherketone thermoplastic composites was observed. In addition to that, no intercalated or exfoliated MMT sheets were detected in the TEM of unmodified MMT/polyetheretherketone thermoplastic composites, which proves the poor dispersion of MMT within polyetheretherketone matrix. After the organophilization of MMT, an intermediate morphology consisted of single-layered exfoliated MMT layers and the multilayered crystallites intercalated with the polyetheretherketone chains were observed. The development of intercalated/exfoliated composites indicated the enhanced interfacial interactions between MMT and polyetheretherketone matrix. This result was in agreement with Al-Samhan et al. (2017).

10.3.3 IN SITU POLYMERIZATION

In situ polymerization is an effective technique in dispersing the MMT evenly within the polymer matrix. The fillers are first swelled in the pre-polymer or monomer solution and then polymerization is carried out at the desired temperature (Figure 10.7). The polymer is able to develop between the layers of clay and the clay layers are pushed apart. As a result, intercalated or exfoliated MMT/thermoplastic composite is formed (Mittal et al. 2015). The advantage of in situ polymerization is that the severe thermodynamic requirements related to the intercalation process can be avoided (Mittal et al. 2015). Furthermore, in situ polymerization also allows various designs of the composites by enabling the different interfacial interactions between MMT and polymeric matrices through the modification on the composition and structure of polymer matrix (Bhattacharya 2016).

In situ polymerization has garnered a great level of interest from researchers in the preparation of MMT and thermoplastic composites. It has recently been applied as an alternative for the processing of MMT-reinforced thermoplastic composites. Fabrication of MMT-reinforced polyamide-6 thermoplastic composite via in situ polymerization was reported (Kherroub et al. 2013). The incorporation of MMT has increased the yield strength and the tensile modulus of polyamide-6 thermoplastic composite. The thermal stability of composites was also greatly enhanced by the

Montmorillonite-Reinforced Thermoplastic Composites

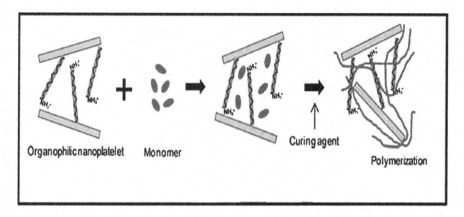

FIGURE 10.7 Schematic diagram of preparation of MMT/polymer composites by in situ polymerization. (Adapted from Huang and Cheng 2017.)

addition of MMT. The TEM showed that the MMT was homogeneously dispersed within the polymer matrix. The composites with 1 and 3 wt% MMT showed an exfoliated structure, whereas 5 wt% MMT/polyamide-6 composite displayed an intercalated composite. The results were in agreement with Strankowski et al. in Kherroub et al. (2013).

The preparation of PLA composites by in situ polymerization of lactide using MMT was reported by Sabatini et al. in Kherroub et al. 2013). To improve the compatibility between MMT and PLA matrix, 3-glycidoxypropyltrimethoxysilane was employed as the coupling agent for the surface modification of MMT. The MMT/PLA composites showed homogeneous dispersion of MMT, especially for the silane-modified MMT/PLA composites. The silane-modified composites also exhibited higher thermal stability compared with unmodified MMT/PLA composites. MMT/poly(methylmethacrylate) (PMMA) composites were fabricated via in situ polymerization in the chloroform solution under probe sonication (Prado and Bartoli 2018). The TEM of MMT/PMMA composites (Figure 10.8) showed a mixed morphology of exfoliated and intercalated structure. The thermogravimetric analyzer (TGA) results also exhibited a significant enhancement in the temperature of PMMA chain scission reaction up to 82°C for the MMT/PMMA composites compared with neat PMMA.

10.4 PROPERTIES OF MONTMORILLONITE-REINFORCED THERMOPLASTIC COMPOSITES

10.4.1 MECHANICAL PROPERTIES

Mechanical properties are the physical properties of thermoplastic composites that reveal the deformation of composites under the exertion of force or load. Under the mechanical testing, the composites are subjected to the forces until the failure occurs (Chakraborty 2012). It plays a significant part during the selection of appropriate polymer for particular applications.

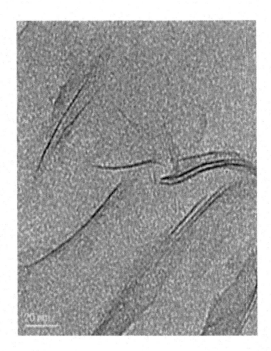

FIGURE 10.8 TEM of MMT/PMMA composite (Adapted from Prado and Bartoli 2018.)

An enhancement in the mechanical properties of PVOH composites by the incorporation of MMT was reported by Gaidukov et al. (2015). The pristine PVOH has a tensile strength and Young's modulus of 85.1 MPa and 1.9 GPa, respectively. On the addition of MMT into PVOH matrix, the tensile strength and Young's modulus of 150.2 MPa and 11.2 GPa could be achieved. This could be attributed to the formation of a strong intermolecular hydrogen bonding network between MMT and PVOH matrix. Also, the polymer comprised approximately 69–85% of the strong and dense crystalline phase, which could lead to an increase in the stiffness of the composites. Similar results were observed by Wilpiszewska et al. (2015), who reported an improvement in the mechanical properties of MMT reinforced starch thermoplastic composites.

Effect of different plasticizers (glycerol and ionic liquid) on the mechanical properties on MMT-reinforced chitosan thermoplastic composite was investigated (Boesel 2015). The ionic liquid-plasticized MMT/chitosan composites showed a higher tensile strength compared with glycerol-plasticized composites. The enhancement in the mechanical properties of ionic liquid-plasticized MMT/chitosan composites was created by the different conformation of chitosan in the MMT layers, which led to the monolayer intercalation to the detriment of a more disorganized or trilayer intercalation.

The mechanical properties of MMT-reinforced polymeric composites can also be improved by physical cross-linking, such as irradiation. The mechanical properties of PLA composites reinforced with various concentration of MMT (1, 3 and 5 wt%)

Montmorillonite-Reinforced Thermoplastic Composites 221

irradiated by electron beam were determined by Salvatore et al. (2016). The addition of MMT improved the mechanical strength and modulus of the PLA composites. The enhancement in the stress at yield and break, elastic modulus and reduction in the elongation at break were observed after the electron beam irradiation. Similar results were also reported by Bee et al. (2014), who observed an improvement in the mechanical properties of electron-beam irradiated MMT/PVOH composites at an irradiation voltage of 15 kV, current of 1 mA and energy of 1 MeV. This could be attributed to the strong MMT interlayer dispersed within the PVOH matrix, which restrained the free movements of electron-beam irradiation free radicals to attack the polymer chains and formed a dense cross-linking network between MMT and PVOH matrix.

Also, chemical cross-linking can also be employed to further enhance the mechanical properties of the thermoplastic composites. Peidayesh et al. (2020) reported the improvement of the mechanical properties of starch thermoplastic composites by the inclusion of MMT and the application of dialdehyde starch as a cross-linking agent. The tensile strength, elongation at break and modulus of neat starch thermoplastic were 2.7 MPa, 136% and 11 MPa, respectively. After cross-linking, the tensile strength and modulus of elasticity of neat starch thermoplastic increased significantly. The dialdehyde starch-cross-linked MMT-starch thermoplastic composite displayed the highest tensile strength and modulus of elasticity of 6.7 and 150 MPa, respectively. The enhanced tensile strength obtained by the addition of MMT and a cross-linking agent was attributed to the intramolecular and intermolecular cross-linking, which led to the formation of a rigid cross-linking network. However, the incorporation of MMT and the cross-linking process had a negative impact on the elongation at break of the MMT-starch thermoplastic composite. The results were in agreement with Chen et al. (2017).

10.4.2 Thermal Properties

10.4.2.1 Dynamic Mechanical Properties

The thermomechanical properties of thermoplastic composites can be investigated by dynamic mechanical analysis (DMA) and thermomechanical analysis (TMA). However, as few TMAs in the literature studied TMA, this chapter focuses on the thermomechanical properties analyzed using DMA instead of TMA. DMAs involve the impact of stress, frequency and temperature on the viscous elastic, relaxation and damping behavior of the thermoplastic composite. DMA can be considered as a more precise technique in detecting the transition state than via differential thermal analysis (DTA) and differential scanning calorimetry (DSC) methods as it measured dynamic modulus and damping coefficient (Ebnesajjad 2014). Also, DMA can detect the minor structure change of polymer as well as the glass transition temperature, T_g, of the thermoplastic composites.

Zheng et al. (2017) observed an improvement in the dynamic mechanical properties of PLA thermoplastics after the addition of MMT. The storage modulus of PLA thermoplastic increased by 23% with the inclusion of 6 wt% MMT. However, there was no significant enhancement on the glass transition temperature of the MMT/PLA composites. Similar results were also reported by Sirousazar et al. (2012), in which the storage modulus of PVOH composites was increased by the reinforcement of MMT. This result was attributed to the higher cross-linking density of the composites, which resulted from the reinforcing effect of MMT within the PVOH matrix. Also, the intensity of tan δ was observed to be decreased with the addition of MMT. This was due to the constraint imposed by the MMT against the mobility of the PVOH matrix, which resulted in a more elastic response in the thermoplastic composites compared with neat PVOH.

The preparation method has a significant influence on the thermal properties of MMT-reinforced thermoplastic composites. Romero-Bastida et al. (2018) investigated the effect of different preparation techniques (using autoclave at 121°C or using a hot-plate stirrer at 90°C) on the storage modulus and glass transition temperature of the MMT/starch thermoplastic composites. The inclusion of MMT has increased the storage modulus of starch thermoplastic composites regardless of the preparation methods. Nevertheless, a higher glass transition temperature was observed in the MMT/starch thermoplastic composite prepared by the autoclave method. This could be from the reduction in amylose content, which lead to a greater interaction with glycerol, and allowed a higher free volume and increased the glass transition temperature of the MMT/starch thermoplastic composite.

The interaction between hydrophilic MMT and hydrophobic polymers has been explored by numerous researchers. The chemical modification of MMT was carried out by using different types of compatible silanes: vinyltriethoxysilane (CVTES) and γ-methacryloxypropyltrimethoxysilane (CMPS) (Romanzini et al. 2015). The properties of surface-modified MMT/unsaturated polyester composites were then compared with those prepared by using commercial Cloisite® 30B (C30B) and Cloisite® 15A (C15A) MMT. The positive reinforcing effect of surface-modified MMT/unsaturated polyester is seen in Figure 10.9 through the strong dependence of storage modulus values with the addition of modified MMT. Among the modified MMT, the silane-modified clays (CVTES and CMPS) exhibited greater storage modulus with the increasing of temperature compared with organic-modified clays (C30B and C15A). This phenomenon suggested a good stress transfer between MMT and polymer matrix at higher temperatures.

10.4.2.2 Thermal Stability

The capability of a substance in resisting the action of heat while retaining physical properties, such as toughness and strength, is a reflection of its thermal stability (Romero-Bastida et al. 2018). In other words, it represents the heat-resistance level of the biopolymer product that could be observed from the temperature at which the respective chains begin to break down into monomers that would be eventually evaporated, and to be recorded as weight loss (Peelman et al. 2015).

Thermal degradation of thermoplastic composites normally are comprised of three major processes. The first step is the removal of evaporation of low-molecular-weight compounds such as absorbed moisture and volatile matter; the second stage is the dehydration process and the third phase is the degradation of carbonaceous matter (Kiziltas et al. 2016). The enhancement in thermal stability of MMT-reinforced LDPE composites was observed by Bumbudsanpharoke et al. (2017). The temperature at 50% weight loss increased from 476°C for neat LDPE to 496°C for 10 wt%

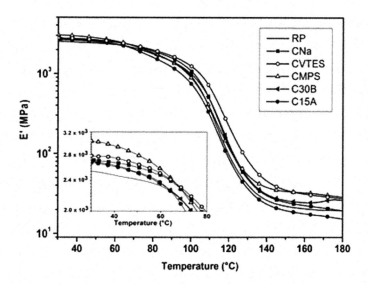

FIGURE 10.9 Variation in storage modulus of MMT/unsaturated polyester composites. (Adapted from Romanzini et al. 2015.)

MMT-reinforced LDPE composites. The enhancement was due to the presence of incombustible carbonaceous char formed on the surface of composites during combustion, which disturbed the degradation of low-molecular-weight compounds and insulated the polymer underneath the char during thermal degradation. The results were in agreement with Silva et al. (2014).

Alshabanat et al. (2013) investigated the effect of sonication time (0.5, 1.0, 1.5 and 2.0 hours) on the thermal stability of MMT-filled PS thermoplastic composites. The thermal degradation of the MMT/PS composites presented a single decomposition step of weight loss from 450 to 500°C, regardless of sonication time. The MMT/PS composites sonicated by 1.0 hours displayed the highest decomposition temperature. The enhancement in thermal stability could be attributed to the incorporation of MMT, which acts as a barrier and insulator between the polymer. Also, the constrained thermal motions of the polymer localized in the galleries also contributed to a higher decomposition temperature of the composites.

Due to the hydrophilic characteristics of MMT, the MMT has an inherent incompatibility issue with hydrophobic matrices due to the lack of similar functional groups for reaction. The significant difference in the surface energy between hydrophilic MMT and hydrophobic matrix could lead to the poor interfacial adhesion and agglomeration of MMT within the polymer matrix. Hence, numerous researchers have performed the chemical modifications on MMT to enhance its compatibility with the polymer matrices, especially a hydrophobic matrix. The MMT could be modified by metallocene-catalyzed linear low-density PE (mLLDPE) to improve the compatibility between MMT and hydrophobic PLA/polycaprolactone (PCL) composites. The addition of 2 parts per hundred (phr) MMT increased the $T_{5\%}$ of the mLLDPE/PLA/PCL composites remarkably from 280°C to 310°C due to the homogeneous dispersion and exfoliated structure of MMT layers within the PLA/PCL matrix. Nevertheless, the further addition of MMT above 2 phr led to the declination in the thermal stability of the composites. Similar results were observed by Xie et al. (2012), who reported the enhancement of thermal stability after the addition of surface-modified MMT in LDPE matrix.

10.4.2.3 Thermal Behavior

Thermal behavior of thermoplastic composites is a crucial parameter that may influence the properties of the final products. The performance of thermoplastic composites is significantly affected by the intermolecular reaction between MMT and polymer matrices. The effect of the addition of MMT on the glass transition and melting temperature of thermoplastic polyurethane was determined by Barick and Tripathy (2010). The glass transition temperature of the thermoplastic polyurethane composites increased slightly with MMT concentration. The interfacial adhesion between MMT and polyurethane matrix restricted the polymer chain movements and increased the rigidity of the composites, which resulted in the improvement in the glass transition temperature of MMT/thermoplastic polyurethane composites. Furthermore, the melting temperature was also increased from 21.91 for neat thermoplastic polyurethane to 30.15°C for 7 wt% MMT/thermoplastic polyurethane composites. This result suggested that the MMT could act as the nucleating agent and interrupted the crystal structure, which in turn led to the increment on the melting temperature of composites.

The organic modification of MMT is usually carried out by the ion-exchange reactions with cationic surfactants by using alkyl ammonium or alkyl phosphonium salts. However, the decomposition temperature of alkyl ammonium salts is less than 180°C and is not suitable for the high temperature processing such as melt mixing (Sarier, Onder, and Ersoy 2010). Therefore, a new approach to modify the surface of MMT for the fabrication of MMT/PCL composite was performed by Yusoh et al. (2018). The surface modification of MMT to increase the d-spacing by aminopropylisooctyl polyhedral oligomeric silsesquioxane (AP-POSS) was conducted and its properties were compared with the unmodified MMT-filled PCL composites. DSC results presented the highest melting and crystallization temperature for 5 wt% AP-POSS-modified MMT/PCL composite, which was 56.6°C and 32.7°C, respectively. However, a slight decrease in the crystallinity degree for AP-POSS-modified MMT/PCL composite was observed compared with unmodified MMT/PCL composite. This could be attributed to the presence of surfactant at the interface, which interrupted the nucleation process and resulted in the declination of the crystallinity of composites.

Numerous processing techniques were used in the preparation of MMT-reinforced thermoplastic composites such as melt mixing, solution casting and in situ polymerization. However, none of it could govern the structural parameters of both the filler (filler aspect ratio and orientation) and the polymeric matrix (crystalline lamellar thickness and lamellar orientation) for the additional facilities to control the morphology and the properties of polymer nanocomposites. Recently, a new processing technique known as equal channel angular extrusion (ECAE) has been introduced. ECAE technique allows the alternation of the aspect ratio and orientation of filler,

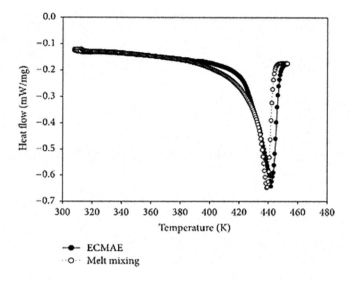

FIGURE 10.10 DSC curve of MMT/PP composites prepared by different techniques. (Adapted from Beloshenko et al. 2016.)

as well as the crystalline lamellar (Seo and Weon 2013; Yang et al. 2010). The positive effect on the melting temperature of MMT/PP composites prepared by melt mixing followed by ECAE technique was observed (Beloshenko et al. 2016). The onset temperature of MMT/PP composites was increased by from 397°C (without ECAE) to 418°C (with ECAE). The higher onset temperature was attributed to the improved part of larger crystallites, and the degree of their perfection in extrudates resulted from the damage of the thinnest crystallites and strain-induced crystallization (Figure 10.10).

10.4.2.4 Barrier Properties

Performance of the barrier properties of the thermoplastic composites plays a crucial role as it can affect the performance of the composites on different applications, particularly for water-sensitive products. The barrier property of thermoplastic composites can be influenced by various factors such as ambient temperature, relative humidity (RH), filler concentration and presence of voids within the composites (Kalachandra and Turner 1987).

Jalalvandi et al. (2015) prepared PLA/starch composite with the addition of unmodified MMT. The barrier property of the composites was determined in terms of the water absorption of the composites. The neat starch exhibited a water uptake of 38%, whereas the composite with the incorporation of the highest MMT content of 7 wt% presented an uptake of only 2%. The enhancement in barrier property of composites resulted from the addition of MMT as a physical barrier and resulted in the drastic reduction in water absorption. A similar finding was also observed by Othman et al. (2019), who varied the concentration of MMT and attained the optimal barrier properties at 3 wt% of MMT in the PLA matrix.

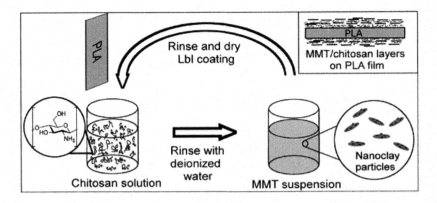

FIGURE 10.11 Schematic illustration of layer-by-layer deposition of MMT and chitosan on extruded (PLA) film. (Reprinted with permission from Svagan et al. 2012. Copyright (2012) American Chemical Society.)

The orientation of MMT within the polymer matrix could significantly influence the barrier property of thermoplastic composites. MMT/PS composites were prepared by extrusion and biaxially stretched to improve the exfoliation level of MMT in the PS matrix (Huang et al. 2015). The barrier properties were investigated in terms of water vapor and oxygen transmission rate. The neat PS showed a high oxygen transmission rate of 7600 cm^3/m^2/day and a water vapor transmission rate of 20 g/m^2/day. On the incorporation of MMT, the oxygen and water vapor transmission rate of biaxially stretched composites were reduced to 5300 cm^3/m^2/day and 10 g/m^2/day, respectively. The enhancement in barrier property of biaxially stretched composites was attributed to the orientation of MMT, which acts as an impermeable barrier and created a more tortuous penetration pathway for permeating molecules to travel through.

Another significant improvement in barrier properties of MMT/PLA composites was attained by the layer-by-layer technique. Svagan et al. (2012) synthesized transparent films of MMT/PLA composites via the layer-by-layer technique and exhibited tunable oxygen barrier properties (Figure 10.11). When multilayers coated with 70 bilayers was used, the oxygen permeability coefficient of the coated PLA was decreased by 99% and 96% at 20% and 50% RH, respectively.

10.4.2.5 Biodegradation Properties

The biodegradation process is a type of biochemical degradation of compounds aided by microorganisms and the material propensity to decompose into its main constituent depending on its natural tendency (Maran et al. 2014). The enzyme method, the microbiological method and the soil burial method have been carried out by numerous researchers to determine the biodegradation properties of the thermoplastic composites, in which the tests employed the weight difference of buried composites as the efficiency of degradation process.

Microbial degradation of thermoplastic composites typically involves two kinds of enzymes, intracellular and extracellular depolymerases (Gu 2003). During the

Montmorillonite-Reinforced Thermoplastic Composites

biodegradation process, the exo-enzymes secreted from microbes break down complex polymers into simpler molecules such as monomers, dimers and oligomers. These molecules are absorbed by the microbes and used as energy and carbon sources. The entire process is recognized as depolymerization (Mohan and Srivastava 2011). The polymers can be degraded by the microbes via anaerobic or aerobic circumstances. Carbon dioxides and water are formed during the aerobic condition. For anaerobic microbial degradation, thermoplastic composites are degraded into carbon dioxide, water and methane under methanogenic conditions or into carbon dioxide, water and hydrogen sulfide under sulfidogenic circumstances as the biodegradation end product (Mohan and Srivastava 2011).

Taghizadeh et al. (2012) studied the effect of MMT incorporation on the degradation properties of starch/PLA composites. α-Amylase was used as the enzyme for the degradation of composites. The results of this work showed that composites with the addition of 5 wt% MMT displayed a remarkable reduced degradation rate compared with neat starch/PLA. This could be attributed to the interactions between MMT and polymer matrix, which prevented the enzymatic attack. The reduction of the degradation rate was also attributed to the reduced water uptake ability of the MMT-reinforced starch PLA composites.

The effect of MMT content and compatibilizer on the biodegradation property of poly(butylene succinate) (PBS) was investigated by Phua et al. (2012). Maleic anhydride-grafted PBS (PBS-g-MA) was utilized as the compatibilizer in this study. Soil burial testing was performed in natural organic humus compost soil for 180 days under controlled conditions. The addition of MMT reduced the weight loss of the composites due to the improved barrier properties after incorporation of MMT, as displayed in Figure 10.12. However, the PBS-g-MA compatibilized MMT/PBS

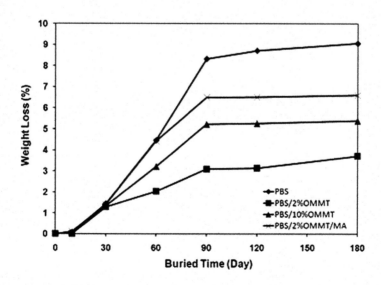

FIGURE 10.12 Weight loss of neat PBS and its composites (OMMT: organo-montmorillonite). (Adapted from Phua et al. 2012.)

composites showed a slightly higher weight loss compared with non-compatibilized composites, suggesting a higher biodegradability.

10.5 CONCLUSIONS

The potential of MMT-filled thermoplastic composites was extensively extended in numerous applications. Nevertheless, the utilization of MMT possesses numerous challenges due to the polarity difference between the MMT and polymer matrix. This chapter discussed the different processing methods of the MMT-reinforced thermoplastic composites. The review on mechanical, dynamic mechanical, thermal, barrier and biodegradation properties of the MMT-reinforced thermoplastic composites was also described in brief. There is an agreement in the literature concerning the improvement in mechanical, thermal, barrier and biodegradation properties of thermoplastic composites by the incorporation of MMT; however, they are restricted to the studies in which the MMTs are homogeneously dispersed and have good compatibility with the polymer matrix. The intermolecular reaction between MMT and polymer matrix plays an important part in enhancing the properties of thermoplastic composites. Therefore, the effect of MMT concentration, the type of matrices and the application of compatibilizers and cross-linking agents on the mechanical, dynamic mechanical, thermal, barrier and biodegradation properties of thermoplastic composites was presented.

REFERENCES

Al-Samhan, Meshal, Jacob Samuel, Fatema Al-Attar, and Gils Abraham. 2017. "Comparative Effects of MMT Clay Modified with Two Different Cationic Surfactants on the Thermal and Rheological Properties of Polypropylene Nanocomposites." *International Journal of Polymer Science* 2017: 5717968. https://doi.org/10.1155/2017/5717968

Allison, P. G., J. A. Caminero-Rodriguez, K. Torres-Cancel, R. D. Moser, J. K. Newman, C. A. Weiss Jr, and M. Q. Chandler. 2015. "Mechanical, Thermal, and Microstructural Analysis of Polyvinyl Alcohol (PVA)/Montmorillonite (MMT) Nanocomposites." *Journal of Nanomaterials* 2015: 291248. http://dx.doi.org/10.1155/2015/291248

Alshabanat, Mashael, Amal Al-Arrash, and Waffa Mekhamer. 2013. "Polystyrene/ Montmorillonite Nanocomposites: Study of the Morphology and Effects of Sonication Time on Thermal Stability." *Journal of Nanomaterials* 2013: 650725. https://doi.org/ 10.1155/2013/650725

Arjmandi, Reza, Azman Hassan, M. K. Mohamad Haafiz, Zainoha Zakaria, and I. M. Inuwa. 2014. "Characterization of Polylactic Acid/Microcrystalline Cellulose/Montmorillonite Hybrid Composites." *Malaysian Journal of Analytical Sciences* 18 (3): 642–50.

Barick, A. K., and D. K. Tripathy. 2010. "Preparation and Characterization of Thermoplastic Polyurethane/Organoclay Nanocomposites by Melt Intercalation Technique: Effect of Nanoclay on Morphology, Mechanical, Thermal, and Rheological Properties." *Journal of Applied Polymer Science* 117: 639–54. https://doi.org/10.1002/app

Batool, Sadia, Rohama Gill, Muhammad Arshad, Humaira Masood Siddiqi, and Shahid Saeed Qureshi. 2018. "Layer-by-Layer Fabrication of Nacre Inspired Epoxy/MMT Multilayered Composites." *Journal of Applied Polymer Science* 135 (14): 1–12. https:// doi.org/10.1002/app.46079

Bee, Soo Ling, M. A. A. Abdullah, Soo Tueen Bee, Lee Tin Sin, and A. R. Rahmat. 2018. "Polymer Nanocomposites Based on Silylated-Montmorillonite: A Review." *Progress in Polymer Science* 85: 57–82. https://doi.org/10.1016/j.progpolymsci.2018.07.003

Bee, Soo Tueen, C. T. Ratnam, Lee Tin Sin, Tiam Ting Tee, David Hui, A. A. H. Kadhum, A. R. Rahmat, and Joshin Lau. 2014. "Effects of Electron Beam Irradiation on Mechanical Properties and Nanostructural-Morphology of Montmorillonite Added Polyvinyl Alcohol Composite." *Composites Part B: Engineering* 63: 141–53. https://doi.org/10.1016/j.compositesb.2014.03.021

Beloshenko, V. A., A. V. Voznyak, Yu V. Voznyak, L. A. Novokshonova, V. G. Grinyov, and V. G. Krasheninnikov. 2016. "Processing of Polypropylene-Organic Montmorillonite Nanocomposite by Equal Channel Multiangular Extrusion." *International Journal of Polymer Science* 2016: 8564245. https://doi.org/10.1155/2016/8564245

Bertuoli, Paula T., Diego Piazza, Lisete C. Scienza, and Ademir J. Zattera. 2014. "Preparation and Characterization of Montmorillonite Modified with 3-Aminopropyltriethoxysilane." *Applied Clay Science* 87: 46–51. https://doi.org/10.1016/j.clay.2013.11.020

Bhattacharya, Mrinal. 2016. "Polymer Nanocomposites-A Comparison between Carbon Nanotubes, Graphene, and Clay as Nanofillers." *Materials* 9 (4): 1–35. https://doi.org/10.3390/ma9040262

Bittmann, Birgit, Frank Haupert, and Alois K. Schlarb. 2009. "Ultrasonic Dispersion of Inorganic Nanoparticles in Epoxy Resin." *Ultrasonics Sonochemistry* 16 (5): 622–28. https://doi.org/10.1016/j.ultsonch.2009.01.006

Boesel, Luciano F. 2015. "Effect of Plasticizers on the Barrier and Mechanical Properties of Biomimetic Composites of Chitosan and Clay." *Carbohydrate Polymers* 115: 356–63. https://doi.org/10.1016/j.carbpol.2014.08.064

Bumbudsanpharoke, Nattinee, Wooseok Lee, Jae Chun Choi, Se Jong Park, Meekyung Kim, and Seonghyuk Ko. 2017. "Influence of Montmorillonite Nanoclay Content on the Optical, Thermal, Mechanical, and Barrier Properties of Low-Density Polyethylene." *Clays and Clay Minerals* 65 (6): 387–97. https://doi.org/10.1346/CCMN.2017.064071

Chakraborty, J N. 2012. "2 – Strength Properties of Fabrics: Understanding, Testing and Enhancing Fabric Strength." In *Woodhead Publishing Series in Textiles*, edited by Patricia A. B. T., 31–58. Woodhead Publishing. https://doi.org/10.1533/9780857097644.1.31

Chen, Chenwei, Youji Chen, Jing Xie, Zhewei Xu, Zhipeng Tang, Fuxin Yang, and Kaijia Fu. 2017. "Effects of Montmorillonite on the Properties of Cross-Linked Poly(Vinyl Alcohol)/Boric Acid Films." *Progress in Organic Coatings* 112: 66–74. https://doi.org/10.1016/j.porgcoat.2017.06.003

Cui, Zhong Kai, Soyon Kim, Jessalyn J. Baljon, Benjamin M. Wu, Tara Aghaloo, and Min Lee. 2019. "Microporous Methacrylated Glycol Chitosan-Montmorillonite Nanocomposite Hydrogel for Bone Tissue Engineering." *Nature Communications* 10 (1): 1–10. https://doi.org/10.1038/s41467-019-11511-3

Ebnesajjad, Sina. 2014. "Surface and Material Characterization Techniques." In *Surface Treatment of Materials for Adhesive Bonding*, 39–75. Amsterdam: Elsevier. https://doi.org/10.1016/b978-0-323-26435-8.00004-6

Fornes, T. D., and D. R. Paul. 2003. "Formation and Properties of Nylon 6 Nanocomposites." *Polímeros* 13 (4): 212–17. https://doi.org/10.1590/s0104-14282003000400004

Gaidukov, S., I. Danilenko, and G. Gaidukova. 2015. "Characterization of Strong and Crystalline Polyvinyl Alcohol/Montmorillonite Films Prepared by Layer-by-Layer Deposition Method." *International Journal of Polymer Science* 2015: 123469. https://doi.org/10.1155/2015/123469

Geyer, Roland, Jenna R. Jambeck, and Kara Lavender Law. 2017. "Production, Use, and Fate of All Plastics Ever Made." *Science Advances* 3 (7): 25–29. https://doi.org/10.1126/sciadv.1700782

Gu, Ji Dong. 2003. "Microbiological Deterioration and Degradation of Synthetic Polymeric Materials: Recent Research Advances." *International Biodeterioration and Biodegradation* 52 (2): 69–91. https://doi.org/10.1016/S0964-8305(02)00177-4

Guidotti, Giulia, Michelina Soccio, Valentina Siracusa, Massimo Gazzano, Elisabetta Salatelli, Andrea Munari, and Nadia Lotti. 2017. "Novel Random PBS-Based Copolymers Containing Aliphatic Side Chains for Sustainable Flexible Food Packaging." *Polymers* 9 (12): 1–16. https://doi.org/10.3390/polym9120724

Huang, Chuanjin, and Qunfeng Cheng. 2017. "Learning from Nacre: Constructing Polymer Nanocomposites." *Composites Science and Technology* 150: 141–66. https://doi.org/10.1016/j.compscitech.2017.07.021

Huang, Wenhan, Songshan Zeng, Jingjing Liu, and Luyi Sun. 2015. "Bi-Axially Oriented Polystyrene/Montmorillonite Nanocomposite Films." *RSC Advances* 5 (72): 58191–98. https://doi.org/10.1039/c5ra09598k

Jalalvandi, E., R. A. Majid, T. Ghanbari, and H. Ilbeygi. 2015. "Effects of Montmorillonite (MMT) on Morphological, Tensile, Physical Barrier Properties and Biodegradability of Polylactic Acid/Starch/MMT Nanocomposites." *Journal of Thermoplastic Composite Materials* 28 (4): 496–509. https://doi.org/10.1177/0892705713486129

Kalachandra, S., and D. T. Turner. 1987. "Water Sorption of Polymethacrylate Networks: Bis-GMA/TEGDM Copolymers." *Journal of Biomedical Materials Research* 21 (3): 329–38. https://doi.org/10.1002/jbm.820210306

Kherroub, Djamal Eddine, Mohammed Belbachir, Saad Lamouri, Larbi Bouhadjar, and Karim Chikh. 2013. "Synthesis of Polyamide-6/Montmorillonite Nanocomposites by Direct in-Situ Polymerization Catalysed by Exchanged Clay." *Oriental Journal of Chemistry* 29 (4): 1429–36. https://doi.org/10.13005/ojc/290419

Kiziltas, Alper, Behzad Nazari, Esra Erbas Kiziltas, Douglas J.S. Gardner, Yousoo Han, and Todd S. Rushing. 2016. "Cellulose NANOFIBER-Polyethylene Nanocomposites Modified by Polyvinyl Alcohol." *Journal of Applied Polymer Science* 133 (6): 1–8. https://doi.org/10.1002/app.42933

Kumar, Mukesh, and Tharanikkarasu Kannan. 2014. "Polymer-Montmorillonite Nanocomposites through Controlled Radical Polymerization Using (4-Vinylbenzyl) Triethylammonium Anchored Organo-Montmorillonite." *Journal of Macromolecular Science, Part A: Pure and Applied Chemistry* 51 (11): 931–40. https://doi.org/10.1080/10601325.2014.953379

Li, Yan, Huafeng Tian, Qingqing Jia, Ping Niu, Aimin Xiang, Di Liu, and Yanan Qin. 2015. "Development of Polyvinyl Alcohol/Intercalated MMT Composite Foams Fabricated by Melt Extrusion." *Journal of Applied Polymer Science* 132 (43): 1–7. https://doi.org/10.1002/app.42706

Maran, J. Prakash, V. Sivakumar, K. Thirugnanasambandham, and R. Sridhar. 2014. "Degradation Behavior of Biocomposites Based on Cassava Starch Buried under Indoor Soil Conditions." *Carbohydrate Polymers* 101 (1): 20–28. https://doi.org/10.1016/j.carbpol.2013.08.080

Mittal, Garima, Vivek Dhand, Kyong Yop Rhee, Soo Jin Park, and Wi Ro Lee. 2015. "A Review on Carbon Nanotubes and Graphene as Fillers in Reinforced Polymer Nanocomposites." *Journal of Industrial and Engineering Chemistry* 21: 11–25. https://doi.org/10.1016/j.jiec.2014.03.022

Mohan, Krishna, and Tanu Srivastava. 2011. "Microbial Deterioration and Degradation of Polymeric Materials." *Journal of Biochemical Technology* 2 (4): 210–15.

Mtibe, Asanda, Thabang Hendrica Mokhothu, Maya J. John, Teboho Clement Mokhena, and Mokgaotsa Jonas Mochane. 2018. Fabrication and Characterization of Various Engineered Nanomaterials. In *Handbook of Nanomaterials for Industrial Applications*. Amsterdam: Elsevier Inc. https://doi.org/10.1016/B978-0-12-813351-4.00009-2

Nagy, Dorottya, and Eszter Kókai. 2018. "Polymer-Based Nanocomposites with Nanoclay." *IOP Conference Series: Materials Science and Engineering* 448 (1). https://doi.org/10.1088/1757-899X/448/1/012021

Nur Aimi, M. N., and H. Anuar. 2016. "Effect of Plasticizer on Fracture Toughness of Polylactic Acid Reinforced with Kenaf Fibre and Montmorillonite Hybrid Biocomposites." In *Nanoclay Reinforced Polymer Composites*, 263–80. Singapore: Springer. https://doi.org/10.1007/978-981-10-0950-1_11

Othman, Siti Hajar, Hee Nyia Ling, Rosnita A. Talib, Mohd Nazli Naim, Nazratul Putri Risyon, and M. Saifullah. 2019. "PLA/MMT and PLA/Halloysite Bio-Nanocomposite Films: Mechanical, Barrier, and Transparency." *Journal of Nano Research* 59: 77–93. https://doi.org/10.4028/www.scientific.net/JNanoR.59.77

Ozdemir, Esra, Tugba Orhan Lekesiz, and Jale Hacaloglu. 2016. "Polylactide/Organically Modified Montmorillonite Composites; Effects of Organic Modifier on Thermal Characteristics." *Polymer Degradation and Stability* 134 (December): 87–96. https://doi.org/10.1016/j.polymdegradstab.2016.09.028

Peelman, Nanou, Peter Ragaert, Kim Ragaert, Bruno De Meulenaer, Frank Devlieghere, and Ludwig Cardon. 2015. "Heat Resistance of New Biobased Polymeric Materials, Focusing on Starch, Cellulose, PLA, and PHA." *Journal of Applied Polymer Science* 132 (48). https://doi.org/10.1002/app.42889

Peidayesh, Hamed, Zahed Ahmadi, Hossein Ali Khonakdar, Majid Abdouss, and Ivan Chodák. 2020. "Fabrication and Properties of Thermoplastic Starch/Montmorillonite Composite Using Dialdehyde Starch as a Crosslinker." *Polymer International* 69 (3): 317–27. https://doi.org/10.1002/pi.5955

Peng, Kang, Hongjie Wang, Xiaoyu Li, Jianwei Wang, Zhixin Cai, Lei Su, and Xingyu Fan. 2019. "Emerging WS2/Montmorillonite Composite Nanosheets as an Efficient Hydrophilic Photocatalyst for Aqueous Phase Reactions." *Scientific Reports* 9 (1): 1–9. https://doi.org/10.1038/s41598-019-52191-9

Phua, Y. J., N. S. Lau, K. Sudesh, W. S. Chow, and Z. A. Mohd Ishak. 2012. "Biodegradability Studies of Poly(Butylene Succinate)/Organo-Montmorillonite Nanocomposites under Controlled Compost Soil Conditions: Effects of Clay Loading and Compatibiliser." *Polymer Degradation and Stability* 97 (8): 1345–54. https://doi.org/10.1016/j.polymdegradstab.2012.05.024

Prado, Bruna Rosa, and Julio Roberto Bartoli. 2018. "Synthesis and Characterization of PMMA and Organic Modified Montmorilonites Nanocomposites via in Situ Polymerization Assisted by Sonication." *Applied Clay Science* 160:132–43. https://doi.org/10.1016/j.clay.2018.02.035

Qaiss, Abouelkacem, Rachid Bouhfid, and Hamid Essabir. 2015. "Effect of Processing Conditions on the Mechanical and Morphological Properties of Composites Reinforced by Natural Fibres." In *Manufacturing of Natural Fibre Reinforced Polymer Composites*, 177–97. Switzerland: Springer International Publishing. https://doi.org/10.1007/978-3-319-07944-8

Rahromostaqim, Mahsa, and Muhammad Sahimi. 2020. "Molecular Dynamics Study of the Effect of Layer Charge and Interlayer Cations on Swelling of Mixed-Layer Chlorite-Montmorillonite Clays." *Journal of Physical Chemistry C* 124 (4): 2553–61. https://doi.org/10.1021/acs.jpcc.9b10919

Ratna, Debdatta. 2009. *Handbook of Thermoset Resins*. Shrewsbury: Smithers Rapra Technology.

Romanzini, Daiane, Alberto Frache, Ademir J. Zattera, and Sandro C. Amico. 2015. "Effect of Clay Silylation on Curing and Mechanical and Thermal Properties of Unsaturated Polyester/Montmorillonite Nanocomposites." *Journal of Physics and Chemistry of Solids* 87: 9–15. https://doi.org/10.1016/j.jpcs.2015.07.019

Romero-Bastida, Claudia A., Miguel Chávez Gutiérrez, Luis A. Bello-Pérez, Estefania Abarca-Ramírez, Gonzalo Velazquez, and Guadalupe Mendez-Montealvo. 2018. "Rheological Properties of Nanocomposite-Forming Solutions and Film Based on Montmorillonite and Corn Starch with Different Amylose Content." *Carbohydrate Polymers* 188 (February): 121–27. https://doi.org/10.1016/j.carbpol.2018.01.089

Salvatore, Marcella, Antonella Marra, Donatella Duraccio, Shima Shayanfar, Suresh D. Pillai, Sossio Cimmino, and Clara Silvestre. 2016. "Effect of Electron Beam Irradiation on the Properties of Polylactic Acid/Montmorillonite Nanocomposites for Food Packaging Applications." *Journal of Applied Polymer Science* 133 (2). https://doi.org/10.1002/app.42971

Sarier, Nihal, Emel Onder, and Sabri Ersoy. 2010. "The Modification of Na-Montmorillonite by Salts of Fatty Acids: An Easy Intercalation Process." *Colloids and Surfaces A: Physicochemical and Engineering Aspects* 371 (1–3): 40–49. https://doi.org/10.1016/j.colsurfa.2010.08.061

Seo, Young Rok, and Jong Il Weon. 2013. "Manipulation of Nanofiller and Polymer Structures by Using Equal Channel Angular Extrusion." *Journal of the Korean Physical Society* 63 (1): 114–19. https://doi.org/10.3938/jkps.63.114

Serwicka, Ewa M., Malgorzata Zimowska, Dorota Duraczyńska, Bogna D. Napruszewska, Malgorzata Nattich-Rak, Grzegorz Mordarski, Lidia Lityńska-Dobrzyńska, and Helena Palkova. 2018. "PDDA-Montmorillonite Composites Loaded with Ru Nanoparticles: Synthesis, Characterization, and Catalytic Properties in Hydrogenation of 2-Butanone." *Polymers* 10 (8). https://doi.org/10.3390/polym10080865

Sidorenko, A. Yu, A. V. Kravtsova, A. Aho, I. Heinmaa, T. F. Kuznetsova, D. Yu Murzin, and V. E. Agabekov. 2018. "Catalytic Isomerization of A-Pinene Oxide in the Presence of Acid-Modified Clays." *Molecular Catalysis* 448: 18–29. https://doi.org/10.1016/j.mcat.2018.01.021

Silva, Bruna Louise, Fernanda Czerkies Nack, Carlos Mauricio Lepienski, Luiz Antonio Ferreira Coelho, and Daniela Becker. 2014. "Influence of Intercalation Methods in Properties of Clay and Carbon Nanotube and High Density Polyethylene Nanocomposites." *Materials Research* 17 (6): 1628–36. https://doi.org/10.1590/1516-1439.303714

Sirousazar, M., M. Kokabi, Z. M. Hassan, and A. R. Bahramian. 2012. "Polyvinyl Alcohol/Na-Montmorillonite Nanocomposite Hydrogels Prepared by Freezing-Thawing Method: Structural, Mechanical, Thermal, and Swelling Properties." *Journal of Macromolecular Science, Part B: Physics* 51 (7): 1335–50. https://doi.org/10.1080/00222348.2011.629870

Sun, Xiaofei, Hrishikesh Kharbas, and Lih-Sheng Turng. 2015. "Fabrication of Highly Expanded Thermoplastic Polyurethane Foams Using Microcellular Injection Molding and Gas-Laden Pellets." *Polymer Engineering and Science* 55 (11): 2643–52. https://doi.org/10.1002/pen

Svagan, Anna J., Anna Åkesson, Marité Cárdenas, Sanja Bulut, Jes C. Knudsen, Jens Risbo, and David Plackett. 2012. "Transparent Films Based on PLA and Montmorillonite with Tunable Oxygen Barrier Properties." *Biomacromolecules* 13 (2): 397–405. https://doi.org/10.1021/bm201438m

Taghizadeh, Mohammad Taghi, Zahra Abbasi, and Zainab Nasrollahzade. 2012. "Study of Enzymatic Degradation and Water Absorption of Nanocomposites Starch/Polyvinyl Alcohol and Sodium Montmorillonite Clay." *Journal of the Taiwan Institute of Chemical Engineers* 43 (1): 120–24. https://doi.org/10.1016/j.jtice.2011.07.006

Uddin, Faheem. 2018. "Montmorillonite: An Introduction to Properties and Utilization." In *Current Topics in the Utilization of Clay in Industrial and Medical Applications.* London: IntechOpen Limited. https://doi.org/http://dx.doi.org/10.5772/57353

Vilarinho, Fernanda, Malia Fátima Vaz, and Ana Sanches Silva. 2019. "The Use of Montmorillonite (MMT) in Food Nanocomposites: Methods of Incorporation,

Characterization of MMT/Polymer Nanocomposites and Main Consequences in the Properties." *Recent Patents on Food, Nutrition & Agriculture* 11 (1): 13–26. https://doi.org/10.2174/2212798410666190401160211

Wilpiszewska, Katarzyna, Adrian Krzysztof Antosik, and Tadeusz Spychaj. 2015. "Novel Hydrophilic Carboxymethyl Starch/Montmorillonite Nanocomposite Films." *Carbohydrate Polymers* 128: 82–89. https://doi.org/10.1016/j.carbpol.2015.04.023

Xie, Li, Xia Yan Lv, Zhong Jie Han, Ji Hao Ci, Chang Qing Fang, and Peng Gang Ren. 2012. "Preparation and Performance of High-Barrier Low Density Polyethylene/Organic Montmorillonite Nanocomposite." *Polymer - Plastics Technology and Engineering* 51 (12): 1251–57. https://doi.org/10.1080/03602559.2012.699131

Yang, Zhe, Hongdan Peng, Weizhi Wang, and Tianxi Liu. 2010. "Crystallization Behavior of Poly(ε-Caprolactone)/Layered Double Hydroxide Nanocomposites." *Journal of Applied Polymer Science* 116 (5): 2658–67. https://doi.org/10.1002/app

Yusoh, Kamal, Shamini Vesaya Kumaran, and Fadwa Sameeha Ismail. 2018. "Surface Modification of Nanoclay for the Synthesis of Polycaprolactone (PCL) - Clay Nanocomposite." In *MATEC Web of Conferences*, 150:1–6. https://doi.org/10.1051/matecconf/201815002005

Zandsalimi, Kavosh, Babak Akbari, Faramarz Mehrnejad, and Reza Bagheri. 2019. "Compatibilization of Clays and Hydrophobic Polymers: The Case of Montmorillonite and Polyetheretherketone." *Polymer Bulletin* 77, 5505–27. https://doi.org/10.1007/s00289-019-03036-y.

Zheng, W., M. Beeler, J. Claus, and X. Xu. 2017. "Poly(Lactic Acid)/Montmorillonite Blown Films: Crystallization, Mechanics, and Permeation." *Journal of Applied Polymer Science* 134 (36): 1–8. https://doi.org/10.1002/app.45260

Zulfiqar, Sonia, Ayesha Kausar, Muhammad Rizwan, and Muhammad Ilyas Sarwar. 2008. "Probing the Role of Surface Treated Montmorillonite on the Properties of Semi-Aromatic Polyamide/Clay Nanocomposites." *Applied Surface Science* 255: 2080–86. https://doi.org/10.1016/j.apsusc.2008.06.184

11 Mineral-Filled Polymer Composites
Reliability, Challenges, Opportunities and Future Perspectives

R.A. Ilyas
Universiti Teknologi Malaysia
Johor Bahru, Malaysia

M. Izzat, S.M. Qusyairi, S.M. Sapuan, M.S.N. Atikah, and H.A. Aisyah
Universiti Putra Malaysia
Serdang, Malaysia

Hanafi Ismail
Universiti Sains Malaysia
Nibong Tebal, Malaysia

CONTENTS

11.1 Introduction 235
    11.1.1 Mineral-Filled Polymer Composite 235
    11.1.2 Polymer 236
11.2 Mineral Fillers 237
11.3 Stress Strain of Filled Polymers 237
11.4 Effect of the Reinforcement Composite: Reliability and Opportunities 239
11.5 Challenges and Future Perspectives 251
11.6 Conclusions 253
References 254

11.1 INTRODUCTION

11.1.1 MINERAL-FILLED POLYMER COMPOSITE

Mineral-filled polymers are widely used in industries across the globe and the applications are continuously increasing (Sapuan et al. 2020). Recently, interest with the

DOI: 10.1201/9781003220947-11

235

exception of polyvinyl chloride (PVC) has increased, where the implementation of fillers is largely justified for technical and technological purposes, as a separate compounding phase greatly raises the price of the composite. Some of these improvements, such as stiffness, increase in thermal deflection temperature and thermal conductivity are beneficial, while others decreased in deformity and impact, thus, processing is less desirable (Pukánszky 2016).

Composite is a product in which one material, serving as a matrix, is combined with one or more materials behaving as a filler (particles, fibers, cellular, etc.) to enhance the strength and other properties but minimize the total size of this new material (Alsubari et al. 2021; Asyraf et al. 2020a,b; Ayu et al. 2020; Omran et al. 2021; Rozilah et al. 2020; Sabaruddin et al. 2020; Syafiq et al. 2020). The matrix and the filler are chemically apart, but develop a solid bond between them with no chemical reaction among them. By way of the composite concept, this interfacial bonding can be enhanced by some chemical or physical treatment of the fibers (Syafri et al. 2019; Asrofi et al. 2020a,b; Kumar et al. 2020; Abral et al. 2021). Thus this chapter reviews mineral-filled polymer composites, their reliability, challenges, opportunities and future perspectives.

11.1.2 POLYMER

A polymer is a chemical compound of molecules linked together in long chains (Ilyas and Sapuan 2020a,b). Polymerization is a method of assembling small monomer molecules into chains bound together by covalent bonds to create synthetic polymers. There are two primary types of polymerization: step-growth and chaingrowth. In chain-growth polymerization, monomer molecules are attached to the chain one at a time. Step-growth polymerization takes place when several monomer molecules are directly bound to each other. Polymers are generally referred to as plastics or thermoplastics composed of molecular chains that can be broken and rebonded (Abral et al. 2020b; Atikah et al. 2019; Ilyas et al. 2018; Ilyas et al. 2019a; Ilyas et al. 2020a,b). Most common plastics can develop into new forms by adding heat, and they are beneficial to the environment because they are recyclable. Because of their composition, polymers have properties that can be used for various applications. They can be man-made and naturally occurring (Wang et al. 2017). Rubber, for example, is a natural polymeric material that has been around for thousands of years. This product of a naturally formed molecular polymer chain has excellent elasticity properties. Shellac, one of the natural product polymers found in East Asia, is a resin produced by a lake insect used as a color primer, sealant and varnish material.

The term polymer is widely used in the plastics and composites industries, often as an alternative word for plastics or resins. In reality, polymers are the integration of materials with a range of properties (Jumaidin et al. 2019a,b; Jumaidin et al. 2020). Polymers mostly can be found in household goods, clothing, toys, construction materials and various other items. Composite multiphase polymer products are obtained when the reinforcing fillers are combined with the polymer matrix, leading to synergistic mechanical properties that cannot be obtained by any element alone (Herrera-Franco and Valadez-González 2004). The most widely used polymer composite in the market is carbon fiber-reinforced polymer (FRP). FRP is a plastic material with

Mineral-Filled Polymer Composites 237

high strength and low weight. The FRP characteristics of "light and strong" have made it the first choice in the selection of materials for automotive parts, aerospace, sports and construction engineering materials.

FRPs typically have high specific strengths, making them versatile for a wide range of industrial applications that require such features (Aisyah et al. 2019). Fiber can be categorized into natural fibers and synthetic fibers. Synthetic fiber such as carbon and glass fibers integrated into polyester resins are the common conventional fiber-reinforced composite materials possessing outstanding mechanical properties (Baihaqi et al. 2021; Mohd Nurazzi et al. 2019; Nurazzi et al. 2019; 2020). However, these materials are non-degradable fibers, hence, they cause adverse effects to the environment. Natural fibers are fibers that are produced by plants (sugar palm, water hyacinth, ginger, flax, hemp, kenaf and sugarcane), animals (silk, wool and alvian fiber) and geological (asbestos, graphite and basalt) processes (Ilyas et al. 2017; Abral et al. 2019, 2020a; Atiqah et al. 2019; Azammi et al. 2019; Halimatul et al. 2019; Ilyas et al. 2019b,c; Hazrol et al. 2020; Ilyas et al. 2021). This motivated the exploration of the use of mineral fillers in composite polymers to proliferate. The characteristics of the composite materials are influenced by the characteristics of the elements, their composition, interfacial interactions and their structure (Wang et al. 2017; Sari et al. 2020). Both the aggregation and orientation of anisotropic filler particles have a strong effect on composite properties. The basic aim of this study is to determine the durability, challenges, opportunities and potential prospects of the natural FRP composites.

11.2 MINERAL FILLERS

Mineral fillers consist of finely dispersed mineral matters, e.g., rock dust, slag dust, hydraulic lime, hydraulic cement, fly ash, loess (pre-existing mineral particles and rock-forming mostly silky sediment formed by wind-blown dust accumulation), or other suitable minerals. Data from several studies have shown that the characteristics of the particulate-filled polymers are determined by the materials, nature, structure and interaction properties of the polymers. These four variables are equally important and interconnected in their outcomes. For example, the exact surface area of the filler defines the size of the contact surface between the filler and the polymer, the structure and even the effect of the composition on the properties as well as the mode of deformation are determined by the energy of the surface. Without defining the role of all factors influencing the properties of the composites and the interrelationship between them, there is a relevant discussion of the adhesion and interaction of particulate-filled polymers (Table 11.1) (Pukánszky and Fekete 1999).

11.3 STRESS STRAIN OF FILLED POLYMERS

The essential part of the polymer is its inherent toughness and resistance to fracture. The term plastic, which describes some type of polymeric material, is not the same as the term plasticity, which is the ability of a solid to experience irreversible stress deformation. The mechanical properties of the material are obviously dependent on strain and temperature. If the strain is low, the deformation of the solid might be

TABLE 11.1
Structure and Characteristics of the Particulate Filler

Filler	Composition	Density (g cm^{-3})	Mohs Hardness	Shape
Calcium carbonate	CaCo$_3$	2.7	3	Sphere
Talc	Mg$_3$(Si$_4$O$_{10}$)(OH)$_2$	2.8	1	Plate
Kaolin	Al$_2$O$_2$·2SiO$_2$·2H$_2$O	2.6	2.5–3.0	Plate
Wollastonite	CaSiO$_3$	2.9	4.5	Needle
Mica	KM(AlSi$_3$O$_{10}$)(OH$_2$)	2.8	2.0–2.5	Plate
Barite	BaSO$_4$	4.5	3.5	Plate

Source: Pukánszky 2016.

elastic. The deformation is homogeneous and the plastic returns to its original size and shape after the deforming load has been withdrawn. The stress (σ) in this regime is equal to the pressure (ε).

$$\sigma = E\varepsilon$$

where E is the plastic tensile (or Young's) modulus, which is a measure of the material's stiffness. This relationship can be defined by Hooke's law: when a plastic sample is pulled at a (constant) strain rate, the stress (or load) applied is directly proportional to the strain (or elongation) observed. Figure 11.1 suggests that the real elongation encountered by the polymer must be greater for a specified elongation of the model (Nielsen 1967). At this point in the study, shear effects around the filler particles, triaxial strains in the polymer and effects attributable to Poisson's ratio are all neglected. Several other more complicated models have been casually explored and seem to give approximately the same results as this base model as a first assumption.

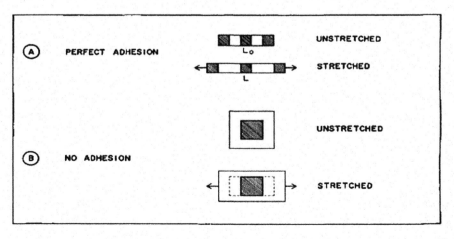

FIGURE 11.1 Models for filled polymers.

Mineral-Filled Polymer Composites

11.4 EFFECT OF THE REINFORCEMENT COMPOSITE: RELIABILITY AND OPPORTUNITIES

The mineral-reinforced composites are available in a wide range of mineral types, such as natural fiber, glass fiber, silica, clay, cement and talc. Of these filler types, natural fiber is one of the most commonly employed for composite manufacturing because of the abundant sources together with the good performance properties. Natural fiber-reinforced composite is fabricated from lignocellulosic fibers, including woof fiber, kenaf, oil palm, bamboo and agricultural wastes. On the other hand, mineral fillers are applied to thermoplastics polymers to lower material costs and enhance the product's performance. In addition, mineral filler, e.g., talc and calcium carbonate, could increase thermal conductivity and shrinkage and impact properties and dimensional stability. Moreover, natural mineral filler in thermoplastics composites are promising materials that can be used in many applications, such as packaging, in the automotive industry, papermaking, construction, and in the furniture industry. Table 11.2 lists some of the common natural fibers and mineral fillers and the effect of their applications.

Mineral polymer composite is mineral filler-reinforced with the multiphase substance combined with a polymer matrix in which reinforcing fillers result in synergistic mechanical properties that cannot be obtained by any part alone. That combination produces a different substance with modified properties. Some of these enhancements (improved rigidity, higher heat deflection temperature [HDT] and higher thermal conductivity) are beneficial, whereas others are less attractive (decreased deformability and impact and wear of the processing equipment).

Recently, several studies were carried out on mineral-filled composites. In research conducted by Nourbakhsh et al. (2010), the influence of the accumulation of particle size and binding agent on the mechanical properties of particulate-filled polymer composites (PFPC) stated that the strength properties of the composites could be moderately strengthened by adding 2 wt% of polypropylene grafted maleic anhydride (PP-g-MA). They also reported that the filler particles provided higher tensile modulus than the bigger ones. The influence of filler particle sizes and coupling agent with the concentrations of 0 and 2 wt% on the composite mechanical properties was studied. Specimens containing 30 wt% poplar wood flour were blended with PP and PP-g-MA as the coupling agent. Wood flour was considered a low-cost source of natural fiber for composites. The best mechanical properties of wood flour-PP composites were obtained on a smaller (0.25-mm) particle scale. The tensile modulus was increased with declining filler particle sizes attributed to the strong interfacial bonding between hydrophilic filler, binding agent and hydrophobic polymer matrix. In a review conducted by Saba et al. (2014) on the potential of nano-filler/natural fiber-filled polymer hybrid composites, the latest details on sources of natural fibers, nano-fillers, cellulosic composite-based fibers, nanocomposites, and natural hybrid composite based fibers/nano-fillers were reported with their specific applications. The researchers outlined the increasing new perspectives in nanotechnology for the improvement of cross-breed composites in a sustainable and greener environment. In the analysis, polymeric matrix materials with suitable and effective filler resulted in a stronger filler/matrix relationship. Along with innovative and

TABLE 11.2
Mineral-Filled Polymer Composites

Polymer Matrix	Fiber	Effect of Reinforcement	Reference
Epoxy resin 615A	Particulate-filled polymer composite	• Increased monomer retention by volume (MRV) and weight (MRW)	Yin et al. (2017)
Methyl methacrylate	Wood flour	• Increased composites' strength	Nourbakhsh et al. (2010)
Plastic composites	Kenaf fiber	• Reinforcing commodity fiber in fiber-thermoplastic composite • Increased water absorption	Rowell et al. (1997)
Polyethylene	Henequen fiber	• Treatment fiber surface did not improve the bond between the fibers in bending, tension and impact loading	Herrera-Franco and Valadez-González (2004)
Nanocrystalline cellulose	Discarded cigarette filter	• Improved ultrasonication process to increase quality of the material	Ditzel et al. (2017)
Polcarb	English clay	• Lowered fillers' surface tension • Lowered polymer interaction	Fekete et al. (1990)
Polyvinylpyrrolidone copolymers	Leaf fiber–polycarbonate	• Increased tensile strength • Decreased thermal stability of the composite	Skorokhoda et al. (2016)
Glass fiber polymer	Portland cement	• Increased compressive strength and split-tensile strength	Revathy et al. (2020)
Polyester matrix	Prawn antenna	• Different interactions of composition with various chemical treatments • Increased tensile strength	Gwon et al. (2010)
Semi-crystalline polymers	Plastic fiber	• Improved compressible plastic flow • Increased tensile strength	Balieu et al. (2014)
Epoxy-based polymers	Epoxy resin	• Increased glass transition temperature • Slightly decreased the mechanical properties after hygrothermal conditioning	Khotbehsara et al. (2019)
Grafted polypropylene	Calcium carbonate	• Increased viscoelastic properties	Yang et al. (2010)

Biobutanol	Rice straw	• Increased the fermentation efficiency	Wickaramasinghe et al. (2019)
Diphenyl phosphate	Polycarbonate composites	• Increased damping efficiency	Jang (2016)
PVC	Calcium carbonate	• Volume strain on the macroscale connected to an empty growth on the microscale • Improved stress-softening reaction of PVC composite material	Olufsen et al. (2019)
Graphite	Pencil lead	• Improved material density	Owuamanam and Cree (2020)
Vinyl-trimethoxy	Wood fiber	• Reduced rigidity and improved ductility by up to 25% of the polymer	Koohestani et al. (2017)
Polystyrene sulfonate	Gypsum fiber	• Increased content of moisture within the material volume	Nicoleau et al. (2019)
Polyanionic cellulose	Bentonite	• Increased toughening effects of the clay filler • Increased material tensile strength at 14% • Increased impact energy value	Lyu et al. (2019)
Bio-calcium carbonate	Eggshell	• Eggshell maintained 75% of talc and calcium carbonate stiffness	Owuamanam and Cree (2020)
Flax fiber	Epoxy	• Trade-off between mechanical properties and environmental sustainability	Huang et al. (2016)
Graphene	Thermal interface materials (TIMs)	• Improved and characterized thermal properties of graphene-filled polymer composite TIMs	Zhang et al. (2017)
$CaCO_3$	Anisotropic	• Increased in stiffness and heat resistance	Pukánszky (2016)
Stearic acid	Polypropylene	• Thermoplastics improved some mechanical properties but decreased others, such as impact strength • Using ultrafine fillers decreased its degradation • The impact force change measured when the second agent was used	Mareri et al. (1998)

(Continued)

TABLE 11.2 (*Continued*)
Mineral-Filled Polymer Composites

Polymer Matrix	Fiber	Effect of Reinforcement	Reference
Mica and talc	Polybutylene terephthalate	• Improved mechanical properties compared with talc-filled composites • Higher aspect ratio and the surface area of the mica relative to the talc resulted in a higher tension transfer at the polymer filler interface	Deshmukh et al. (2011)
Rice husk	Epoxy resin	• Sliding velocity, filler material and normal load were major factors influencing the particular rate of wear	Rout and Satapathy (2012)
Amino acid	Hydrolyzed polyoxazoline	• Water- and oil-resistant materials had good heat distortion properties	Meyers (1985)
Stearic acid	Polymethyl methacrylate	• Enhanced tensile and impact strength properties of the composites when compared with the untreated filled composite	Hanumantha Rao et al. (1998)
Glass fiber	Bulk molding compounds	• The mechanical loading on the suspension rheology emphasized	Guiraud et al. (2010)
Basalt fabric	Polyester-based polymer	• The mechanical properties of basalt fiber-reinforced composites were improved • Acid-treated basal fiber-reinforced composites had higher tensile strength ratings than other combinations	Manikandan et al. (2012)
Wollastonite	Ethylene-propylene and polypropylene	• Increased tensile modulus of polymeric materials and minimized plastic deformation of the polymer matrix	Misra et al. (2004)
Glass fiber	Isothermal crystallization kinetics of polyamide 6	• Two fillers provided a substantial improvement in the PA6 storage module	Şanlı et al. (2012)
Glass fiber	Polyamide-6 nanocomposites	• PA6/NC achieved a high reinforcement efficiency even at 2–5 wt% of clay, achieving high specific modulus, power and temperature distortion under load (DTUL)	Akkapeddi (2000)

Fillers mica, zeolite, and vansil	Poly (lactic acid)	• Interface filler/matrix adhesion was the key component assessing the thermal and mechanical properties of reinforced composite materials	Gregorova et al. (2012)
Sepiolite clay	Nanocomposites	• Strengthened performance and an impressive filler-matrix interaction due to strong hydrogen bonds	Mohd Zaini et al. (2017)
Nylon 6/clay hybrids	Polypropylene	• Extensive cavitation activity when sustaining a reasonably large strain at break, as long as the deformation occurred above the glass transition temperature of the matrix	Gloaguen and Lefebvre (2001)
Single-walled carbon nanotubes	Acrylonitrile-butadiene-styrene	• The tensile strength and modulus of the VGCF-filled ABS improved by an average of 39% and 60%, respectively, over the unfilled ABS	Shofner et al. (2003)
Basalt fiber	Thermoplastic and thermoset	• Significantly increased the deformation and energy absorption capacities	Fiore et al. (2015)
Nanoclay	Bio-based elastomer	• Enhanced the properties of the bio-based elastomers • The tensile strength improved as well as the elongation with the loading	Zhu and Wool (2006)
Asphalt mixtures	Polyester, polyacrylonitrile, lignin and asbestos	• Optimal asphalt content, air void, mineral void and Marshall stability increased, while actual bulk gravity decreased as fibers were added to asphalt mixtures • Optimum asphalt material, Marshall stability and dynamic stability gradually increased and then decreased with increasing fiber content.	Chen et al. (2009)

Abbreviations: ABS, acrylonitrile-butadiene-styrene; VCGF, vapor-grown carbon fibers.

modern technologies or techniques that would support any use in the growth of major manufacturing and building sectors, it was concluded that the strengthening of nanoparticles increases the efficiency and mechanical properties of the composites that favor the fiber-reinforced composite industry. A great possibility has appeared by the incorporation of nanoparticles as the reinforcing materials in composites.

In a study conducted by Yang (2018) on the influence of grafted PP on the mechanical properties of mineral-filled PP composites, it was revealed that the coupling agents improved the tensile strength of the composites significantly, and the extent of the coupling effect depended on the nature of the interface that formed. In Yang (2018), several mineral fillers were selected to study the reaction in a PP matrix when PP modified with MA and/or itaconic acid (IA) was used as a coupling agent in the preparation of mineral-filled PP composites. The composites were then scanned under electron microscopy; the films' surface from fractured tensile test specimens was examined. The appearance of microstructures confirmed the mechanical results with respect to the observed homogeneous or optimized dispersion of the mineral filler phase in these composites. A study on mineral-filled composite was carried out by Rowell et al. (1997) on the utilization of natural fibers in plastic composites. The study revealed that agro-based fibers are potential alternatives to inorganic or material-based fibers as reinforcement in synthetic thermoplastic composite materials with a certain condition and indicated that adequate processing conditions and higher water absorption are crucial for applications in which water absorption need is high. The kenaf fibers were selected because of their low density and excellent basic properties. The non-abrasive design naturally permitted a high amount of composite filling. During testing, various forms of natural fiber were blended with PP and then injected. The fractions of the fiber weight reduced by 60%. Improvement on the interaction and adhesion was applied between the non-polar matrix and the polar lignocellulosic fibers as the binding agent or the compatibilizer. In this research, it was concluded that high-fiber loading could result in substantial material cost savings, especially in the plastics industry. In comparison, for the same weight of plastic and natural fiber, production of natural fibers was higher by 20% with the cellulose-dependent system. Cellulose fibers are smooth and non-abrasive, and high filling amounts are possible.

In a study conducted by Khotbehsara et al. (2019) on the effect of elevated in-service temperature on the mechanical properties and microstructure of particulate-filled epoxy polymers, the mechanical properties during service at elevated temperature were achieved by increasing the filler percentages. Compressive and split tensile strength retention resulted in higher net epoxy. Different particulate fillers were used to improve the mechanical properties that included epoxy resin and lightweight fillers. Improving the retention of mechanical properties at high in-service temperatures was accomplished by rising the percentage of fillers. Compressive and split tensile strength retention at 80°C for the mix with 60% fillers was 72% and 52%, respectively. From the research, the particulate-filled epoxy-based polymer resin density was increased with increasing filler concentration. A recent study on mineral composite conducted by Yin et al. (2017) on porosity, mechanical properties and damping ratio of PFPC for precision machine tools showed a significant correlation of porosity and mechanical properties with the discovery of the damping ratio of PFPCs. It was revealed that the mechanical properties (damping ratio) of the PFPC were improved significantly as porosity was increased. The correlation of pores and mechanical properties on resin epoxy was studied. A mechanical test was performed using a hydraulic pressure test machine and proceeded with the measurement of porosity. The mechanical properties reached maximum when the porosity of PFPC was zero. In contrast, the damping ratio was at the lowest when there was zero porosity. In a study conducted by Stokes (2018) on mineral-filled polymer, providing the method of forming thermally stable polymer compositions and mineral-filled polymer compositions was emphasized. Composition of polymer consisting of a crystalline polymer, a mineral filler of more than 15 wt%, on the basis of the overall weight of the polymer mixture was used in the methods that included shaping the polymer composition into mold, forming the polymer composition into a composite within the mold and removing the product from the mold. The process might involve the extrusion of the polymer composition onto a layer without crystallization prior to the disposal of the polymer composition in the mold. The study revealed a detailed method in polymer fabrication, which is useful for future reference.

Moreover, in a work conducted by Gwon et al. (2010) on the effects of chemical treatments of hybrid fillers on the physical and thermal properties of wood-plastic composites, the melting enthalpy of the wood composite decreased by the addition of the fillers. This was due to the reduced volume of crystallized resin and interference of fillers during the crystallization. Wood fibers and mineral fillers were used in the study and the changes in tensile strength, water absorption and thermal properties of composites on chemical treatment were measured. The researchers concluded that chemical treatments of wood fibers and mineral fillers gave a better effect on the physical properties of plastic wood composites by modifying the chemical composition of the wood fibers and the surface structure of the mineral fillers. A study conducted by Balieu et al. (2014) on non-associated viscoplasticity coupled with an integral-type nonlocal damage model for mineral-filled semi-crystalline polymers built an elastoviscoplastic model combined with a non-local damage model to simulate the behavior and damage of a mineral-filled semi-crystalline polymer. Finite-element and numerical methods were used to find the yield strength and deformation in semi-crystalline polymer materials. They concluded that the non-local formulation of the isotropical damage model has solved the unfounded mesh-dependency issue due to the softening action of the polymer-filled materials.

Several studies were carried out on mineral-filled composite, where a study was conducted by Sakthi et al. (2020) on the effect of chemical treatment on mechanical properties of prawn antenna-reinforced waste plastic PFPCs. Reinforcement in the polyester matrix used was from prawn antennas. The results of chemical treatments were observed through the application of fibers with three types of chemicals: hydrogen peroxide, potassium hydroxide and sodium hydroxide. The composition and treatment of the composites were developed in MINITAB software using the experimental design of Taguchi to find the result of water absorption, tensile strength and flexural strength. The researchers concluded that the prawn antenna improved the tensile properties and flexural properties of the composites. Adding all fibers and fillers at lower stages resulted in lower composite density. In a study conducted by Revathy et al. (2020) on the experimental investigation on concrete-filled glass FRP tubular beams under flexural loading showed that the FRP tubular beams filled with type 2 concrete enhanced the ultimate load more than the FRP tubular beams filled with type 1 concrete. The concrete-filled unidirectional FRP tubular beams showed a better performance than the woven roving FRP tubular beams. In the experiment, two different strengths of concrete (types 1 and 2) were used to fill the FRP tubular beams of two configurations (S-type and B- type). The tubular beams were operated at a four-point loading system. The strength of concrete that infilled the FRP tubular beams and configurations of FRP were recorded. The researchers concluded that the performance of type 2 concrete-filled FRP tubular beams showed a greater ultimate load-carrying capacity. FRP tubes filled with a type 2 grade of concrete showed an increase in maximum deflection of about 22.09%. In another study by Rueda et al. (2017) on rheology and heavily packed polymer applications, the presence and composition of the particles, correlations, maximal packing fraction and matrix viscosity were the main factors affecting the rheological behavior of these composites. Hard particles, such as aluminum nitride and boron nitride, with sizes ranging from several hundred nanometers to a few microns, were used in the experiments. By using quantitative filler detection instruments in microscopic local experiments and other global approaches like light scattering, X-ray diffraction (XRD), scanning electron microscopy (SEM) and SEM-EDX techniques, the particles were analyzed. Particle surface alteration might improve the diffusion or reinforce the interactions of the particle matrix that likely result in reinforcing the composite. A work performed by Devasahayam et al. (2019) on mineral and metallurgical manufacturing, polymers and recycled polymers summarized the uses of recycled polymers, their energy, pollution benefits and drawbacks, the elimination of non-renewables and dematerialization. During the testing, several plastics were tested, including styrene resin with calcium carbonate and aluminum trihydrate fillers. To evaluate their pollution, the products were tested in a coke oven, the iron ore-reducing agent in blast furnaces and in chemical feedstock. Recently, global consensus has resurfaced that plastics are environmental threats, leading many countries to ban single-use plastic products. These actions come with strict rules and several methods to overcome the problem.

A study conducted by Skorokhoda et al. (2016) on porous composites based on polyvinylpyrrolidone copolymers with bactericidal properties were indeed mineral filled. The research was to invent new composites containing silver based on copolymers of polyvinylpyrrolidone (PVP)/methacrylic esters with mineral fillers and analyzing the effects of the form and quantity of filler on the composites' polymerization kinetics, structure and properties. The results demonstrated that higher composite reactivity with montmorillonite and wollastonite was higher relative to the polymerization of kinetic curves for composites with different fillers. In a different study conducted by Tekin et al. (2020) on sodium dodecatungstophosphate hydrate-filled silicone formulations with nuclear radiation shielding, various additives were used in the sodium dodecatungstophosphate hydrate ($H_2Na_3O_{41}PW_{12}$)-doped polymer composite materials process. The composite materials produced were measured using the WinXcom theoretical software at different energies. The findings derived from the first study were then compared with the results measured using the MCNP-X simulation software. Based on the result, it was observed that the glass content had stronger shielding properties compared with other composites. The highest density of NPW20 polymer composite materials and the sodium dodecatungstophosphate hydrate additive had exceptional abilities to protect charged particles and gamma rays from nuclear radiation. Owuamanam and Cree (2020) in their work on the progress of eggshell and seashell fillers with bio-calcium carbonate waste in polymer composites cured thermoplastic polymers and composites at high temperature and room temperature following temperature elevation, respectively. Thermoplastic polymers, waste eggshell and seashell fillers required high processing temperatures to melt the polymers, whereas thermoplastic composites were cured at room temperature and continued at elevated temperatures. Results showed that the analyses demonstrated improvement in composite materials with the inclusion of fillers, even without surface modifications relative to pure polymer matrices. The recycling of these bio-materials, waste eggshells, and seashells for a range of uses could generate extra revenue for eggs and seafood processors without deteriorating the environmental-related issues.

In recent years, there has been a growing interest in mineral-filled polymer composites. In a study conducted by Szajerski et al. (2020), the strength increment of sulfur polymer concrete composites based on waste and residual filler was caused by radiation. The results obtained indicated the compounds under investigation had a high tolerance to radiation. Irradiated samples displayed up to 35% higher compressive strain. Sulfur-based polymer concrete composites (SPCs) were tested under high radiation exposure conditions for future applications. Research specimens included compressive testing, SEM analysis, water absorption capillary testing, XRD, Fourier transform infrared spectroscopy (FTIR) and differential scanning calorimetry (DSC) research. The results revealed a the compounds under investigation had a high tolerance to radiation. For hydraulic cement concrete composites, in particular the radiation and nuclear technology industries, SPC materials could be recognized as a promising choice. Another study by Frank et al. (2020) on the influence of carbon nanotube (CNT)/polymer nanocomposite (PNC) biodegradation of the polymer forms and the carbon nanotube properties revealed that PNCs did not prevent complete polymer matrix biodegradation, but decreased the biodegradation rate by a certain threshold and beyond. In the experiment, a sequence of CNT loads of 0–5 w/w% were integrated into the poly-β-caprolactone (PCL) and polyhydroxyalcanoate (PHA) matrices. They were biodegraded into the anaerobic microbial community with the volumetric biogas measurements and cinétical simulation of biodegradations as a function of the polymer form and CNT properties used. The study revealed that the CNT's effect in inhibiting polymer biodegradation rates was greater under the conditions of slowest biodegradation, i.e., the polymer form, microbiome phenotype and CNT dispersion. Research was conducted by Balan and Ravichandran (2020) on the study of moisture absorption characteristics of jute fiber-reinforced waste plastic-filled polymer composite. The percolation of the water can be avoided by minimizing, closing holes or by adding more fillers. The specimens were created by varying reinforcement and filler levels at various weight proportions. The Taguchi method has developed process parameters, e.g., weight percentage of plastic pellets, jute strengthening and a chemical processing type for jute fiber.

Apart from that, in a study performed by Rod et al. (2020) on polymer-modified and self-repaired cement for geothermal and fossil energy applications with high temperatures, the introduction of these polymers resulted in auto-healing capabilities of at 200°C for 30 days. There were two polymer cement mixtures discovered, where the thermal stability of the polymeric materials showed that the total organic carbon and NMR spectroscopy were calculated for the stability of the composites. These advanced polymer cement composites with better ductility and self-healing properties can be used for geothermal and fossil energy purposes as alternative wellbore cement materials.

Lashari et al. (2018) studied high strength and thermally stable organic composite polymer gels characterized by gelation time, gel strength, morphology, long-term thermal stability and pH effect. The effects of bulk gelling properties were investigated in various concentrations. Traditional (organic) gel and modern combined gel microstructures were analyzed by electron microscopy (SEM), providing insight into the gel power mechanism. The gelation time and gel strength were measured with the nanoparticle, cross-connector, and polymer concentrations. The composite gel also displayed high thermal stability and negligible syneresis at 60°C for 90 days at pH 8.0–8.5, suggesting that the thermal stability results of the composite polymer gel were better than the normal polymer gel and thermal stability. In a research by Lin et al. (2020), the usage of waste materials in a novel mortar-polymer-laminar composite to be applied in constructing three-dimensional (3D) printing was investigated. The laminar-mortar-polymer composite was developed. Three separate composites were tested using displacement-controlled compression experiments. The first was a standard mortar, with two components of waste: biochar or fly ash. The improvements in the ductility were seen despite the fact that polymer inclusion decreased the overall peak compressive pressure in just one case. When the mortars were either biochar or fly ash, the inclusion of plastic reinforcement would give the strengthened mortar equivalent ductility without such pollution. Although the reinforcement was made with ABS polymers, other polymers might also be considered for a lower cost, higher sustainability or more attractive mechanical properties. Even theoretic ones with a large fraction of the recycled component might be consider.

Apart from that, Venkatarajan and Athijayamani (2020) evaluated the natural cellulose FRP composites. The potential of natural cellulose fibers in polymer matrix composites to replace synthetic fibers, for example, glass, aramid, and carbon, revealed that they were not as strong as synthetic fibers. Natural fibers are widely available at low cost, have low density and are recyclable and biodegradable. Resin transfer molding methods were used to study the stretching and effects of hemp fiber-strengthened polyester composites. Increasing trends of the flexural stress at breakage and flexural modules of the fiber material were observed. The intensity of the effect was observed with low fiber content and then was increased with the addition of the fiber content. Natural cellulose fillers such as fibers and particulates are light weight, environmentally friendly and reusable.

In a study conducted by Deshmukh et al. (2011) on the analysis of the effect of mineral addition on the mechanical, thermal and structural properties of poly(butylene terephthalate) (PBT) composites, they demonstrated the mechanical properties of mica and talc-containing PBT composites with different concentrations of the two fillers. BASF Ultradur, grade ultradur B 2550 with a density and melt flow index of 1.30 g/cm^3 and 18 g/10 minutes, respectively, supplied the PBT used for this

Mineral-Filled Polymer Composites

function. In this work, it was stated that PBT composites containing talc and mica were prepared using the melting technique and that the structures were tested for their mechanical, thermal and structural properties. As a result of hydrogen bonding and without the use of any surface-altering or binding agent, the most striking discovery was the presence of heavy interfacial contact in both the composite systems of mica and talc. Another study by Manikandan et al. (2012) on the investigation of the influence of surface modifications on the mechanical properties of basalt FRP composites showed that natural fibers are now known to be serious alternatives to glass fibers for reinforcing agent applications in composite materials. Low cost, low density, high strength to weight ratio, resistance to breakage during processing, low energy content and recyclability are among the advantages of natural fibers over glass fibers. The fibers can be corroded by diffusion through the material by a degraded interface or as a result of matrix fracturing. The fibers in composite materials play a significant role in deciding the strength of the material. In this analysis, the production of composites reinforced with basalt fiber with unsaturated polyester was stated to be superior to those reinforced with glass fiber.

The increasing interest in mineral-filled polymer composite in recent years is also illustrated by the study carried out by Zhang et al. (2017) on the thermal properties of graphene-filled polymer composite thermal interface materials (TIMs). This work was motivated by the exponential growth in the power density of modern electronic devices. The high-power density heat characteristic limits the performance, reliability and further production of such devices. Matrix products of graphene-filled polymer composite TIMs are primary polymers such as butyl rubber, mineral oil, PVC, epoxy resin, polyethylene (PE), nylon 6 and butyl chloride. The same study was aimed to demonstrate recent advances in the TC enhancement of graphene-filled composite polymer TIMs. In addition, Pukánszky (2016) reviewed mineral-filled polymers and found several extensive areas of particulate-filled polymer applications. With the exception of PVC, the implementation of fillers is largely justified for technical and technological purposes, as a separate compounding phase greatly raises the price of the composite. Until the product is made, the polymer and the filler must be homogenized. The minimum requirements for fast production and execution are through the homogenization of the components, where inadequate homogenization leads to aggregation. These composites had improved mechanical properties, decreased gas permeation and flame retardation as well as significant weight savings that were planned to be supplemented by the improved properties. Much of the standards had not been met, as it turned out that these components were still used in small quantities in niche applications. In this research, the use of mineral fillers was reported to continue to increase, for instance, injection of the filler into the nylon results in new fabrics. The features of the elements, structure, interfacial relationship and shape determine the properties of the composites.

Research work performed by Patnaik et al. (2010) was based on the wear properties of rigid particle degradation of fiber and PFPCs. It showed that wear is defined as the damage to a solid surface that typically results in a progressive loss of material due to relative movement between the surface and the touching object or substance. Statistical approaches have been widely used for the study, estimation and/or optimization of a variety of engineering processes. Such approaches help the consumers to identify and study the impact of each potential situation in an experiment where a variety of variables are involved. In this research, it was reported that the detailed literature survey presented above indicates that although much work has been reported on the characteristics of the erosion of polymers and their composites, the likelihood of integrating both particles and fibers into polymers has not yet been adequately addressed in terms of improved wear resistance.

Guiraud et al. (2010) worked on the simulation of the mold filling with mineral fillers and short FRP composites. Bulk molding compounds are widely used in the electrical industry for the manufacture of small parts with fair surface quality and complicated shapes, and the manufacturing of car frames in the automotive industry as some examples. The stress-strength curves demonstrated a remarkable strain hardening, independent of the mechanical loading, and the strain severity was considered. Viscoelastic effects might be responsible for the first spike in stress, i.e., at $\varepsilon 33 < 0.25$. In this analysis, it was stated that the research initiated to understand the rheology of bulk molding compounds was pursued. Once again, studies showed that these polymer composites exhibit complex rheology during the forming phase of the extremely condensed non-newtonian fiber-reinforced suspensions.

Gregorova et al. (2012) investigated the mineral-filled poly(lactic acid) (PLA) composites' viscoelastic properties and revealed that the global annual production of petroleum-produced polymers has reached 150 million tonnes, with an anticipated 5% rise. It has taken millions of years for fossil fuels to evolve and their production has been limited due to heavy use. PLA 7000D pellets from Nature-Works LLC (Minnetonka, MN) were used as the matrix. PLA, having an average molecular weight (Mw) of 140 000 gmol^{-1}, a polydispersity index of 2.06 g and a density of 1.22 g cm^{-3}, was used in this study. In the tensile surface study of fracture, the multiple filler particle forms in the composites were observed under SEM micrographs. Mica was mainly platy, with a blocky structure in the zeolites, and fibrous aggregates were formed by Vansil.

Sharma et al. (2017) studied the curing tests and mechanical properties of silanized clay minerals of glass fiber-reinforced composites and revealed that the modification of clay minerals allowed the possibility to achieve a good dispersion of clay minerals into the polymer matrix and used their high aspect ratio and wide surface area to interact with the polymer molecules of clay mineral layers. For clay mineral weight, the amount of silane coupling agents (SCAs) used were 0.1×, 0.5×, 2×, 4×, and 6× (×). Each SCA was mixed in a solvent and hydrolyzed for 30 minutes with a continuous stirring solution. Thermogravimetric analysis of silane-modified clay minerals was carried out in a systematic review of silane grafting on clay minerals. In this study, an optimized curing schedule was recorded for the development of fiber-reinforced clay-epoxy nanocomposites containing Cloisite 15A and silylated Cloisite 15A clay minerals. Maximum mechanical properties were achieved by curing the epoxy at a temperature slightly below the temperature of the fully cured network using differential calorimetric scanning.

Carmisciano et al. (2011) worked on the vinylester composites reinforced with basalt woven fiber to study the flexural and electrical properties. They revealed that the growing use of polymer composite materials for non-structural and structural applications involves the development of goods capable of compliance with

Mineral-Filled Polymer Composites

the environmental requirements. The qualitative elementary analysis of E-glass and basalt fibers on SEM Philips XL40 was performed using energy dispersion spectroscopy (EDS). There are many differences between basalt and glass fibers. Compared with E-glass fiber, the elements in basalt fiber are more complex. SiO_2 and Al_2O_3 are the main compounds in the chemical system. In this research, it was stated that there is room for widespread applications of basalt fibers as an alternative to glass fibers as a reinforcement in polymer composites, according to the results of this preliminary investigation. Flexural modulus and interlaminar properties were especially promising, although dielectric behavior was almost identical in the 10 kHz^{-1} frequency range.

Atay and Çelik (2013) evaluated the mechanical properties of flame-retardant huntite and hydromagnesite-reinforced polymer composites and showed that the relative performance of polymer hydrated fire retardant fillers depended heavily on the presence and origin of the form of filler and the chemical properties of the host polymer, in particular the mechanism of decomposition. Pre-processing involves drilling, crushing, grinding and arranging mineral powders by size delivery, as in the brief details illustrated here. The 10-mm mineral powder XRD pattern showed that hydromagnesite ($Mg_4(OH)_2(CO_3)3\cdot3H_2O$), huntite ($Mg_3Ca(CO_3)_4$) and dolomite ($CaMg(CO_3)_{22}$) are important minerals. Morphologically, these rocks consist of differing amounts of dolomite, monohydrocalcite, hydromagnesite, huntite, magnesite-cemented silicic and carbonate-clastic debris. In this analysis, it was stated that the mechanical properties were examined in the continuation of the experiments in these studies, and subsequent results were found until a loading level of 64% decreased the tensile strength by increasing the particles. However, up to 64% of the tensile strength was improved by increasing the volume of the filler. Increased additive size of mineral powder led to a reduction in tensile strength.

Sreekanth et al. (2011) studied the effects of mica aggregation on the properties of polyester thermoplastic elastomer composites. They revealed that the performance of filled polymers is typically measured on the basis of the attraction of the filler and the polymer interface. The injection of inorganic mineral fillers into plastic resins had improved various physical properties of the materials, such as mechanical strength and modulus. The tensile strength reduced at higher filler concentrations after a slight increase in the initial concentration of mica. The increase might be due to the arrangement of the mica plate, providing a good reinforcement. In this analysis, inorganic mica fillers were added to the polymer that resulted in improved rigidity, strength and thermal resilience, but greatly reduced the elongation of the crack. Through an increase in the strength of the filler, there was a substantial increase in flexural capacity and modulus. Effect strength decreased with filler aggregation due to reduced substrate elasticity from the addition of the filler, resulting in decreased matrix deformability.

11.5 CHALLENGES AND FUTURE PERSPECTIVES

The mineral-filled polymer composites have shown that they are very useful and have potential applications in many fields via the manufacturing technique that requires reinforcing different polymers to vary the compositions and features.

The characteristics of these materials are desirable because they have comparable strength and toughness ratios to those used in metal alloys while being lightweight and more economical. A wide variety of these composite applications were found in the shipping, manufacturing and renewable energy sectors. This is one of the reasons making the durability of polymeric materials and polymer composites a crucial field for future research and development.

However, current traits of mineral polymers have shown that they are susceptible to degradation. These polymers tend to have a short lifetime and slowly lose their functional properties over a period of time under harsh environmental conditions. Another challenge for polymer composites is that they are easily damaged during manufacturing; irregular manufacturing resulted in cracks on the materials' surface. Because of the presence of these voids, the filler is a necessary element to add in the polymeric substances, not only to fill the voids but to enhance the desired properties, especially thermal, mechanical and conductivity.

The interphase layers in the mineral filler-reinforced composite involve the interactions between the polymer and mineral filler to enhance the required properties of the composite. The physical and chemical interactions between the interphases have been extensively studied to optimize the mechanical behavior of various types of mineral filler composites (Liang and Wu 2012). Some of the mineral fillers require surface modification when mixed with polymer matrices to provide decent surface area for better adhesion across the interface. The surface treatment was found to improve the mechanical strength and chemical resistance of composites by improving the filler spreading and creating a good distribution of the mineral filler into polymeric means. In addition to this, the surface treatment also promoted the reduction of the viscosity of the mixture, as well as improve curing behavior of polymers with the mineral filler surface (Yang 2018). One of the main purposes of surface treatment is to improve the moisture resistance of the composite. The surface of mineral fillers is commonly hydrophilic because it contains metallic elements such as silicon. Mineral filler treatment might alter the surface of the mineral from hydrophilic to hydrophobic or modifying it to a chemically reactive surface (Gorrasi et al. 2008).

The mineral filler has different hardness values, for instance, silica has higher hardness than talc. When utilizing silica in the composite production, extra abrasiveness was introduced that lowered the equipment life span. In the case of machinery and processing parameters, tooling needed several design improvements, in particular clay in the form or platelet. It is important to control the expansion of the clay during the dispersion process to avoid the clay from getting sloughed. Several processing parameters such as feeding speed and size needed to be considered to ensure good distribution and dispersion of fillers into the polymeric matrix. Another challenge during the processing of composite using mineral filler is the surface area of the filler. Filler that has high surface area offers excellent processability, including determining the viscosity of the flowing resin, as well as enhanced flow and dispersion by producing well-wetted filler composite. In mineral-filled polymer composite, the key factor for good incorporation between filler and the polymer is the filler volume, particularly when processing highly viscous material. High filler content means a lot of air inserted in the process, which makes discharge and airing a challenging task. This requires some modification on the compound formulation, as

Mineral-Filled Polymer Composites

well as the processing parameters such as segmented screw geometries. High filler content requires stable, high volumetric dosing and proper processing die heads to handle a large number of filled compounds.

It was noted that some drawbacks of using mineral filler in composite production exist. Nilugal and Kumar (2015) found that the addition of calcium sulfate increased the mechanical properties of E-glass epoxy-based composites, but their thermal properties were reduced. Calcium sulfate was also found to degrade the mechanical properties of some plastics, with its main limitations of poor handling and mechanical properties (Lewis et al. 2006). Further, it was found that glass beads, silica, calcium carbonate and talc generally deteriorated plastics by hindering plastic flow and increased the viscosity of the mixture (Leong et al. 2004; Wang et al. 2013).

Most of the recent developments in the composite industry are motivated by the need for light weight and green, particularly in the automotive industry. The composite materials are lightweight but still can offer high performance and comparable mechanical properties. The use of mineral fillers as reinforcement materials in composites provides cost benefits, aside from environmental sustainability. Mineral-filled polymer composites are promising materials that can be used to improve some composite properties, particularly thermal and electrical, in many applications (Jiang et al. 2009; Anyszka et al. 2018). Proper research and development of mineral-filled polymer composites also can improve the composite durability and life span. A certain mineral can be grown, which is a positive sign of them replacing the non-renewable minerals such as copper. Using mineral-filled composites from grown plants or animals should not harm the environment as they decompose over a short period of time. Some consideration and specific techniques need to be developed to tackle the mineral filler drawbacks with the aim of improving the compatibility with the matrix, and final product performance.

11.6 CONCLUSIONS

This chapter provides an overview of mineral-filled polymer composites. Because of their abundance, low cost, versatility and advantageous properties, they are used in many industries including construction, automotive, housing and furniture. Proper types, size, shape and volume of mineral filler in composites associated with filler treatment further improve the mineral-filled polymer composite properties. The use of mineral filler, e.g., talc and calcium carbonate in mineral-filled polymer, widely increases composite production due to the technology developments. The properties of this material are determined by the characteristic of the parts, composition, interfacial relations and form. The exhaustive literature survey presented indicated that a great deal of study has been reported on this kind of composite. These estimated hypotheses clearly demonstrate the influence of the reinforcement between the mineral and the polymer compound by improvements in the mechanical properties and the adhesive bond strength between the polymer and the filler phases. The theory should be as applicable to any form of substance as the matrix, although only composites were discussed.

In addition, mineral-filled polymer composites have achieved some marketable success. The use of sustainable mineral fillers demonstrated the enormous potential for lightweight sustainable composites with improved specific properties. Due to the properties offered by the addition of mineral filler, such as improving both thermal and mechanical performance, considering the composite weight is an advantage that might have implications in the structural applications. The effective compatibilization of mineral filler and polymer matrices allows a good balance of properties that can be achieved by using accurate filler and processing techniques. Nevertheless, progress is already ongoing to address these obstacles in a more cost-effective and eco-friendly fashion without losing their properties to ensure wider usage. Because of this, it is possible to foresee a bright future for these products.

REFERENCES

Abral, Hairul, Jeri Ariksa, Melbi Mahardika, Dian Handayani, Ibtisamatul Aminah, Neny Sandrawati, Angga Bahri Pratama, Nural Fajri, S.M. Sapuan, and R.A. Ilyas. 2020a. "Transparent and Antimicrobial Cellulose Film from Ginger Nanofiber." *Food Hydrocolloids* 98 (January): 105266. https://doi.org/10.1016/j.foodhyd.2019.105266

Abral, Hairul, Jeri Ariksa, Melbi Mahardika, Dian Handayani, Ibtisamatul Aminah, Neny Sandrawati, S.M. Sapuan, and R.A. Ilyas. 2019. "Highly Transparent and Antimicrobial PVA Based Bionanocomposites Reinforced by Ginger Nanofiber." *Polymer Testing* 81 (October): 106186. https://doi.org/10.1016/j.polymertesting.2019.106186

Abral, Hairul, Arief Atmajaya, Melbi Mahardika, Fadli Hafizulhaq, Kadriadi, Dian Handayani, S.M. Sapuan, and R.A. Ilyas. 2020b. "Effect of Ultrasonication Duration of Polyvinyl Alcohol (PVA) Gel on Characterizations of PVA Film." *Journal of Materials Research and Technology* 9 (2): 2477–2486. https://doi.org/10.1016/j.jmrt.2019.12.078

Abral, Hairul, Melati Krista Chairani, Muhammad Dinul Rizki, Melbi Mahardika, Dian Handayani, Eni Sugiarti, Ahmad Novi Muslimin, S.M. Sapuan, and R.A. Ilyas. 2021. "Characterization of Compressed Bacterial Cellulose Nanopaper Film after Exposure to Dry and Humid Conditions." *Journal of Materials Research and Technology* 11 (March–April), 896–904. https://doi.org/10.1016/j.jmrt.2021.01.057

Aisyah, H. A., M. T. Paridah, S. M. Sapuan, A. Khalina, O. B. Berkalp, S. H. Lee, C. H. Lee, et al. 2019. "Thermal Properties of Woven Kenaf/Carbon Fibre-Reinforced Epoxy Hybrid Composite Panels." *International Journal of Polymer Science* 2019: 5258621. https://doi.org/10.1155/2019/5258621

Akkapeddi, M. K. 2000. "Glass Fiber Reinforced Polyamide-6 Nanocomposites." *Polymer Composites* 21 (4): 576–585. https://doi.org/10.1002/pc.10213

Alsubari, S., M. Y. M. Zuhri, S. M. Sapuan, M. R. Ishak, R. A. Ilyas, and M. R. M. Asyraf. 2021. "Potential of Natural Fiber Reinforced Polymer Composites in Sandwich Structures: A Review on Its Mechanical Properties." *Polymers* 13 (3): 423. https://doi.org/10.3390/polym13030423

Anyszka, Rafał, Dariusz M. Bieliński, Zbigniew Pędzich, Grzegorz Parys, Przemysław Rybiński, Magdalena Zarzecka-Napierała, Mateusz Imiela, et al. 2018. "Effect of Mineral Filler Additives on Flammability, Processing and Use of Silicone-Based Ceramifiable Composites." *Polymer Bulletin* 75 (4): 1731–1751. https://doi.org/10.1007/s00289-017-2113-0

Asrofi, Mochamad, S. M. Sapuan, R. A. Ilyas, and M. Ramesh. 2020a. "Characteristic of Composite Bioplastics from Tapioca Starch and Sugarcane Bagasse Fiber: Effect of Time Duration of Ultrasonication (Bath-Type)." *Materials Today: Proceedings*, August. https://doi.org/10.1016/j.matpr.2020.07.254

Asrofi, Mochamad, Edi Syafri Sujito, S. M. Sapuan, and R. A. Ilyas. 2020b. "Improvement of Biocomposite Properties Based Tapioca Starch and Sugarcane Bagasse Cellulose

Nanofibers." *Key Engineering Materials* 849 (June): 96–101. https://doi.org/10.4028/www.scientific.net/KEM.849.96

Asyraf, M. R. M., M. R. Ishak, S. M. Sapuan, N. Yidris, and R. A. Ilyas. 2020a. "Woods and Composites Cantilever Beam: A Comprehensive Review of Experimental and Numerical Creep Methodologies." *Journal of Materials Research and Technology* 9 (3): 6759–6776. https://doi.org/10.1016/j.jmrt.2020.01.013

Asyraf, M. R. M., M. Rafidah, M. R. Ishak, S. M. Sapuan, R. A. Ilyas, and M. R. Razman. 2020b. "Integration of TRIZ, Morphological Chart and ANP Method for Development of FRP Composite Portable Fire Extinguisher." *Polymer Composites* 1–6. https://doi.org/10.1002/pc.25587

Atay, Hüsnügül Yılmaz, and Erdal Çelik. 2013. "Mechanical Properties of Flame-Retardant Huntite and Hydromagnesite-Reinforced Polymer Composites." *Polymer-Plastics Technology and Engineering* 52 (2): 182–188. https://doi.org/10.1080/03602559.2012.735310

Atikah, M. S. N., R. A. Ilyas, S. M. Sapuan, M. R. Ishak, E. S. Zainudin, R. Ibrahim, A. Atiqah, M. N. M. Ansari, and R. Jumaidin. 2019. "Degradation and Physical Properties of Sugar Palm Starch/Sugar Palm Nanofibrillated Cellulose Bionanocomposite." *Polimery/Polymers* 64 (10). https://doi.org/10.14314/polimery.2019.10.5

Atiqah, A., M. Jawaid, S. M. Sapuan, M. R. Ishak, M. N. M. Ansari, and R. A. Ilyas. 2019. "Physical and Thermal Properties of Treated Sugar Palm/Glass Fibre Reinforced Thermoplastic Polyurethane Hybrid Composites." *Journal of Materials Research and Technology* 8 (5): 3726–3732. https://doi.org/10.1016/j.jmrt.2019.06.032

Ayu, Rafiqah S., Abdan Khalina, Ahmad Saffian Harmaen, Khairul Zaman, Tawakkal Isma, Qiuyun Liu, R. A. Ilyas, and Ching Hao Lee. 2020. "Characterization Study of Empty Fruit Bunch (EFB) Fibers Reinforcement in Poly(Butylene) Succinate (PBS)/Starch/Glycerol Composite Sheet." *Polymers* 12 (7): 1571. https://doi.org/10.3390/polym12071571

Azammi, A. M. Noor, R. A. Ilyas, S. M. Sapuan, Rushdan Ibrahim, M. S. N. Atikah, Mochamad Asrofi, and A. Atiqah. 2019. "Characterization Studies of Biopolymeric Matrix and Cellulose Fibres Based Composites Related to Functionalized Fibre-Matrix Interface." In *Interfaces in Particle and Fibre Reinforced Composites – From Macro to Nano Scales*, 1st ed., 1–68. London: Woodhead Publishing. https://doi.org/10.1016/B978-0-08-102665-6

Baihaqi, N. M. Z. Nik, A. Khalina, N. Mohd Nurazzi, H. A. Aisyah, S. M. Sapuan, and R. A. Ilyas. 2021. "Effect of Fiber Content and Their Hybridization on Bending and Torsional Strength of Hybrid Epoxy Composites Reinforced with Carbon and Sugar Palm Fibers." *Polimery* 66 (1): 36–43.

Balan, G. Sakthi, and M. Ravichandran. 2020. "Study of Moisture Absorption Characteristics of Jute Fiber Reinforced Waste Plastic Filled Polymer Composite." *Materials Today: Proceedings* 27: 712–717. https://doi.org/10.1016/j.matpr.2019.11.260

Balieu, R., F. Lauro, B. Bennani, T. Matsumoto, and E. Mottola. 2014. "Non-Associated Viscoplasticity Coupled with an Integral-Type Nonlocal Damage Model for Mineral Filled Semi-Crystalline Polymers." *Computers and Structures* 134: 18–31. https://doi.org/10.1016/j.compstruc.2013.12.006

Carmisciano, Salvatore, Igor Maria De Rosa, Fabrizio Sarasini, Alessio Tamburrano, and Marco Valente. 2011. "Basalt Woven Fiber Reinforced Vinylester Composites: Flexural and Electrical Properties." *Materials and Design* 32 (1): 337–342. https://doi.org/10.1016/j.matdes.2010.06.042

Chen, Huaxin, Qinwu Xu, Shuanfa Chen, and Zhengqi Zhang. 2009. "Evaluation and Design of Fiber-Reinforced Asphalt Mixtures." *Materials and Design* 30 (7): 2595–2603. https://doi.org/10.1016/j.matdes.2008.09.030

Deshmukh, Gauri S., D. R. Peshwe, S. U. Pathak, and J. D. Ekhe. 2011. "A Study on Effect of Mineral Additions on the Mechanical, Thermal, and Structural Properties of

Poly(Butylene Terephthalate) (PBT) Composites." *Journal of Polymer Research* 18 (5): 1081–1090. https://doi.org/10.1007/s10965-010-9510-5

Devasahayam, Sheila, R. K. Raman, K. Chennakesavulu, and Sankar Bhattacharya. 2019. "Plastics—Villain or Hero? Polymers and Recycled Polymers in Mineral and Metallurgical Processing—A Review." *Materials* 12 (4): 655. https://doi.org/10.3390/ma12040655

Ditzel, Fernanda I., Eduardo Prestes, Benjamim M. Carvalho, Ivo M. Demiate, and Luís A. Pinheiro. 2017. "Nanocrystalline Cellulose Extracted from Pine Wood and Corncob." *Carbohydrate Polymers* 157: 1577–1585. https://doi.org/10.1016/j.carbpol.2016.11.036

Fekete, Erika, Béla Pukánszky, András Tóth, and Imre Bertóti. 1990. "Surface Modification and Characterization of Particulate Mineral Fillers." *Journal of Colloid And Interface Science* 135 (1): 200–208. https://doi.org/10.1016/0021-9797(90)90300-D

Fiore, V., T. Scalici, G. Di Bella, and A. Valenza. 2015. "A Review on Basalt Fibre and Its Composites." *Composites Part B: Engineering* 74 (June): 74–94. https://doi.org/10.1016/j.compositesb.2014.12.034

Frank, Benjamin P., David G. Goodwin, Pavlo Bohutskyi, Duc C. Phan, Xier Lu, Leo Kuwama, Edward J. Bouwer, and D. Howard Fairbrother. 2020. "Influence of Polymer Type and Carbon Nanotube Properties on Carbon Nanotube/Polymer Nanocomposite Biodegradation." *Science of The Total Environment* 742 (November): 140512. https://doi.org/10.1016/j.scitotenv.2020.140512

Gloaguen, J. M., and J. M. Lefebvre. 2001. "Plastic Deformation Behaviour of Thermoplastic/Clay Nanocomposites." *Polymer* 42 (13): 5841–5847. https://doi.org/10.1016/S0032-3861(00)00901-0

Gorrasi, Giuliana, V. Vittoria, Marius Murariu, Amália Da Silva Ferreira, Michaël Alexandre, and Philippe Dubois. 2008. "Effect of Filler Content and Size on Transport Properties of Water Vapor in PLA/Calcium Sulfate Composites." *Biomacromolecules* 9 (3): 984–990. https://doi.org/10.1021/bm700568n

Gregorova, Adriana, Michal MacHovsky, and Rupert Wimmer. 2012. "Viscoelastic Properties of Mineral-Filled Poly(Lactic Acid) Composites." *International Journal of Polymer Science* 2012: 252981. https://doi.org/10.1155/2012/252981

Guiraud, Olivier, Pierre J. J. Dumont, Laurent Orgéas, Jean Pierre Vassal, Thai Hung Le, and Denis Favier. 2010. "Towards the Simulation of Mould Filling with Polymer Composites Reinforced with Mineral Fillers and Short Fibres." *International Journal of Material Forming* 3 (Suppl. 2): 1313–1326. https://doi.org/10.1007/s12289-009-0658-7

Gwon, Jae Gyoung, Sun Young Lee, Sang Jin Chun, Geum Hyun Doh, and Jung Hyeun Kim. 2010. "Effects of Chemical Treatments of Hybrid Fillers on the Physical and Thermal Properties of Wood Plastic Composites." *Composites Part A: Applied Science and Manufacturing* 41 (10): 1491–1497. https://doi.org/10.1016/j.compositesa.2010.06.011

Halimatul, M. J., S. M. Sapuan, M. Jawaid, M. R. Ishak, and R. A. Ilyas. 2019. "Water Absorption and Water Solubility Properties of Sago Starch Biopolymer Composite Films Filled with Sugar Palm Particles." *Polimery* 64 (9): 27–35. https://doi.org/10.14314/polimery.2019.9.4

Hanumantha Rao, K., K. S. E. Forssberg, and W. Forsling. 1998. "Interfacial Interactions and Mechanical Properties of Mineral Filled Polymer Composites: Wollastonite in PMMA Polymer Matrix." *Colloids and Surfaces A: Physicochemical and Engineering Aspects* 133 (1–2): 107–117. https://doi.org/10.1016/S0927-7757(97)00130-1

Hazrol, M. D., S. M. Sapuan, R. A. Ilyas, M. L. Othman, and S. F. K. Sherwani. 2020. "Electrical Properties of Sugar Palm Nanocrystalline Cellulose Reinforced Sugar Palm Starch Nanocomposites." *Polimery* 65 (05): 363–370. https://doi.org/10.14314/polimery.2020.5.4

Herrera-Franco, P. J., and A. Valadez-González. 2004. "Mechanical Properties of Continuous Natural Fibre-Reinforced Polymer Composites." *Composites Part A: Applied Science and Manufacturing* 35 (3): 339–345. https://doi.org/10.1016/j.compositesa.2003.09.012

Huang, Kede, Abhishek Vishwanath Rammohan, Umeyr Kureemun, Wern Sze Teo, Le Quan Ngoc Tran, and Heow Pueh Lee. 2016. "Shock Wave Impact Behavior of Flax Fiber Reinforced Polymer Composites." *Composites Part B: Engineering* 102: 78–85. https://doi.org/10.1016/j.compositesb.2016.07.014

Ilyas, R. A., and S. M. Sapuan. 2020a. "Biopolymers and Biocomposites: Chemistry and Technology." *Current Analytical Chemistry* 16 (5): 500–503. https://doi.org/10.2174/157341101605200603095311

Ilyas, R. A., and S. M. Sapuan. 2020b. "The Preparation Methods and Processing of Natural Fibre Bio-Polymer Composites." *Current Organic Synthesis* 16 (8): 1068–1070. https://doi.org/10.2174/157017941608200120105616

Ilyas, R. A., S. M. Sapuan, M. S. N. Atikah, M. R. M. Asyraf, S. Ayu Rafiqah, H. A. Aisyah, N. Mohd Nurazzi, and M. N. F. Norrrahim. 2021. "Effect of Hydrolysis Time on the Morphological, Physical, Chemical, and Thermal Behavior of Sugar Palm Nanocrystalline Cellulose (Arenga Pinnata (Wurmb.) Merr)." *Textile Research Journal* 91 (1–2): 152–167. https://doi.org/10.1177/0040517520932393

Ilyas, R. A., S. M. Sapuan, A. Atiqah, R. Ibrahim, H. Abral, M. R. Ishak, E. S. Zainudin, et al. 2020a. "Sugar Palm (Arenga Pinnata [Wurmb.] Merr) Starch Films Containing Sugar Palm Nanofibrillated Cellulose as Reinforcement: Water Barrier Properties." *Polymer Composites* 41 (2). https://doi.org/10.1002/pc.25379

Ilyas, Rushdan Ahmad, Salit Mohd Sapuan, Rushdan Ibrahim, Hairul Abral, M. R. Ishak, E..S. Zainudin, Mochamad Asrofi, et al. 2019a. "Sugar Palm (Arenga Pinnata (Wurmb.) Merr) Cellulosic Fibre Hierarchy: A Comprehensive Approach from Macro to Nano Scale." *Journal of Materials Research and Technology* 8 (3): 2753–2766. https://doi.org/10.1016/j.jmrt.2019.04.011

Ilyas, R. A., S. M. Sapuan, R. Ibrahim, H. Abral, M. R. Ishak, E. S. Zainudin, M. S. N. Atikah, et al. 2019b. "Effect of Sugar Palm Nanofibrillated Celluloseconcentrations on Morphological, Mechanical Andphysical Properties of Biodegradable Films Basedon Agro-Waste Sugar Palm (Arenga Pinnata(Wurmb.) Merr) Starch." *Journal of Materials Research and Technology* 8 (5): 4819–4830. https://doi.org/10.1016/j.jmrt.2019.08.028

Ilyas, R. A., S. M. Sapuan, Rushdan Ibrahim, Hairul Abral, M. R. Ishak, E. S. Zainudin, A. Atiqah, et al. 2020b. "Thermal, Biodegradability and Water Barrier Properties of Bio-Nanocomposites Based on Plasticised Sugar Palm Starch and Nanofibrillated Celluloses from Sugar Palm Fibres." *Journal of Biobased Materials and Bioenergy* 14 (2): 234–248. https://doi.org/10.1166/jbmb.2020.1951

Ilyas, R. A., S. M. Sapuan, M. R. Ishak, and E. S. Zainudin. 2017. "Effect of Delignification on the Physical, Thermal, Chemical, and Structural Properties of Sugar Palm Fibre." *BioResources* 12 (4): 8734–8754. https://doi.org/10.15376/biores.12.4.8734-8754

Ilyas, R. A., S. M. Sapuan, M. R. Ishak, and E. S. Zainudin. 2019c. "Sugar Palm Nanofibrillated Cellulose (Arenga Pinnata (Wurmb.) Merr): Effect of Cycles on Their Yield, Physic-Chemical, Morphological and Thermal Behavior." *International Journal of Biological Macromolecules* 123 (February): 379–388. https://doi.org/10.1016/j.ijbiomac.2018.11.124

Ilyas, R. A., S. M. Sapuan, M. R. Ishak, and E. S. Zainudin. 2018. "Development and Characterization of Sugar Palm Nanocrystalline Cellulose Reinforced Sugar Palm Starch Bionanocomposites Development and Characterization of Sugar Palm Nanocrystalline Cellulose Reinforced Sugar Palm Starch Bionanocomposites." *Carbohydrate Polymers* 202 (September): 186–202. https://doi.org/10.1016/j.carbpol.2018.09.002

Jang, Keon Soo. 2016. "Mineral Filler Effect on the Mechanics and Flame Retardancy of Polycarbonate Composites: Talc and Kaolin." *E-Polymers* 16 (5): 379–386. https://doi.org/10.1515/epoly-2016-0103

Jiang, X., Y. Rui, and G. Chen. 2009. "Effect of Single-Mineral Filler and Hybrid-Mineral Filler Additives on the Properties of Polypropylene Composites." *Journal of Vinyl Additive Technology* 21 (2): 129–133. https://doi.org/10.1002/vnl

Jumaidin, Ridhwan, R. A. Ilyas, Mohamed Saiful, Firdaus Hussin, and M. T. Mastura. 2019a. "Water Transport and Physical Properties of Sugarcane Bagasse Fibre Reinforced Thermoplastic Potato Starch Biocomposite." *Journal of Advanced Research in Fluid Mechanics and Thermal Sciences* 61 (2): 273–281.

Jumaidin, Ridhwan, Muhammad Afif Akmal Khiruddin, Zulhelmi Asyul Sutan Saidi, Mohd Sapuan Salit, and Rushdan Ahmad Ilyas. 2020. "Effect of Cogon Grass Fibre on the Thermal, Mechanical and Biodegradation Properties of Thermoplastic Cassava Starch Biocomposite." *International Journal of Biological Macromolecules* 146 (March): 746–755. https://doi.org/10.1016/j.ijbiomac.2019.11.011

Jumaidin, Ridhwan, Zulhelmi Asyul Sutan Saidi, Rushdan Ahmad Ilyas, Mohd Nazri Ahmad, Mohammad Khalid Wahid, Mohd Yuhazri Yaakob, Nurul Ain Maidin, Mohd Hidayat Ab Rahman, and Mohd Hairizal Osman. 2019b. "Characteristics of Cogon Grass Fibre Reinforced Thermoplastic Cassava Starch Biocomposite: Water Absorption and Physical Properties." *Journal of Advanced Research in Fluid Mechanics and Thermal Sciences*, 62 (1): 43–52.

Khotbehsara, Mojdeh Mehrinejad, Allan Manalo, Thiru Aravinthan, Kakarla Raghava Reddy, Wahid Ferdous, Hong Wong, and Ali Nazari. 2019. "Effect of Elevated In-Service Temperature on the Mechanical Properties and Microstructure of Particulate-Filled Epoxy Polymers." *Polymer Degradation and Stability* 170: 108994. https://doi.org/10.1016/j.polymdegradstab.2019.108994

Koohestani, Babak, Ikram Ganetri, and Erol Yilmaz. 2017. "Effects of Silane Modified Minerals on Mechanical, Microstructural, Thermal, and Rheological Properties of Wood Plastic Composites." *Composites Part B: Engineering* 111: 103–111. https://doi.org/10.1016/j.compositesb.2016.12.021

Kumar, T. Senthil Muthu, M. Chandrasekar, K. Senthilkumar, R. A. Ilyas, S. M. Sapuan, N. Hariram, A. Varada Rajulu, N. Rajini, and Suchart Siengchin. 2020. "Characterization, Thermal and Antimicrobial Properties of Hybrid Cellulose Nanocomposite Films with in-Situ Generated Copper Nanoparticles in Tamarindus Indica Nut Powder." *Journal of Polymers and the Environment* 29: 1134–1142. https://doi.org/10.1007/s10924-020-01939-w

Lashari, Zeeshan Ali, Hongbin Yang, Zhou Zhu, Xuechen Tang, Changxiao Cao, Muhammad Waseem Iqbal, and Wanli Kang. 2018. "Experimental Research of High Strength Thermally Stable Organic Composite Polymer Gel." *Journal of Molecular Liquids* 263 (August): 118–124. https://doi.org/10.1016/j.molliq.2018.04.146

Leong, Y. W., M. B. Abu Bakar, Z. A. Mohd. Ishak, A. Ariffin, and B. Pukanszky. 2004. "Comparison of the Mechanical Properties and Interfacial Interactions between Talc, Kaolin, and Calcium Carbonate Filled Polypropylene Composites." *Journal of Applied Polymer Science* 91 (5): 3315–3326. https://doi.org/10.1002/app.13542

Lewis, K. N., M. V. Thomas, and D. A. Puleo. 2006. "Mechanical and Degradation Behavior of Polymer-Calcium Sulfate Composites." *Journal of Materials Science: Materials in Medicine* 17 (6): 531–537. https://doi.org/10.1007/s10856-006-8936-0

Liang, J. Z., and C. B. Wu. 2012. "Effects of the Glass Bead Content and the Surface Treatment on the Mechanical Properties of Polypropylene Composites." *Journal of Applied Polymer Science* 123 (5): 3054–3063. https://doi.org/10.1002/app.34850

Lin, Alexander, Yu Kiat Tan, Chi-Hwa Wang, Harn Wei Kua, and Hayden Taylor. 2020. "Utilization of Waste Materials in a Novel Mortar–Polymer Laminar Composite to Be Applied in Construction 3D-Printing." *Composite Structures* 253 (December): 112764. https://doi.org/10.1016/j.compstruct.2020.112764

Lyu, Shuaifeng, Shengwei Wang, Xiaojun Chen, S. M. Shah, Rui Li, Yuhang Xiao, Qingxiang Dong, and Yuanyuan Gu. 2019. "Journal of Petroleum Science and Engineering Experimental Study of a Degradable Polymer Drilling Fl Uid System for Coalbed Methane Well." *Journal of Petroleum Science and Engineering* 178 (February): 678–690. https://doi.org/10.1016/j.petrol.2019.03.065

Manikandan, V., J. T. Winowlin Jappes, S. M. Suresh Kumar, and P. Amuthakkannan. 2012. "Investigation of the Effect of Surface Modifications on the Mechanical Properties of Basalt Fibre Reinforced Polymer Composites." *Composites Part B: Engineering* 43 (2): 812–818. https://doi.org/10.1016/j.compositesb.2011.11.009

Mareri, P., S. Bastide, N. Binda, and A. Crespy. 1998. "Mechanical Behaviour of Polypropylene Composites Containing Fine Mineral Filler: Effect of Filler Surface Treatment." *Composites Science and Technology* 58 (5): 747–752. https://doi.org/10.1016/S0266-3538(97)00156-5

Meyers, Paul A. 1985. United States Patent (19), no. 19.

Misra, R. D. K., R. Hadal, and S. J. Duncan. 2004. "Surface Damage Behavior during Scratch Deformation of Mineral Reinforced Polymer Composites." *Acta Materialia* 52 (14): 4363–4376. https://doi.org/10.1016/j.actamat.2004.06.003

Mohd Nurazzi, N., A. Khalina, S. M. Sapuan, and R. A. Ilyas. 2019. "Mechanical Properties of Sugar Palm Yarn/Woven Glass Fiber Reinforced Unsaturated Polyester Composites: Effect of Fiber Loadings and Alkaline Treatment." *Polimery/Polymers* 64 (10). https://doi.org/10.14314/polimery.2019.10.3

Mohd Zaini, Nurul Aizan, Hanafi Ismail, and Arjulizan Rusli. 2017. "Short Review on Sepiolite-Filled Polymer Nanocomposites." *Polymer - Plastics Technology and Engineering* 56 (15): 1665–1679. https://doi.org/10.1080/03602559.2017.1289395

Nicoleau, Luc, Alexander E. S. Van Driessche, and Matthias Kellermeier. 2019. "A Kinetic Analysis of the Role of Polymers in Mineral Nucleation. The Example of Gypsum." *Cement and Concrete Research* 124 (July): 105837. https://doi.org/10.1016/j.cemconres.2019.105837

Nielsen, Lawrence E. 1967. "Simple Theory of Stress Strain Properties of Filled Polymers." *Rubber Chemistry and Technology* 40 (3): 801–805. https://doi.org/10.5254/1.3539094

Nilugal, R. P., and D. Amaresh Kumar. 2015. "Effect of Silicon Carbide and Calcium Sulphate on E-Glass/Epoxy Composites." *International Journal of Mechanical Engineering and Technology (IJMET)* 6: 8–15.

Nourbakhsh, Amir, Abolfazl Karegarfard, Alireza Ashori, and Anita Nourbakhsh. 2010. "Effects of Particle Size and Coupling Agent Concentration on Mechanical Properties of Particulate-Filled Polymer Composites." *Journal of Thermoplastic Composite Materials* 23 (2): 169–174. https://doi.org/10.1177/0892705709340962

Nurazzi, N. Mohd., A. Khalina, M. Chandrasekar, H. A. Aisyah, S. Ayu Rafiqah, R. A. Ilyas, and Z. M. Hanafee. 2020. "Effect of Fiber Orientation and Fiber Loading on the Mechanical and Thermal Properties of Sugar Palm Yarn Fiber Reinforced Unsaturated Polyester Resin Composites." *Polimery* 65 (02): 115–124. https://doi.org/10.14314/polimery.2020.2.5

Nurazzi, N. Mohd., A. Khalina, S. M. Sapuan, R. A. Ilyas, S. Ayu Rafiqah, and Z. M. Hanafee. 2019. "Thermal Properties of Treated Sugar Palm Yarn/Glass Fiber Reinforced Unsaturated Polyester Hybrid Composites." *Journal of Materials Research and Technology* 9 (2): 1606–1618. https://doi.org/10.1016/j.jmrt.2019.11.086

Olufsen, Sindre, Arild Holm Clausen, and Odd Sture Hopperstad. 2019. "Influence of Stress Triaxiality and Strain Rate on Stress-Strain Behaviour and Dilation of Mineral-Filled PVC." *Polymer Testing* 75 (February): 350–357. https://doi.org/10.1016/j.polymertesting.2019.02.018

Omran, Abdoulhdi A Borhana, Abdulrahman A. B. A. Mohammed, S. M. Sapuan, R. A. Ilyas, M. R. M. Asyraf, Seyed Saeid Rahimian Koloor, and Michal Petrů. 2021. "Micro- and Nanocellulose in Polymer Composite Materials: A Review." *Polymers* 13 (2): 231. https://doi.org/10.3390/polym13020231

Owuamanam, Stephen, and Duncan Cree. 2020. "Progress of Bio-Calcium Carbonate Waste Eggshell and Seashell Fillers in Polymer Composites: A Review." *Journal of Composites Science* 4 (2): 70. https://doi.org/10.3390/jcs4020070

Patnaik, Amar, Alok Satapathy, Navin Chand, N. M. Barkoula, and Sandhyarani Biswas. 2010. "Solid Particle Erosion Wear Characteristics of Fiber and Particulate Filled Polymer Composites: A Review." *Wear* 268 (1–2): 249–263. https://doi.org/10.1016/j.wear.2009.07.021

Pukánszky, B. 2016. "Mineral Filled Polymers." In *Reference Module in Materials Science and Materials Engineering* Amsterdam: Elsevier, 1–6. https://doi.org/10.1016/b978-0-12-803581-8.02598-4

Pukánszky, Béla, and Erika Fekete. 1999. "Adhesion and Surface Modification." *Advances in Polymer Science* 139: 109–153. https://doi.org/10.1007/3-540-69220-7_3

Revathy, J., P. Gajalakshmi, and P. Pavithra. 2020. "Experimental Investigation on Concrete Filled Glass Fibre Reinforced Polymer Tubular Beams under Flexural Loading." *Materials Today: Proceedings* 33: 440–445. https://doi.org/10.1016/j.matpr.2020.04.869

Rod, Kenton A., Carlos A. Fernandez, Phillip K. Koech, Gao Dai, Miguel Correa, Nicolas Huerta, Sarah Burton, Quin R. S. Miller, and Charles T. Resch. 2020. "Self-Repairing Polymer-Modified Cements for High Temperature Geothermal and Fossil Energy Applications." *Geothermics* 85 (May): 101790. https://doi.org/10.1016/j.geothermics.2019.101790

Rout, Arun, and Alok Satapathy. 2012. "Analysis of Dry Sliding Wear Behaviour of Rice Husk Filled Epoxy Composites Using Design of Experiment and ANN." *Procedia Engineering* 38: 1218–1232. https://doi.org/10.1016/j.proeng.2012.06.153

Rowell, Roger M., Anand R. Sanadi, Daniel F. Caulfield, and Rodney E. Jacobson. 1997. "Utilization of Natural Fibers in Plastic Composites: Problems and Opportunities." *Lignocellulosic-Plastic Composites*, 23–51.

Rozilah, A., C. N. Aiza Jaafar, S. M. Sapuan, I. Zainol, and R. A. Ilyas. 2020. "The Effects of Silver Nanoparticles Compositions on the Mechanical, Physiochemical, Antibacterial, and Morphology Properties of Sugar Palm Starch Biocomposites for Antibacterial Coating." *Polymers* 12 (11): 2605. https://doi.org/10.3390/polym12112605

Rueda, Martha Margarita, Marie-Camille Auscher, René Fulchiron, Thomas Périé, Grégory Martin, Philippe Sonntag, and Philippe Cassagnau. 2017. "Rheology and Applications of Highly Filled Polymers: A Review of Current Understanding." *Progress in Polymer Science* 66 (March): 22–53. https://doi.org/10.1016/j.progpolymsci.2016.12.007

Saba, Naheed, Paridah Md. Tahir, and Mohammad Jawaid. 2014. "A Review on Potentiality of Nano Filler/Natural Fiber Filled Polymer Hybrid Composites." *Polymers* 6 (8): 2247–2273. https://doi.org/10.3390/polym6082247

Sabaruddin, Fatimah Athiyah, M.T. Paridah, S M Sapuan, R A Ilyas, Seng Hua Lee, Khalina Abdan, Norkhairunnisa Mazlan, Adlin Sabrina Muhammad Roseley, and H.P.S. Abdul Khalil. 2020. "The Effects of Unbleached and Bleached Nanocellulose on the Thermal and Flammability of Polypropylene-Reinforced Kenaf Core Hybrid Polymer Bionanocomposites." *Polymers* 13 (1): 116. https://doi.org/10.3390/polym13010116

Sakthi, G., S. Nandha Gopan, V. Santhosh, and M. Ravichandran. 2020. "Materials Today: Proceedings Effect of Chemical Treatment on Mechanical Properties of Prawn Antenna Reinforced Waste Plastic Particulates Filled Polymer Composites." *Materials Today: Proceedings* 33 (7): 3668–3375. https://doi.org/10.1016/j.matpr.2020.05.797

Şanlı, Selen, Ali Durmus, and Nevra Ercan. 2012. "Isothermal Crystallization Kinetics of Glass Fiber and Mineral-Filled Polyamide 6 Composites." *Journal of Materials Science* 47 (7): 3052–3063. https://doi.org/10.1007/s10853-011-6137-9

Sapuan, S. M., H. S. Aulia, R. A. Ilyas, A. Atiqah, T. T. Dele-Afolabi, M. N. Nurazzi, A. B. M. Supian, and M. S. N. Atikah. 2020. "Mechanical Properties of Longitudinal Basalt/Woven-Glass-Fiber-Reinforced Unsaturated Polyester-Resin Hybrid Composites." *Polymers* 12 (10): 2211. https://doi.org/10.3390/polym12102211

Sari, Nasmi Herlina, Catalin Iulian Pruncu, Salit Mohd Sapuan, Rushdan Ahmad Ilyas, Agus Dwi Catur, Suteja, Yusuf Akhyar Sutaryono, and Gareth Pullen. 2020. "The Effect of Water Immersion and Fibre Content on Properties of Corn Husk Fibres Reinforced Thermoset Polyester Composite." *Polymer Testing* 91 (November): 106751. https://doi.org/10.1016/j.polymertesting.2020.106751

Sharma, Bikramjit, Rahul Chhibber, and Rajeev Mehta. 2017. "Curing Studies and Mechanical Properties of Glass Fiber Reinforced Composites Based on Silanized Clay Minerals." *Applied Clay Science* 138 (March): 89–99. https://doi.org/10.1016/j.clay.2016.12.038

Shofner, M. L., K. Lozano, F. J. Rodríguez-Macías, and E. V. Barrera. 2003. "Nanofiber-Reinforced Polymers Prepared by Fused Deposition Modeling." *Journal of Applied Polymer Science* 89 (11): 3081–3090. https://doi.org/10.1002/app.12496

Skorokhoda, Volodymyr, Nataliya Semenyuk, Iryna Dziaman, and Oleg Suberlyak. 2016. "Mineral Filled Porous Composites Based on Polyvinylpyrrolidone Copolymers with Bactericidal." *Chemistry and Chemical Technology* 10 (2): 187–192. https://doi.org/10.23939/chcht10.02.187

Sreekanth, M. S., S. Joseph, S. T. Mhaske, P. A. Mahanwar, and V. A. Bambole. 2011. "Effects of Mica and Fly Ash Concentration on the Properties of Polyester Thermoplastic Elastomer Composites." *Journal of Thermoplastic Composite Materials* 24 (3): 317–331. https://doi.org/10.1177/0892705710389293

Stokes, Paul. 2018. Patent et Application 1.

Syafiq, R., S. M. Sapuan, M. Y. M. Zuhri, R. A. Ilyas, A. Nazrin, S. F. K. Sherwani, and A. Khalina. 2020. "Antimicrobial Activities of Starch-Based Biopolymers and Biocomposites Incorporated with Plant Essential Oils: A Review." *Polymers* 12 (10): 2403. https://doi.org/10.3390/polym12102403

Syafri, Edi, Sudirman, Mashadi, Evi Yulianti, Deswita, Mochamad Asrofi, Hairul Abral, S. M. Sapuan, R. A. Ilyas, and Ahmad Fudholi. 2019. "Effect of Sonication Time on the Thermal Stability, Moisture Absorption, and Biodegradation of Water Hyacinth (Eichhornia Crassipes) Nanocellulose-Filled Bengkuang (Pachyrhizus Erosus) Starch Biocomposites." *Journal of Materials Research and Technology* 8 (6): 6223–6231. https://doi.org/10.1016/j.jmrt.2019.10.016

Szajerski, Piotr, Joanna Celinska, Andrzej Gasiorowski, Rafal Anyszka, Radoslaw Walendziak, and Michal Lewandowski. 2020. "Radiation Induced Strength Enhancement of Sulfur Polymer Concrete Composites Based on Waste and Residue Fillers." *Journal of Cleaner Production* 271 (October): 122563. https://doi.org/10.1016/j.jclepro.2020.122563

Tekin, H. O., M. R. Kaçal, Shams A. M. Issa, H. Polat, G. Susoy, F. Akman, O. Kilicoglu, and V. H. Gillette. 2020. "Sodium Dodecatungstophosphate Hydrate-Filled Polymer Composites for Nuclear Radiation Shielding." *Materials Chemistry and Physics* 256 (December): 123667. https://doi.org/10.1016/j.matchemphys.2020.123667

Venkatarajan, S., and A. Athijayamani. 2020. "An Overview on Natural Cellulose Fiber Reinforced Polymer Composites." *Materials Today: Proceedings* 37 (2): 3620–3624. https://doi.org/10.1016/j.matpr.2020.09.773

Wang, Guolong, Demei Yu, Ajit D Kelkar, and Lifeng Zhang. 2017. "Progress in Polymer Science Electrospun Nanofiber : Emerging Reinforcing Filler in Polymer Matrix Composite Materials." *Progress in Polymer Science* 75: 73–107. https://doi.org/10.1016/j.progpolymsci.2017.08.002

Wang, K., N. Bahlouli, F. Addiego, S. Ahzi, Y. Rémond, D. Ruch, and R. Muller. 2013. "Effect of Talc Content on the Degradation of Re-Extruded Polypropylene/Talc Composites." *Polymer Degradation and Stability* 98 (7): 1275–1286. https://doi.org/10.1016/j.polymdegradstab.2013.04.006

Wickaramasinghe, W. A.W. I. C., D. S. Lasitha, A. M.P. B Samarasekara, D. A.S. Amarasinghe, and L. Karunanayake. 2019. "Extraction and Characterization of Nano Crystalline Cellulose (NCC) from Sri Lankan Agricultural Waste." *MERCon 2019 – Proceedings, 5th International Multidisciplinary Moratuwa Engineering Research Conference*, 616–620. https://doi.org/10.1109/MERCon.2019.8818904

Yang, M. 2018. "Preparation and Mechanical Properties of Polypropylene Composite for Seats." *Chemical Engineering Transactions* 66: 133–138. https://doi.org/10.3303/CET1866023

Yang, Zhe, Hongdan Peng, Weizhi Wang, and Tianxi Liu. 2010. "Crystallization Behavior of Poly(ε-Caprolactone)/Layered Double Hydroxide Nanocomposites." *Journal of Applied Polymer Science* 116 (5): 2658–2667. https://doi.org/10.1002/app

Yin, Jicai, Jianhua Zhang, Yi Zhang, and Wenqiang Wang. 2017. "Porosity, Mechanical Properties, and Damping Ratio of Particulate-Filled Polymer Composite for Precision Machine Tools." *Journal of Applied Polymer Science* 134 (6): 1–7. https://doi.org/10.1002/app.44435

Zhang, Ping, Jianhua Zeng, Siping Zhai, Yaoqi Xian, Daoguo Yang, and Qiang Li. 2017. "Thermal Properties of Graphene Filled Polymer Composite Thermal Interface Materials." *Macromolecular Materials and Engineering* 302 (9): 1–18. https://doi.org/10.1002/mame.201700068

Zhu, Lin, and Richard P. Wool. 2006. "Nanoclay Reinforced Bio-Based Elastomers: Synthesis and Characterization." *Polymer* 47 (24) 8106–8115. https://doi.org/10.1016/j.polymer.2006.07.076

Index

Note: Locators in *italics* represent figures and **bold** indicate tables in the text.

A

Accelerated ageing, 94–107
Accelerators, 119
Acoustic emission (AE), 41
Acrylic rubber (ACM), 89
Acrylonitrile butadiene styrene (ABS), 212
Ageing (weathering), mineral-reinforced polymer composites, 90–91
   accelerated ageing, 94–107
   cyclic ageing, 105–107
   e-beam irradiation, 105
   natural ageing, **91**, 91–94
   thermal ageing, 99–101
   UV ageing, 94–99
   water ageing, 101–105
Agglomeration, 76, 206, *206*
7Å-halloysite, 150
Al-OH libations, 120
Alumina (Al_2O_3), 85–86, 161–164, 171
   classification, 162
   filled rubber composites, 160–161
   fillers in polymer matrix composites, 164–166
   mineral corundum, *162*
   properties of, **163**
Alumina-filled natural rubber-based composites, **174–175**
Alumina-filled polymer composites, **165**
Alumina-filled rubber, 191
Alumina-filled synthetic rubber-based composites, **176**
Alumina-reinforced rubber composites
   application as insulator in power transmission and distribution lines, 172–173
   for electronic application, 170–172
   mechanical properties of, 173–178
      alumina loadings on tensile properties, 173–178
      alumina particle sizes (micro vs nano) to tensile properties, 179
      alumina surface treatment, 179–180
      curing agent on tensile properties, 180
      hardness, 182–183
      hybrid alumina particle sizes on tensile properties, 181–182
      matrix modification on tensile properties, 181

      morphological characteristics, 183
      scanning electron microscopy (SEM), 184–187
   processability of, 190–191
Aluminols, 73
Aluminosilicate minerals, 72
Aluminosilicate nanotubes, 71
Aluminum hydroxide, 162
Aluminum nitride (AlN), 171
Amino silane, 5
   coupling agent, 5
   seashell powder, reaction, 5
Ammonium benzoate (AmBz), 89
Anhydride-grafted polyethylene (PE-g-MA), 86
Anhydrous alumina, 162
Antiferromagnetism, 200–201
Antiparallel spin coupling interactions, 201
Aramid fiber-reinforced polymer (AFRP), 41
ASTM D471, 116
ASTM D624, 117
ASTM D790, 36
ASTM D2240, 117
ASTM D3039, 36
Attenuated total reflection (ATR), 116

B

Bar-reinforced concrete slabs (BRCSs), 39
Basalt fabric-reinforced epoxy composite, 102
Basalt fiber (BF), 32–34, **34**
   chemical constituents, *34*, 37
   fabric, *33*
   hybridization, 46
   mechanical properties of, **34**
   strands, *33*
Basalt fiber-reinforced polymer (BFRP), 31–32, 36–49
   applications
      laminates and pre-pregs, 59
      transportation, 59–60
   bar-reinforced concrete slabs (BRCSs), 39
   composites, **50–54**
   mechanical properties, 49–57
   strain-rate variation, *56*
   thermal properties, 57–58
Basalts rocks, 34
Bauxite, 162
Bayerite, 162

263

Index

BF, *see* Basalt fiber
Binary mixture, 181
Bio-based epoxy resin, **53**
Bio-calcium carbonate, 247
Biodegradable polymers, 71
Bio-fibers, 35
Bio mineral fillers, 1–2
    calcium carbonate ($CaCO_3$), 1, *3*, **4**
    defined, 2
    hybrid composites, 10, **11**
    modification, 5–10, *7*
    in polymer composites, gaps and challenges, 10
    preparation, *3*
    production, 3–4
    resources, *2*
Bio silica, 5
Bisphenol A diglycidyl ether (DGEBA), 19
Boehmite, 162
Bond formation, 5
Boron nitride (BN) nanotubes, 171
Brabender Plastigraph®, 115
Bragg's law, 150
4-Bromobenzoic acid, 140
Burst test, 25, *25*
1-n-Butyl-3-methylimidazolium (BMI), 218

C

Calcination, 8
Calcination of chicken eggshell powder, *9*
Calcium carbonate ($CaCO_3$), 1, *3*, 86, 107
    bio mineral fillers, **4**
Calcium hydroxide (Ca(OH)2) bonds, 9
Calcium oxide (CaO), 8
Carbon black, 88
Carbon fiber, **34**
    fabric, *33*
    reinforced polymer (CFRP), 32, 41, 48
    strands, *33*
Carbon nanofiber (CNF), 38
Carbon nanotubes (CNTs), 112, 171, 247
Carbon-woven fabrics, 32
Carboxy-terminated liquid natural rubber
    (CTNR), 113–114
Cellulose fibers, 244
Charge-coupled device (CCD) detector, 140
Chicken eggshell bio-filler, **4**, 8
Clay, 85–86
Clay nanofillers, 72
Clay-reinforced PA6, 101
Clay-reinforced polymer composites, 90
CNT, *see* Carbon nanotubes
Cockerel shell bio-filler, **4**
Coefficient of thermal expansion (CTE), 164
Commercialization, 76
Commercial silica, **4**
Compatible silanes: vinyltriethoxysilane
    (CVTES), 222

Composite glass fiber polyester resin pipes, 16
Composite material, 32, 36
Compressive strength of nanocomposite filled
    with fly ash geopolymer, 23–25
Condensation, 5
Copolymerization, 76
Crack propagation, 55
Cross-linking agent, 180
Cure rate index (CRI), 118
Curie temperature, 198
Cyclic ageing, 105–107
    Charpy impact strength, **107**
    flexural strength and flexural modulus as
        function of water exposure time, **106**

D

De-agglomeration, 76
Decomposition of polymeric materials, 78
Deformations, 204
Degradation, 85
Degree of crystallinity, 140, 146
Degree of magnetization, 198
Depolymerization, 227
Diamagnetism, 198
Dicumyl peroxide (DCP), 180
Differential scanning calorimetry (DSC), 221
Differential thermal analysis (DTA), 221
Diglycidyl ether of bisphenol A (DGEBA), 89
Dispersion fibers, 41
Dynamic mechanical analysis (DMA), 48, 221

E

E-beam irradiation, 105
Eggshell, *3*
    powder, 5
E-glass epoxy-based composites, 253
E-glass fiber, 32, **34**
    quasi-static crush energy absorption
        capability, 47
Energy absorption by magnetostriction, 208
Energy dispersion spectroscopy (EDS), 251
Energy dissipation, 205
Environmental-benign technique, 217
Epoxidized natural rubber (ENR), 89, 114, 164,
    168, 168–169
Epoxies/thermosetting polymers, 16
Epoxy, 35, **50–54**
Epoxy-based polymer resin density, 244
Epoxy composites, *8*, 38
Epoxy-layered silicate nanocomposites, 19
Epoxy LY556 resin, **11**
Epoxy resin, 18, **53**, 88–89
Escherichia coli, 86
Ethylene, 169
Ethylene propylene diene monomer (EPDM)
    rubber, *169*, 169–170

Index

265

Ethylene propylene diene rubber (EPDM)-grafted maleic anhydride (MA), 114
Ethylene vinyl alcohol (EVOH), 212

F

Facsimile machines, 161
Ferrimagnetism, 201–202
Ferrites, 201
Ferromagnetic materials, 200
Ferromagnetism, *199*, 199–200
Fiber/fly ash-reinforced polymer composite, 40
Fiber-reinforced composites, 16, 19, 244
Fiber-reinforced/mineral-filled epoxy composites
    bamboo fiber/epoxy, **17**
    fiberglass/SiO_2/epoxy, **17**
    fly ash/epoxy, 18, **18**
    glass/carbon fiber/epoxy, **18**
    properties, **17–18**
    SiO_2/epoxy nanocomposite, **17**
    slag/epoxy, **17**
Fiber-reinforced plastic (FRP) pipe, 16
Fiber-reinforced polyester composites, 32
Fiber-reinforced polymer (FRP), 35, 236
Fiber-spinning process, 49
Field-effect transistors (FETs), 180
Field emission scanning electron micrograph (FESEM), 215
Filaments, comparative analysis properties, **60**
Filled polymers, models for, *238*
Filler agglomeration, 123
Filler-filler interactions, 123, 143
Fire resistance, 18
Fishbone, **11**
Flax fiber, **34**
Flexural strength and flexural modulus as function of water exposure time, **106**
Fly ash, 40
Fly ash-based geopolymers, 19–21, 25
    burst test, *26*
    filler, 22
Fourier transform infrared spectroscopy (FTIR), 8–9, 115–116, 138

G

Geopolymer filler, 15–18
    in epoxy glass fiber composites, 22
        fly ash-based geopolymer filler loading on compressive strength, 22–25
        fly ash-based geopolymer filler on hydrostatic pressure strength, 25–26
    in epoxy hybrid composite, 20–21
        fly ash-based geopolymer filler, 21
    in polymeric materials, 18–20
Glass-basalt reinforced hybrid composite, 37
Glass bead, 86, 90, 107
Glass fiber, 22, 32, 37, 86, 107

Glass fiber-reinforced epoxy (GRE) composite pipes, 16
    compressive strength, *23–24*
    -filled fly ash-based geopolymer pipe, *23*
Glass fiber-reinforced plastic (GFRP) pipes, 16
Glass-fiber reinforced polyester (GFRP), 32
Glass fiber-reinforced polymer (GFRP) composites, 97
Glass-reinforced polymer (GRP), 172
Glass transition, 169
3-Glycidoxypropyltrimethoxysilane, 219
Γ-methacryloxypropyltrimethoxysilane (CMPS), 222
Graphene, 171
Grounded commercial calcium carbonate (GCC), 4

H

Halloysite, 72–73
    dehydrated, 73
    hydrated, 73
    irreversible, 73
Halloysite-filled natural rubber composite, 112–114, 136–137
    composites, preparation of, 114–115
    HNT loading
        morphological property, 143–144
        tensile properties, 141–143
        wide angle X-ray scattering, 144–147
        X-ray diffraction analysis, 140–141
    HNT loading on properties of natural rubber composites
        curing characteristic, 118–119
        dynamic properties, 121
        FTIR analysis, 119–120
        mechanical properties, 121–124
        swelling resistance and cross-link density, 120–121
    maleated natural rubber-compatibilized NR/HNT composites
        cure characteristics, 125–127
        dynamic properties, 127–129
        functionalities of, 124–125
        mechanical properties, 129
        SEM, 129–130
    MNR, preparation of, 115
    NR/HNT composites, 138
    palm stearin, 137–138
    palm stearin on straininduced crystallization of NR/HNT composites
        cure characteristics, 148–149
        MPS, 147–148
        MPS and halloysite Nanotubes, 149–150
        reinforcement and strain-induced crystallization, 152–156
        XRD study of composites in the presence of MPS, 150–152

preparation, 137
testing and characterization
cross-link density, 116–117
cure characteristics, 115–116
curing characteristics, 139
dynamic property, 117
Fourier-transform infrared (FTIR)
spectroscopic analysis, 116
mechanical properties, 117–118
swelling resistance, 116
tensile properties, 139
wide angle X-ray diffraction analysis
(WAXD), 139–140
x-ray diffraction analysis (XRD), 139
Halloysite nanotubes (HNTs), 71–72, 112, 136
crystal structure, 73
loading efficiencies, 72
mineral filler for PLA, 72–73
PLA nanocomposites with ZnO-
functionalized, 74–80
single-tube dispersion of, 73
structure, *113*
surface modification, 72
TEM image, 75, *75*
template for immobilization of ZnO
nanoparticles, 73–74
tensile modulus, *77*
Heat deflection temperature (HDT), 239
Heat head substratum, 161
Hermann equation, 140
Hevea brasiliensis, 112, 166–167
1-n-Hexyl-3-methylimidazolium [HMI], 218
High-density polyethylene (HDPE), 5, 86
High-performance packaging materials, 171
HNT, *see* Halloysite nanotubes
HNT loading on properties of natural rubber
composites
curing characteristic, 118–119
dynamic properties, 121
formulation of, **114, 137**
FTIR analysis, 119–120
mechanical properties, 121–124
mixing procedures, **115**
stress-strain dependence of HNT-filled NR,
122
swelling resistance and cross-link density,
120–121
HNT-ZnO hybrid filler, 78
Hooke's law, 202
Hybrid bio-based mineral-filled composites, 12
Hybridization, 41
Hybrid phenolic, **51**
Hydrargillite, 162
Hydrochloric acid (HCl), 19, 89
Hydrogen bonding, 5, 72
Hydrolysis, 5, 101
Hydrophobicity test, 48

Hydrostatic pressure leak tests, 25, *25*
Hygrothermal ageing, **104**

I

Industrialization, 76
Inorganic fillers, 85
In situ polymerization, 218–219
Instron VHS, 43
Integrated circuits (ICs), 161
Interfacial damping, 204–206
Intumescent flame retardant (IFR), 88
Isotactic PP films, 88
Itaconic acid (IA), 244

J

Jute fiber, **34**

K

Kaolin, 86
Kaolin-based geopolymer, 19
Kenaf fibers, 244

L

Layer-by-layer deposition of MMT and chitosan
on extruded (PLA) film, *226*
Life cycle assessment (LCA), 46
Light-emitting diodes (LEDs), 180
Light scattering, 246
Limestone, 1
Limiting oxygen index (LOI) values, **100**
Long glass fiber-reinforced PP (LGFPP), 88
Low-density PE (LDPE) composites, 217
Low-density polyethylene (LDPE), 20, 86–87
Lucalox, 162

M

Magnetic dipoles, 197, *199*
orientation, *200*
Magnetite, 196, 202
Magnetorheological elastomers (MREs),
195–196
anisotropic, 196, 204
chemical properties, 197
damping mechanisms of MRE
interfacial damping, 204–206
magnetostrictive damping, 206–208
viscoelastic damping, 202–204
isotropic, 196
magnetic properties, 197–198
antiferromagnetism, 200–201
diamagnetism, 198
ferrimagnetism, 201–202

Index

ferromagnetism, 199–200
paramagnetism, 198–199
magnetite mineral, distribution of, 196–197
Magnetostrictive damping, 206–208
Maleated natural rubber-compatibilized NR/
HNT composites
cure characteristics, 125–127
dynamic properties, 127–129
functionalities of, 124–125
mechanical properties, 129
SEM, 129–130
Maleated NR (MNR), 115, 181
Material durability, 60
Matrix material, 161
Mechanical test, 46
Medium-acrylonitrile-content nitrile rubber, 169
Melt mixing, 217–218
Mesoporous silica, *3*
Metakaolin-based geopolymer, 20
Metal oxide nanofillers, 72
Metamorphic rocks, 1
Methanol, 137
Mica, 85–86
Microbial degradation of thermoplastic
composites, *226*
Mineral-filled polymer composites, 95, 235–236,
240–243, 249, 254
challenges and perspectives, 251–253
mineral fillers, 237
reinforcement composite, 239–251
stress strain of filled polymers, 237–238
Mineral fillers, 1–2, 237
properties of, **87**
Mineral polymer, 239
Mineral-reinforced polymer, 107
Mineral-reinforced polymer composites, 85–86,
90
ageing (weathering), 90–91
accelerated ageing, 94–107
cyclic ageing, 105–107
e-beam irradiation, 105
natural ageing, 91–94
thermal ageing, 99–101
UV ageing, 94–99
water ageing, 101–105
applications, 90
compounding and processing, 86–89
Minibars (MBs), 41–42
MINITAB, 245
MMT, *see* Montmorillonite
Modified palm stearin (MPS), 137–138, *138*
Molecule grafting, 72
Montmorillonite (MMT), 212–214
crystal structure of, 212
dispersion state in polymer matrix, *215*
hydrophilic, 214
physical properties, **214**

polymer composites, *216*
SEM image of, *213*
structure of, *213*
TEM image of, *213*
Montmorillonite-reinforced thermoplastic
composites, 212–214
mechanical properties, 219–221
processing methods
melt mixing, 217–218
in situ polymerization, 218–219
solution blending, 214–217
thermal properties
barrier properties, 225–226
biodegradation properties, 226–228
dynamic mechanical properties, 221–222
thermal behavior, 224–225
thermal stability, 222–223
Moving die rheometer (MDR), 115, 138
MREs, *see* Magnetorheological elastomers
(MREs)

N

Nano-alumina-filled NR, 181
Nanofillers, 112
Natural ageing, **91**, 91–94
Charpy impact strength, **94**
melting temperature and crystallinity index,
91–92
whiteness and yellowness index, **93**
yield stress, young's modulus and elongation,
93
Natural fiber-filled polymer hybrid composites,
239
Natural fiber-reinforced composite, 239
Natural fiber-reinforced polyester (NFRP), 32
Natural fibers, 237
Natural rubber (NR), 161, 166–168
crystallization behavior, 136, 156, 167
glass transition temperature, 167
NR/HNT composites, mechanical properties,
152, *156*
Newton's law, 202
Non-halogen rubber, 170
Non-renewable resources, 12
Novel fiber, 32
NPW20 polymer composite materials, 247
NR/HNT composites, **129**
with and without MPS, **138**
NR-toluene, 117
Nuclear radiation, 247

O

1-n-Octyl-3-methylimidazolium (OMI), 218
Organo-modified montmorillonite (OMMT), 87
Oyster shells, 5

268

P

Paraffin lubricant, 86
Paramagnetism, 198–199
Particulate-filled polymer composites (PFPC), 239
Particulate-shaped fillers, 161
PA6/wollastonite composites, 101
Payne effect, 121, 127
Perlite, 90
Petroleum-based carbon/silica, 7
Phenol, 35
Pigment, 88
PLA, *see* Poly(lactic acid)
PLA/HNT-ZnO3 nanocomposite, 76
Plastic, 237
Plasticity, 237
Plastic tensile, 238
Polyamide, **51**
Polyamide 6 (PA6), 87
Polybenzoxazines, 48, **52**
Poly(butylene adipate-*co*-terephthalate) (PBAT), 88
Poly(butylene terephthalate) (PBT), 247
Polycrystalline materials, 199
Polydimethylsiloxane, **51**
Polyester, **50**, **52–53**
    composite structures, 47
    and hybrid E-glass-basalt, 47
    matrix, 32
    resin, **51**
    resin hybrid composites, 37
    resins, 35
Polyetheretherketone (PEEK), 88
Polyethylene (PE), 35, 212
Polyhydroxyalcanoate (PHA), 247
Poly(3-hydroxybutyrate-*co*-3-hydroxyvalerate) (PHBV), 88
Cis-1,4-Polyisoprene, 112, 167
Poly(lactic acid) (PLA), 71
    based clay nanocomposites, 72
    composites, *9*
    crystallization, 71
    matrix, 10
    mechanical and thermal properties, 72
    oxidative degradation, 72
    thermal stability, 78
    thermoplastic composites, 215
Polymer blending strategy, 76
Polymer chains, 5
Polymer composites, 15–16, 35, 90
Polymer-HNT nanocomposites, 113
Polymeric materials, 85
Polymerization, 236
Polymer macromolecules, 6
Polymer matrix, 160, 177, 214
    composites, 172
Polymer nanocomposite, 74, 76
Polymer nanocomposite (PNC) biodegradation, 247
Polymers, 236–237
Poly(methylmethacrylate) (PMMA) composites, 219
Polymethylsiloxane, 56
Polymetric matrix, 35
Polymorphs, 73
Poly(oxymethylene) (POM), 105
Polypropylene grafted maleic anhydride (PP-g-MA), 239
Polypropylene (PP), 5, 18, 35, **51**, 88, 212
Polysiloxane resin, **53**
Polystyrene (PS), 212
Polyvinyl alcohol (PVOH), 5, 215
    short fibers, 18
Poly(vinyl chloride) (PVC), 35, 86, 236
Poly-β-caprolactone (PCL), 247
Porous silica, 6
Positive magnetization, 199
PP/talc composite films, 90
Propylene, 169

R

Red pottery clay (RPC), 86
Reinforced concrete (RC) slab, 39
Reinforcing fillers, 161
Reinforcing index (RI), 177
Reinforcing material, 161
Renewable biomaterials, 2
Rice husk, *3*, 10
Rice husk carbon/silica, 6–7, *7–8*
Rise angle (RA), 41
Rock deposits, 1
Rubber, 236
    abrasive properties, 166
    alumina loadings on tensile properties of, 178–179
    alumina particle sizes (micro vs nano) to tensile properties, 179
    alumina surface treatment to tensile properties of, 179–180
    curing agent on tensile properties of, 180
    electrical properties, 166
    physical and mechanical properties, 166
    thermal conductivity, 171
    thermal properties, 166
    viscoelastic behavior, 166
    viscoelastic material, 202
Rubber-filler interaction, 150
Rubber matrices in alumina-filled rubber composites, 166
    epoxidized natural rubber (ENR) matrix, 168–169
    ethylene propylene diene monomer (EPDM) rubber, 169–170

Index

269

natural rubber, 166–168
silicone rubber (SiR), 168
Rubber matrix, 119, 190
Rubbers, 89
Rubber technology, 112

S

Sand, 1
Scanning electron microscopy (SEM), 19, 38,
124, 129–130, 136, 184–187, 246
Sea sand concrete, **52**
Seashell powder, modification, with amino silane
coupling agent, *6*
Semiconductor substratum, 161
SEM Philips XL40, 251
Silane coupling agent, 5, 86
Silane-treated BN-filled SBR, 173
Silanols, 73, 118
Silica (SiO_2), 1, 85–86, 162, 171
based geopolymer comosites, 20
bio minerals, **4**
nanoparticles, 112
Silicon carbide, 171
Silicone rubber (SiR), 164, 168
Silicon nitride (Si_3N_4), 85–86
Sillikolloid, 90
Siloxane, 73
Siloxane functionalities, 118
Sodium chloride (NaCl), 104
Sodium dodecatungstophosphate hydrate, 246
Sodium hydroxide (NaOH), 21–22
Sodium ion conductor, 163
Sodium silicate solution (Na_2SiO_3), 21–22
Solar cells, 180
Solution blending, 214–217
Specific energy absorption (SEA), 47
Staphylococcus aureus., 86
Starch, 35
Stearic acid, 138
Steel fibers (SFs), 41
Strain amplitudes, 205
Strain-induced crystallization, 136, 141–142,
144, 152
Stress transfer, 122
Styrene-butadiene rubber (SBR), 173
Styrene-ethylene/butylene-styrene (SEBS), 89–90
Sulfur-based polymer concrete composites
(SPCs), 247
Sulfur polymer concrete, 247
Surface-anchored polymers in brush
conformation, *189*
Susceptibility, 200
Sustainable Development Goal (SDG), 208
Swelling resistance, 116
Synthetic fiber, 237
Synthetic rubber, 161

T

Talc, 1, 86, 107
Tensile strength, 152
Tensile stress, 208
TENSOR27, 116
Testing pipe sample, *23*
Tetraethoxysilane (TEOS), 89
Thermal ageing, 99–101, 108
conditions, **99**
Cone Calorimeter Test (CCT), **100**
limiting oxygen index (LOI) values, **100**
mechanical properties of OMMT/IFR/
LGFPP, **101**
TGA data for OMMT/IFR/LGFPP
composites, **100**
Thermal conductivity, 8, 10
Thermal cycling, 48
Thermal degradation of thermoplastic
composites, 222
Thermal expansion coefficient, 60
Thermal interface materials (TIMs), 170
Thermal stability, 18
Thermal stability of polymer nanocomposite,
78
Thermomechanical analysis (TMA), 219,
221
Thermoplastic elastomer (TPE), 89
Thermoplastic epoxy composites, 55
Thermoplastic resins, 35
Thermoplastics, 35, 161, 212, 236
Thermoset polymer, 166
Thermosets, 35, 161
Titanium dioxide (TiO_2), 85–86, 88–89, 92
Titanomagnetite, **197**
Torque, 119
Transmission electron microscopy (TEM), 75,
188–189

U

Ultra-large-scale integration (LSI), 161
Ultrasonication excitation, 216
Ultraviolet (UV) light, 72
Uniform magnetic polarization, 206
Unsaturated polyester (UP), **11**, **50**, 89
UV ageing, **94**, 94–99
average compressive modulus of unaged and
aged specimens, **99**
average dynamic compressive modulus of
unaged and aged specimens, **99**
differential scanning calorimetry (DSC) data
for PHBV/TiO2, **96**
mechanical properties of PHBV/TiO2
composite, **97**
melt flow index (MFI) values for PHBV/
TiO2, **96**

270 Index

results before (initial) and after, **98**
thermogravimetric analysis (TGA) Data for
PHBV/TiO2, **96**
water absorption and thickness swelling,
95
UV irradiation, 90

V

Vacuum-assisted resin transfer molding
(VARTM), 38
van der Waals forces, 72
Vinyl ester (VE), **50**, 89
matrix, 42
resin, **52–53**
Virgin polymer, 160
Virgin rubber, 172
Viscoelastic damping, 202–204
Viscoelasticity of composites, 32
Viscous stress, 202
Vulcanizing reaction, 127

W

Waste white scallop powder (WWSP),
9, *9*
Water ageing, 101–105
flexural strength retention, **104**
hygrothermal ageing, **104**
moisture uptake, **103**
shear strength retention, **105**
tensile strength and elongation, **102**

time for VE-Based GFRP under
hygrothermal ageing, **105**
weight gain of basalt-reinforced epoxy
composites, **103**
Wide-angle X-ray scattering (WAXS), 136, 140,
155
Wollastonite, 86, 107
Wollastonite-reinforced polymer composites, 86
Wood, 88
Wood fiber, 86
Wood/PP composite, 90
Woven fabrics, *33*

X

X-ray diffraction (XRD), 138, 246

Y

Young's modulus, 36, *36*, 93, 204, 220

Z

Zinc acetate dihydrate, 74
Zinc-neutralized carboxylate ionomer, 87
Zinc oxide (ZnO), 85–86
functionalized HNT-reinforced PLA
nanocomposites, 76, 80
nanoparticles, 72
functionalized HNT, 74–75
HNT as template for immobilization of,
73–74